UNSUNG GENIUS

UNSUNG GENIUS
A LIFE OF JAGADISH CHANDRA BOSE

KUNAL GHOSH

ALEPH

ALEPH

ALEPH BOOK COMPANY
An independent publishing firm
promoted by *Rupa Publications India*

First published in India in 2022
by Aleph Book Company
7/16 Ansari Road, Daryaganj
New Delhi 110 002

ISBN: 978-93-91047-45-0

3 5 7 9 10 8 6 4 2

Printed in India

Utsarga[1] Pradeep[2]

This
book is
dedicated
to Mrs Sara
Chapman Bull.
To Swami Viveka-
-nanda, she was a
saint and his
American
mother.

She protected India's lone scientist with motherly care when he was
struggling to survive. She nurtured scientific research in India in
multiple ways, when it was in its most vulnerable nascent state.
Mrs Bull is hardly known in India for this beneficence because
she always remained behind the scenes, never caring for fame
and recognition. The least that my fellow countrymen
can do is to remember her with gratitude,
love, and reverence.

---

[1]Utsarga is Sanskrit for dedication.
[2]Pradeep is Sanskrit for a diya, a clay lamp. The observant reader will note that the
dedication on this page is shaped like a diya.

CONTENTS

PREFACE

At the intersection of the twentieth and the twenty-first centuries, as the world celebrated 100 years of wireless communication and the radio, there arose a question—who invented the crystal semiconductor diode, perhaps the most crucial part of a functioning radio at the time? Researchers of science history in the US were surprised to find that it was Jagadish Chandra Bose, an Indian physicist, who held the first American patent on this piece of technology, also the first in the world. This resulted in renewed interest in this unconventional scientist and from that interest arose this book about Bose, the man, the quintessential nationalist, and the physicist-cum-physiologist, and an inventor par excellence whom the world has almost forgotten. This is also the story of the development of radio, its pioneers (Bose being one), and the controversy surrounding the Nobel Prize for Physics for the invention of radio.

The life of Bose the scientist followed a strange trajectory. Between 1895 and 1900, Bose made rapid and remarkable contributions to certain fundamental aspects of modern physics. His legacy to the field of radio engineering was a by-product of this which came about naturally, as though it was almost inevitable, considering the extraordinary inventor that he was. Then there was a sudden shift of his interest from physics to physiology, particularly to plant physiology. Here, too, startling discoveries were made and new inventions created.

Bose was a noted scientist between 1896 and World War II and many early twentieth century textbooks in physics featured his methods and apparatuses. He was elected a fellow of the Royal Society of London and appointed a member of the International Committee on Intellectual Cooperation after World War I. However, within a couple of decades of his death in 1937, the scientific world outside India seemed to forget him. In the face of this, I felt a need to examine the why and wherefore of this blackout through a fresh appraisal of history—what better way to achieve this than to write a biography of the man in question! It is my express desire to write an objective biography with a depiction of both strengths and weaknesses.

As early as 1895, newspapers and science journals in London were agog with the possibility of wireless communication using Bose's inventions. It is no wonder then that Bose's name figured in the controversy that started soon after the announcement of the Nobel Prize for Physics in 1909 or the 'Radio Nobel', as it was popularly known afterwards. The award was for research leading to wireless communication and Bose, an acknowledged pioneer in that subject, was altogether ignored by the Nobel committee. The prize was awarded to two other pioneers, the Italian Guglielmo Marconi and the German Karl F. Braun.

Since then, a few generations in India have grown up hearing rumours that Marconi had somehow made use of Jagadish Chandra Bose's ideas to construct his device for wireless communication. There was a hint of foul play. The rumours almost attained the status of folklore amongst students of science in eastern and northern India, suggesting that Bose was denied proper recognition by the western world in an unjust manner. One variation of this lore is set in the early twentieth century in London. Bose, on an excursion to the capital of the United Kingdom from Calcutta, finds that a man has stolen his notes from his hotel room under the guise of paying the scientist a visit.

During the Victorian era, Calcutta was the capital of British India, and London the capital of the worldwide British empire at its pinnacle. At this time, Bose faced discrimination on the grounds of his race and nationality and was denied a fair salary on his appointment as a college professor in Calcutta. Clearly, the life of a native scholar working under British rule was difficult. It is, therefore, natural to suspect that race and colonial prejudice might have interfered with a fair assessment of his research contributions as well.

There was another complicating factor that played a role in his delayed recognition as a scientist par excellence—his refusal to accept hard and fast subject boundaries. He was a physicist, but he started researching physiology in all earnest, applying the tools of physics to that subject, to the chagrin of many. Physiologists, in general, did not approve of a physicist transgressing into their field of study. His troubles began when he started comparing the response of living tissues and non-living matter, thereby antagonizing some of the eminent plant and animal physiologists of the time. He refers to these acts of his own as breaching the 'etiquette of a caste system'[1] that seemed to prevail among the scientists of the era. Within a few years, he produced startling results. Using his own invention, an instrument called the crescograph, he made plant growth visible to the naked eye. His other remarkable achievement was proving that plants were sensitive beings.

On occasions, at the end of a lecture or seminar, he expressed a profound philosophical belief in the unity of existence among all matter, living and non-living, which seemed far-fetched. But his published research papers and books were all matter of fact and never contained such flourish. His inventions, experiments, and discoveries, both in physics and plant physiology, stood repeated tests flawlessly. Yet the picture is not one of unmixed deprivation and suppression—a significant section of the scholars, academicians, scientists, press, administrators, and policy makers of the ruling nation tried to give him due recognition, but their efforts were thwarted by another group, in which some were motivated by pique, some by a combination of business interests and prejudice, and some, perhaps, by imperial policy.

There is a popular misconception, even in Indian academic circles, that Bose's contribution is not so much to the science of wireless communication, but to the production and study of millimetre waves, which are today also called microwaves, a subcategory of radio waves. He did develop a device to produce millimetre waves, but studying them was not his purpose per se, nor was wireless communication.

Bose was aiming to verify certain fundamental laws of physics regarding radio waves, with the express purpose of putting to test Maxwell's theory of electromagnetism, and to continue Heinrich Hertz's work. This was necessary because Maxwell's theory, at that juncture, had not been fully accepted by physicists who were still looking for comprehensive experimental verification of the theory. The generation

---

[1]'Reply to the Address of the Citizens of Calcutta on 25th January 1921', P. Bhattacharyya (ed.), *Acharya J. C. Bose: A Scientist and a Dreamer*, Vol. 4, Calcutta: Bose Institute, 1997, pp. 96–100.

of millimetre-size radio waves by Bose was only one of the steps in this endeavour. The task involved several other stages and inventions, and Bose's effort was eminently successful and conclusive. Surprisingly, modern authors give sole credit for this to Hertz alone, although early twentieth-century textbooks had duly acknowledged Bose.

Bose was enthusiastic about bringing the study of science to the masses. Following in the footsteps of his teacher Father Lafont, he would organize public lectures on a variety of subjects. He understood that abstruse theory did little to excite public imagination and took to performing simple and attractive experiments in his lectures. One such lecture, in which he demonstrated the power of wireless signalling, attracted the attention of the world and came to acquire historic significance. He sometimes signalled playfully from one part of the college to another, much to the amusement of his students and friends. He invented a series of increasingly efficient receivers and other paraphernalia for these radio waves during the natural course of his research; these instruments formed his contribution to wireless communication.

Father Eugene Lafont, a Jesuit priest of Belgian origin and a renowned professor of physics in St. Xavier's College, Calcutta, stated in a public meeting that if Bose had taken out a patent on his wireless apparatus, he would have forestalled Marconi, and this was widely reported in the newspapers. It is not clear whom the professor blamed for this lapse. Was it Bose for not patenting his inventions? Or was it the Nobel committee for relying too heavily on patents? How was one to make sure that the rumours about Marconi's misdeeds were true? Were they mere fulminations of an overheated nationalist imagination of the suppressed Indian people? The Nobel committee is known to take decisions after much consultation and deliberation, and might not have been unjust, after all. But there have been a few instances of the Nobel being awarded under the influence of political power or otherwise. These outliers have usually occurred in peace and literature, though there is at least one in the field of science, awarded in the 1940s, that would fall in this category. In the end, however, the fact remains that Bose's name was not even in the running for the 1909 Nobel Prize for Physics.

In the late 1990s, the scientific world was amazed at the new discoveries and historical research on wireless communication that started appearing in some renowned journals in the English-speaking world. At this time, I began doing a bit of historical research myself and looked into Bengali and English records and writings available in India. I did not discover much except a small, seemingly innocuous, event that was likely to have some bearing on the entire saga. I decided to include all the bits of information, episodes, and evidences that I found scattered in various books, letters, and scientific journals in this biography. I acknowledge my debt to all historical researchers and will give adequate references whenever necessary. I am especially indebted to Probir K. Bandyopadhyay for performing a kind of detective investigation into the history of the matter. The subject of apportioning credit between Bose and Marconi, which forms a part of this biography, is controversial and the case is balanced on a knife's edge. Hence, I wish to put all materials under one cover for the benefit of an inquisitive reader, and let them draw their own conclusions.

I am grateful to Patrick Geddes, a polymath of Scottish descent who left his mark on the fields of biology, sociology, philanthropy, and urban planning. An admirer of Bose's work on physics and physiology, he came to India from Britain to teach sociology and became a friend of Bose. He went on to write an excellent biography[2] of the latter from which I have liberally drawn. Bose lived seventeen more productive years after this biography was written. Hence, I have drawn also from other writings on Bose, the principal among these being a biography[3] and the correspondence[4] Bose had, at the turn of the century, with his friend Rabindranath Tagore, who was destined to win the Nobel Prize for Literature in 1913. I am indebted to Dibakar Sen, who collected, edited, and clarified the content of the letters with appropriate footnotes.

There were two extraordinary individuals who, most unexpectedly,

---

[2]Patrick Geddes, *The Life and Work of Sir Jagadis C. Bose*, London: Longmans Green and Co., 1920.

[3]Gopalchandra Bhattacharya, Bimalendu Mitra, Manoj Roy, et al. (eds.), *Acharya Jagadis Chandra Bose* (written in Bengali), Calcutta: Basu Bigyan Mandir (Prakaashan Bibhaag), 2008.

[4]Dibakar Sen (ed.), *Patraabali*, Calcutta: Basu Bigyan Mandir (Prakaashan Bibhaag), 1994.

came to the assistance of Bose, when he was passing through the most difficult period of his life. They were Sister Nivedita, alias Miss Margaret Noble, and Mrs Sara Chapman Bull, both Swami Vivekananda's disciples. The former was of Northern Irish origin who had become a Hindu nun. I have borrowed from her biographies written by Lizelle Reymond[5] and Pravrajika Atmaprana[6], and an anthology of her contributions[7]. Mrs Sara Chapman Bull was American and considered a saint by Swami Vivekananda; I have gleaned much material from her biography as well[8]. Another disciple of the Swami and a close friend of Nivedita and Sara, Josephine MacLeod, also offered an occasional helping hand to Bose—I have drawn from his hitherto unpublished letters to MacLeod.

In the prime of his life, Bose had a brilliant student cum assistant, named Basiswar Sen alias Boshi Sen. After assisting Bose for twelve years he departed, due to some disagreements, to set up his own laboratory, first in Calcutta and later in Almora. I have drawn a fair amount from a conjoined biography of Boshi Sen and his wife Gertrude Emerson, a famous globe-trotting geographer.[9]

Although this is not a biography of Marconi, I still required introductory biographical information about him. Marconi's life became eventful only once he started experimenting with wireless telegraphy and tried to get various governments interested. His biographies authored by O. G. Dunlap[10] and Degna Marconi[11] have been useful. I gathered material also from Marconi's own lecture at the Nobel award banquet in Stockholm and various conference and journal papers, as well as some online sources.

---

[5]Lizelle Reymond, *The Dedicated: A Biography of Nivedita*, tr. Jean Herbert, New Delhi: Bee Books, 2017.

[6]Pravrajika Atmaprana, *Sister Nivedita of Ramakrishna-Vivekananda*, Calcutta: Sister Nivedita Girls' School, 1961.

[7]Pravrajika Jnanadaprana (ed.), *The Divine Legacy*, Calcutta: Sri Sarada Math, 2017.

[8]Pravrajika Prabuddhaprana, *Saint Sara: The Life of Sara Chapman Bull, the American Mother of Swami Vivekananda*, Calcutta: Sri Sarada Math, 2014.

[9]Girish N. Mehra, *Nearer Heaven Than Earth: The Life and Times of Boshi Sen and Gertrude Emerson Sen*, New Delhi: Rupa and Co., 2007.

[10]Orrin E. Dunlap Jr, *Marconi: The Man and His Wireless*, New York: The Macmillan Company, 1937.

[11]Degna Marconi, *My Father, Marconi*, New York: McGraw-Hill Book Company, 1962.

This book is divided into nine chapters. The first two chapters 'Making of a Nationalist with a Flair for Invention' and 'Education Abroad and Struggle for Honour at Home' are introductory and give glimpses into the upbringing of Bose, his life in a small town in mid-nineteenth century India, the higher education he received, and the nature of British colonial administration at the time.

'Success Against All Odds and the European Sojourn' gives a non-mathematical, lucid introduction to the physics of waves, the wave theory of light and its properties, aided by simple illustrative diagrams. I have occasionally resorted to over-simplification and repetition in order to reach the uninitiated—my apologies to the purist. Even so if a lay reader is not interested, they may choose to skim through or entirely skip the chapter and still find continuity in the narrative. However, this slightly 'heavy' material adds a new dimension to the reading of a scientist's life, and will make the reader appreciate this biography better; a scientist's life without his science is like a rose without its distinctive fragrance. This third chapter also presents a historical perspective to contextualize Bose's work. It describes his initial research, forays into wireless telegraphy, and his first trip to Europe as a scientist.

Initial success followed by the trials and tribulations of a lonely researcher are depicted in the fourth chapter. In the background, the British rulers are shown preoccupied with containing the nascent Indian freedom movement. Bose's friendship with certain prominent Indian personalities, including Rabindranath Tagore, is also discussed in this chapter. This is also when Sister Nivedita enters the life of the scientist and encourages Mrs Sara Bull to do the same. 'Help Out of the Blue: Rabindranath Tagore, Sister Nivedita, and the Vedanta Circle' also explains the phenomenon of polarization with diagrams, and describes, in some detail, Bose's brilliant research on the rotation of the plane of polarization. His inventions that facilitated wireless communication and his growing interest in physiology are also featured in this chapter.

'Fall from Grace and Redemption' describes his second trip to Europe, and follows Bose as conflicts arise due to his breaking of the unspoken rules of the scientific community with his entry into the field of plant physiology. At this time, he became a victim of blatant plagiarism and had a hard time winning back due credit for his accomplishments.

During these troubled times, Tagore, Sister Nivedita, and Mrs Bull stood by him. The inception of the Nobel prizes at the turn of the twentieth century was a notable event at this time, and finds mention in this chapter. The first Nobel Prize for Physics was awarded to Wilhelm C. Röntgen, whose contribution is compared with Bose's in this book.

'Marconi and Bose: The Paths Cross' gives a brief account of Marconi's achievements and the meeting of the two pioneers of the radio. It deals with old controversies and new historical discoveries. The narrative explores the events leading up to the Nobel Prize awarded for wireless communication, and reveals the principal characters, in the context of controversies and events played across in several countries. 'Bose Turns to Plant Physiology and Tagore Wins the Nobel' discusses Bose's contribution to the field of botany, in particular to plant physiology. Bose's friend Rabindranath Tagore wins the Nobel Prize for Literature but Bose's initial jubilance is dampened due to an unexpected response from Tagore. The founding of the Bose Institute and the benefactions that came in from Sister Nivedita's legacy and from individuals inspired by her are described in 'The Bose Institute and Sister Nivedita'. The last chapter attempts to understand why Bose never acknowledged Sister Nivedita and Mrs Bull. 'The Elderly Scientist and His Declining Years' also gives an account of the life of an ageing scientist, gradually fading into the inevitable sunset, but engaged until the very end with scientific study and its furtherance.

The book uses place name spellings that are historically accurate and in vogue during Bose's times but spells his name as 'Jagadish', in keeping with modern English conventions. That the author should not intrude into a biography is a cardinal principle. I have had to breach this rule, in a few places, in the interest of doing justice to Bose, the unsung genius, and also to some other people in his life. My apology to the discerning reader who may notice.

I am indebted and grateful to several persons for their inspiration and support in writing this biography.

First of all, Dr Arun Kumar[12], a physicist turned economist and a friend, who read some of the early chapters and critiqued them. Initially, I wished to write a monograph on the Bose–Marconi controversy, quite limited in its scope, and these chapters were a part of that. When a potential publisher, on reading these chapters, suggested that I write a full-scale biography of Bose, I was initially daunted by the enormity of the task. It was Arun who said that I had a fresh point of view which should be given expression, and heartened me by saying, 'Kunal, rise to the occasion.'

Dr Vikas Lakhera, a friend, colleague, and professor in the mechanical engineering department of Nirma University, Ahmedabad, who offered constant encouragement. He painstakingly read all the chapters and made valuable corrections and suggestions, over a span of more than two years.

My artist friend Dipak Ghosh who searched the web and downloaded a free soft copy of the biography of Bose by Patrick Geddes.

My niece Amita Majumdar-Giri who found an authentic account of literary events in England culminating with the Nobel Prize award to Rabindranath Tagore.

Many students and one former student, Bhaumik Patel, and my friend Rajveer Upadhyay, an auto-rickshaw driver in Ahmedabad, who helped in constructing the diagrams and figures of the early chapters. Alka Ben Darji and Chirag Patel, both members of the staff in the aforesaid mechanical engineering department, Nirma University, who volunteered occasionally to type up some portions of the early chapters. Neehar Agastya Balantrapu, another former student, who was pursuing a PhD at Virginia Tech in the USA, who helped me in procuring one important reference.

My wife, Snigdha, son Ayanesh, and daughter-in-law Antara who gave constant support and care for the long time that I took to write this book. Ayanesh and Antara also helped me with various intricacies of using a computer.

The mechanical engineering department of Nirma University, Ahmedabad, which provided a congenial environment and good facilities.

---

[12]Malcolm S. Adiseshiah Chair Professor, Institute of Social Sciences, New Delhi.

Last but not least, the team at Aleph: Aienla Ozukum, publishing director, who read the draft of the first five chapters and approved; and Kanika Praharaj, copy editor, for her objective assessment of what was necessary to make the book read better, followed by her meticulous editing; and also, David Davidar, publisher, who first suggested that a scientist of the stature of Professor Jagadish Chandra Bose deserved a new biography written in this century.

MAKING OF A NATIONALIST WITH A FLAIR FOR INVENTION

On a bright morning in February 1899, a man's damaged spine was being X-rayed in a physics laboratory in Calcutta. The laboratory was in Presidency College, the most prestigious college in the capital of the British empire in India and the X-ray operator was Jagadish Chandra Bose, an Indian scientist in his early forties, who had already attained considerable fame within India and abroad. He had acquired a Natural Science Tripos from the University of Cambridge and a B.Sc. from the University of London in 1884 and had been serving as a professor for about fifteen years in the college. He had also been awarded a doctoral degree three years earlier in 1896 by the University of London in recognition of his research on Hertzian waves.

X-ray photography was still in its infancy and the X-ray machine had not gained currency in those days. Bose had built the machine himself, following a newspaper report, and called it Röntgen machine, after its German inventor Wilhelm Röntgen. He had an extremely busy schedule with his lecturing duties and experimental research, and yet he took time off to take X-rays of patients with broken bones, referred to him by a few eminent doctors of the city. Dr Nil Ratan Sarkar, a physician, philanthropist, and educationist and a pioneer in the national science movement, was one of them. Thus, Bose pioneered the use of X-ray in India within four years of its discovery. He gladly accepted this use of his time, thankless in terms of money or fame and irrelevant to his research, only for the sake of the advancement of science and its applications in his home country.

Jagadish Chandra Bose was born on 30 November 1858 to Bhagaban Chandra Bose and his wife Bamasundari Devi in Mymensingh town, located in the northeastern part of the Bengal Presidency. Bhagaban was the headmaster of a school, and had been inspired by the Brahmo

yours Sincerely
J.C. Bose

Professor J. C. Bose

leader Raja Ram Mohan Roy. He had a zeal for social reform and institution building, and a desire to help the common people. True to the Brahmo faith, he had given up all forms of idol worship by the time his son was born.

Bhagaban's ancestral home was in a village in the Bikrampur region located in the western part of Dhaka district in the same Presidency. It was once a flourishing Buddhist centre and had always been considered a seat of learning. The Buddhist period was followed by a Hindu revival; in the twelfth century, the Bikrampur region contained the capital of a Hindu kingdom. The area became a centre for learning the Shastras and attracted students from far afield.

When, after a long period of British rule, a nationalist movement was taking place in nineteenth century India, it was natural that this would take deep roots in the Bikrampur region. It always had a highly cultured middle and upper class, drawn, for the most part, from the upper caste Hindu society, and they took early to 'English education'. This type of education was modelled on the pattern of education prevailing in contemporary England. The learning of the English language was compulsory, but the medium of instruction in general was the vernacular, in this case Bengali. Bhagaban belonged to this elite class. As one of the earliest beneficiaries of this kind of education, he was recruited directly into the service of the British government.

When young Jagadish grew just enough to be aware of his surroundings at about ten years of age, Bhagaban Chandra Bose became a deputy magistrate, and was posted in the Faridpur district adjoining Bikrampur and lived in its capital town, also called Faridpur. During those days a deputy magistrate, in addition to his judicial duties, was required to lead the police force to protect the subjects under his magistracy. He had to be a capable horse rider as well because speedy mobility was essential.

In keeping with his duties, Bhagaban would lead police parties in raiding the hideouts of local criminals in a riverine district full of jungles. Once, a gang of criminals, whom he had captured and sentenced, issued a threat against him while being led away, 'When we get out, we will make the red horse fly.' They kept their unholy promise and set his house on fire in the middle of the night; the family barely escaped with their lives, losing everything else. But Bhagaban remained undaunted and continued to pursue criminals with the same vigour.

A bandit, released from jail after serving his sentence, told Bhagaban that he aspired to reform himself. But he could get no steady means of survival, for who wanted to employ a convict? Bhagaban engaged the man, quite conspicuous due to the many scars on his body, and he served the family faithfully until Bhagaban was transferred from Faridpur.

A young Jagadish would be carried on the servant's shoulders to school and the man would tell thrilling stories of his past exploits to the naive boy. During those days in the riverine parts of Bengal, people often travelled by boat. One day, when the Bose family was travelling by boat to their rural ancestral home at Rarhikhal, several small boats surrounded their large boat in the middle of the river. The bandit turned servant jumped onto the terrace of their houseboat and yelled out a peculiar sonorous call. The raiders understood the meaning of that call—their boats backed off at once and quickly vanished into the nooks of the river.

Bhagaban, after a tiring day at work, still found time to spend with his son, who was now just past the toddling age. He would lie down beside the child after dinner and the latter would ply him with a flood of questions. The father answered them patiently, if he knew the answers. On other occasions, he frankly admitted ignorance. Never did he discourage Jagadish by common utterances such as, 'I am too tired, keep quiet' or 'You are too young to understand this'. Nor did he give evasive answers. He tried his best to find an explanation that the child would be able to comprehend. He thus stoked the fire of enquiry already present in the curious child. Here is an example which adult Jagadish reminisced about:

'Father, today I saw a bush on fire. Going near I found, it was not the bush, but some flies and mosquitoes which had been set on fire. Who did that? Why?' His father explained they were not mosquitoes but a special kind of insects. 'They are called jonaaki pokaa, fireflies; nobody has set them aflame. Their rear glows at night, on its own, to enable them to see in the dark. I do not know how it happens. We know too little about such things.'

In Faridpur, and later in life when Bhagaban was transferred to Burdwan and still later to Calcutta, his characteristic stubbornness and pluck showed up in the things he pursued beyond the pale of his duties. There was, as if, an inner call to pursue these activities that he considered good for his subjugated country. Bhagaban observed how the handloom industry that supplied the common people with their textiles was fast dwindling due to imports of cheap cloth, produced by steam-powered machines from England. Many other traditional crafts were weakening and people were becoming impoverished due to colonial policy, and he foresaw the looming economic danger. As a means to avert it, he established an agricultural and industrial exhibition in Faridpur. Wherever he went, he tried to revive the ancient arts and crafts and put together melas, where handcrafted products could be marketed.

He noticed how the poor were often in need of loans and fell prey to moneylenders who offered credit at exorbitant rates of interest. He set up a bank in Faridpur some time in the 1860s and called it 'Peoples' Bank', which perhaps was the first cooperative society in Bengal that offered easy credit to the needy. He purchased many shares of this bank as the founder-director, and, soon enough, the enterprise prospered. But he did not consider the bank a business, rather his contribution to society, and soon left it to others to manage. He gave away his shares to those friends whom he considered to be in great need. The bank continued to prosper even after he left Faridpur. Had he retained his shares, the earnings would have provided for his family in the times of distress that were soon to come.

That Jagadish was a determined and plucky boy became apparent early in his life. When he was only five years old, his father bought him a pony. He became an expert pony rider, strutting about on his pony. During a horse race in Faridpur, one of the organizers saw Jagadish atop his pony and, much to the amusement of everyone, put him in line for the race. The little boy was least afraid among the much larger beasts, and took part in the race all the way, though he came in last. The public's applause for the boy on the pony was tumultuous.

As a young child, Jagadish became fond of clay modelling. His grandmother, who had continued the traditional Hindu way of worship, would make a clay model of Lord Shiva every day and, at the end of the day, would throw it away. Jagadish would wait for this moment, pick up the well-kneaded clay, and make toys of his own. This was the beginning of his fondness for making and shaping objects of utility, a quality so necessary for an inventor.

Jagadish was sent at age five to a pathshala, established by his father in Faridpur. Here he received his early education in reading and writing in Bengali; arithmetic; Indian epics, such as the Mahabharata and Ramayana; Hindu mythologies; fables imparting moral education; and ancient culture woven around the teachings of the rishis. These sages were embodiments of virtue and renunciation, and remained an inspiration to this nationalist in the making for the rest of his life. His schoolmates were children of farmers, fishermen, and cowherds who told him stories of their own lives, woven around the land and its animals and creatures, found in forests and at great depths of mighty rivers, which instilled in him a love for plants and animals.

The flip side of these traditional schools was that they encouraged learning by rote and discouraged games and sports of any sort. The teacher at Jagadish's pathshala strictly forbade the pupils to play even during the free hours in the afternoon and kept an alert watch. He wanted them to memorize their lessons and multiplication tables instead. But the children always found ways of eluding him. They played cricket on a road crossing, well away from the school, and kept scouts on the approach road to give an early warning in case their teacher suddenly appeared. Occasionally, the master came looking and the boys dived into the shallow ditch running by the roadside and covered themselves with dry leaves. Once the danger passed, they came out and resumed their game with renewed glee.

What was remarkable in this game was the ball. The bats and stumps were crudely made by the local carpenter, but the ball was made by extracting latex from the local rubber tree and rolling the matter carefully into a round shape. It was done by the boys themselves as per the description given by Jagadish; he never claimed credit for this boyish innovation.

Even as late as in the 1950s, when this author was a boy, factory made rubber balls were not to be found in rural India, and though boys played many home-grown games, cricket was never one of them due to the absence of a ball. The most popular game was gulli danda, which involved a two-foot-long stick and a small piece of round wood tapered at both ends, easily made by chiselling. Latex-oozing trees were available but nobody ever thought to make an improvised ball, as that art was not known. One wonders whether the improvised ball was an early innovation of young Jagadish, who certainly was the leader of the group.

In nineteenth-century Bengal, performing theatre troupes travelled from one place to another, enacting scenes and episodes from the Ramayana and Mahabharata. Young Jagadish understood these performances easily, since his teacher in school also dwelt on these epics at length. He found the characters in the Ramayana—Rama, Sita, and Lakshmana—too perfect, but certain characters in the Mahabharata, particularly those of Karna and Arjuna, captivated him. They were chariot-borne great warriors fighting on the opposite sides of an epic battle. Karna was abandoned in a river by his warrior-caste Kshatriya mother Kunti as a newborn and was brought up by a lower-caste couple of humble origins. As he grew older, Karna gravitated towards various martial arts, particularly archery, which he learnt from a famous guru.

Kunti, Karna's biological mother, was also the mother of the five brothers who are the central characters in the epic. The third brother in the Pandavas, Arjuna, is a hero, a spiritually inclined warrior who was compelled to fight unfairly on occasion, and suffered due to pangs of regret. Kunti approached Karna just before the battle started, divulged the secret of his birth, and tried to reclaim her 'lost' motherhood, begging him to change sides. Karna would neither disown his foster parents, whom he continued to love and respect until the end, nor would he change sides. Then, Kunti begged him to spare the life of her five sons. Karna promised not to harm any of her sons, except Arjuna, whose death at the hands of Karna was set as the ultimate challenge by his friend and master Duryodhana.

In the end, the two confront each other in battle. Karna had reserved a weapon, a special arrow, for slaying Arjuna. When he let the arrow fly, Arjuna's charioteer Krishna—who was actually an avatar of Vishnu—shook the earth and the arrow missed Arjuna by a hair's breadth. However, the missed arrow did not fall to the ground at all but returned to Karna's hand on its own; Karna had not known that the arrow was magical and was surprised. The arrow begged him to be launched again. But Karna always fought fair and did not want to use a magical arrow to fell his enemy. When he took out another arrow from his quiver, Krishna made one of the wheels of Karna's chariot sink into the earth. Karna jumped down to lift the wheel and then, advised by Krishna, Arjuna launched his most lethal arrow to cut down an unarmed Karna. Jagadish, as he grew up, saw a reflection of Karna in his father, who was always heroically battling to do good for his people, but failed repeatedly, forever ill-treated by fate.

In Bose's own words:

> All this also gave a lower and lower idea of all ordinary worldly success—how small the so-called victories are!—and with this a higher and higher idea of conflict and defeat; and of the true success born of defeat. In such ways I have come to feel one with the highest spirit of my race...that the only real and spiritual advantage and victory is to fight fair, never to take crooked ways, keep to the straight path, whatever be in the way.

This, of course, is Bose's interpretation of the 'highest spirit' of the Indian race. In the episode narrated above, Arjuna at first refused to take aim at the unarmed Karna. Promptly, Krishna reminded Arjuna how his sixteen-year-old son, Abhimanyu, had been surrounded by seven charioteers and killed in a most unfair manner earlier in the war. Karna was one of the seven and a reluctant participant—his hands had been forced by his master Duryodhana. The dithering Arjuna was roused to indignation by Krishna's recollection of the slaying of his son and he took Karna's life.

The message of the Mahabharata is not at all as simplistic as the one Bose chose to imbibe. The ultimate goal is to establish 'dharma', which is a combination of truth, justice, and righteousness, but if the enemy plays unfair, it is necessary to stoop to their level to exact revenge. The truth is that Bose idolized Karna as his tragic hero, because his role model was his noble but unlucky father.

Jagadish's early schooling was an exception rather than a rule, for most children from his caste and class were sent to schools established by the British, where they had to learn the English language, although the medium of instruction was Bengali. Very few in this class in Bengal sent their boys to English-medium schools, which were only located in big cities like Calcutta and Dacca. Bhagaban decided to send his son to a traditional school because he wanted Jagadish to become firmly anchored in ancient Indian culture right in the beginning of his life and feel one with the common folk of his motherland and their struggles. Bhagaban viewed the presumptuous air of superiority of the upper class, products of English education, with distaste.

In 1869, when Jagadish was only ten years old, his father was posted to Burdwan district as an assistant commissioner. In 1870, after an epidemic of the newly arrived malaria disease in the district, many perished leaving behind numerous orphans. Bhagaban organized relief with full vigour and founded small training units to provide vocational training to orphaned boys. Since no building was available, he used a part of his large house and compound to open workshops in carpentry, metal turning, and even foundry. Here, young Jagadish's inventive tendency found an expression. Convincing his mother to give up some brass vessels and utensils, traditionally used in Indian households those days, he conceived of a toy cannon. He then persuaded a foundry man to melt the brass and cast the cannon. This was large enough to be fired and was later used on occasions of his choosing.

In Burdwan, Bhagaban took another remarkable decision—he sent his son to a school in Calcutta, named Hare School. Jagadish had to live in a hostel in Mirzapur Street, where some of the boarders were his older relatives. This was a hostel run by the Brahmo religious sect and here Jagadish came in contact with the Brahmo religious thoughts in a more intensive way.[1]

---

[1]The 'a' in Brahmo simulates the sound of the 'a' as in 'father'.

He studied in Hare School for a few months, after which he was shifted to St. Xavier's School, where the medium of instruction was English and his classmates were mostly children of the British residents of Calcutta. His situation was utterly perplexing, an Indian boy in the midst of English boys, a country boy in the midst of boys used to city life, and, above all, a boy whose knowledge of English was merely alphabetical in the midst of boys whose mother tongue was English. It speaks volumes of his resilience and merit that he coped with teasing and occasional bullying from his classmates, and the foreign language as the medium, and managed to pass his examinations. Perhaps his preceding stay at the Hare School had provided him with a cushion to absorb all the shocks.

In the hostel, other boys were all college students and took no notice of the little chap. During his leisure hours, devoid of any company, the young lad went back to his village hobbies and pursuits. He acquired pets and tended to them, and laid out a garden in one corner of the compound of his hostel where he grew flowers and vegetables. When he was younger, he had been fascinated by a stream near his home in the village, with a small bridge over it. When it was in spate, Jagadish would stand on the bridge and look at the rushing waters in wonder. As an expression of his engineering instinct, in this little garden he created a replica, albeit on a much smaller scale, of the stream of his childhood and constructed a wooden bridge over it. This required some elaborate piping and a manual pump and some carpentry. The money for this came from the small allowance given by his father for his incidental expenses.

His happiest times were during the vacations when he returned home to the company of his sisters. On one such occasion, he constructed a house with bricks and mud for his pet animals in one corner of the large compound. His merry sisters were his assistants in this endeavour. Much later, when he was to found a research institute in Calcutta, he again returned to the theme of a flowing stream with an overbridge while designing the surrounding landscape. He had a love for a hands-on approach to all kinds of practical work, an essential quality in all inventors.

Soon, Jagadish grew to be a healthy and spirited adolescent, having inherited some of the pluck of his father. The senior Bose, as a deputy magistrate, maintained a fair stable of horses. During his vacations

Jagadish took lessons in horse riding from the hired hand that looked after the horses and became a skilled rider. Once, the adventurous spirit of early youth led him to take a fearful risk that could have cost him his life. At age fifteen, while riding in the countryside he came across a stream in spate and attempted to ford it on horseback. The riverbed in the middle had been cut deep by swirling waters; the horse stepped into a cavity, lost his balance, and turned over, trapping the rider underneath. Jagadish not only disentangled himself but also rescued the horse and led it to safety. Thereafter, the animal would tolerate no other rider, not even his father.

As deputy magistrate, Bhagaban had an attendant who was a retired Rajput sepoy who taught a young Jagadish how to shoot a gun. During one vacation, Jagadish went game hunting in the Terai jungles in the foothills of the Himalayas. This was his first brush with dense jungles and wildlife and would stay with him forever.

In 1875, Bhagaban became the executive officer, in charge of the Katowa subdivision. In 1880, a great famine struck these parts and he plunged into relief work wholeheartedly, often neglecting his own needs. By the time the famine passed, his health was in ruins and he suffered a mild stroke of paralysis that forced him to take a two-year sick leave at a reduced salary.

Even during this period of illness, Bhagaban kept on planning activities that he considered necessary for his country. He reasoned that if Scotsmen could come to his land and start tea plantations by converting jungles, then Indians too should be able to match such enterprise. When he recovered a little, he purchased acres of land in Assam—although conditions there were not conducive to good health—and started a tea garden. The returns were slow and the debts he incurred in the process were heavy; his considerable savings dwindled fast. The business languished for a long time but did not die, and eventually became successful in the hands of his daughters' sons, though, sadly, not in his lifetime.

His next project came in the form of a Bombay weaving mill, into which he invested his remaining capital. He felt this would be his way of helping make his country independent of foreign clothes, only to later realize that he had been a victim of fraud when the directors of the mill vanished with his money. He had stood security for others' kindred enterprises, and when those failed too, the burden of their debt fell on him. Fortunately, he recovered sufficiently to return to work at the end of his leave, and again started drawing his regular and considerable salary. However, he could never discharge his debts fully even after retirement from his job.

Years later, when Jagadish started earning, he sold some of the family's ancestral properties, added his own savings to the fund, and paid off his father's debts and the outstanding interests. Within one year of this Bhagaban breathed his last. In all likelihood, this was in 1895; it is not known what happened to Jagadish's mother after this. It is obvious that Bhagaban was a man with a kind, patriotic heart who worked towards the betterment of his fellow countrymen, and who had lived much ahead of his times. In the eyes of most people and the society at large, Bhagaban was a failure, a person who had wrecked his health through reckless and unwise activities, and died in penury; but not so for young Jagadish. His father was a role model and left an imprint on him, and later he was to refer to his father as 'a failure that was great' in a public address.

In 1875, Jagadish passed Calcutta University's entrance examination with a first division and earned a scholarship at the age of sixteen and began attending St. Xavier's College for a degree in natural science. Father Lafont, a Jesuit priest of Belgian origin, who had come to India in 1865, was one of his teachers. Lafont had established a well-equipped laboratory for scientific experiments in the college and a makeshift meteorological observatory on the terrace of the college building. He would make notes of meteorological data in this observatory daily and once accurately predicted the arrival of a cyclone well in advance, so that precautionary measures could be initiated by the government, saving many lives and considerable property.

Lafont's students, young Jagadish among them, were taught many a lesson in the college laboratory and observatory. They admired his dedication to teaching, his lucid expositions, and innovative experimental demonstrations. Jagadish's performance at the college was not extraordinary but respectable. Though he was inspired by his teacher, he showed no external sign of it at that time. Later in life, after being well known as a scientist, he attributed his love for physics and experiments in general to this excellent teacher.

After he graduated from college with a B.A. degree in 1880, Jagadish was faced with a conflict. On one hand, his father's financial affairs were in a sorry state and he was paying enormous amounts in interest to his creditors; Jagadish understood that it was time to stand by his father and look for profitable employment. On the other hand, he wanted to pursue higher education in England. So, he decided to compete for the Indian Civil Service (ICS), which offered the most lucrative career at that time. For this he would need to travel all the way to London. The preparatory classes and the qualifying examination were held in London, and Indians who aspired for this service had to live in the city.

There was another fact that might have influenced his decision; if one had the ability, it did not take long to qualify and get recruited into the ICS. Surprisingly, Bhagaban's refusal as regards that particular career was absolute—his son was to rule nobody but himself, to paraphrase Jagadish's own words in this context. Why this was so requires an explanation and has much to do with the kind of education the British government had instituted for creating a special class of people, from whom many in the ICS were drawn. The architect of the colonial education policy, Thomas B. Macaulay, came to India in 1834 as a member of the council of the governor general, the top administrator of the country. Macaulay laid out the principles of a new education system with the concurrence of the then Governor General Lord Bentinck. Macaulay asserted:

> [I]t is impossible for us, with our limited means, to attempt to educate the body of the people. We must at present do our best to form a class who may be interpreters between us and the millions whom we govern—a class of persons Indian in blood and colour, but English in tastes, in opinions, in morals, and in intellect. To that class we may leave it to refine the vernacular dialects of the country, to enrich those dialects with terms of science borrowed from the Western nomenclature, and to render them by degrees fit vehicles for conveying knowledge to the great mass of the population.

To the credit of Macaulay, he had no disdain for the Indian languages or dialects; on the contrary, he wished his anglicized brown sahibs to 'refine the vernacular dialects'. The English Education Act 1835 that was promulgated by Bentinck closely resembled the recommendations of Macaulay, and India's first English-medium school named La Martiniere was established in the following year in Calcutta.

However, the government, and the British businessmen residing in Calcutta and their Indian collaborators did not succeed in multiplying such English-medium schools, and their numbers remained few. Meanwhile, the government and British businesses also needed a large number of clerks who were required to have only a rudimentary and working knowledge of English in addition to other skills, and therefore the authorities had to compromise and did not implement the education policy strictly.

Unknown to Macaulay, Indians themselves had started learning English and appreciating the suitability of the western education system for the times. These modernist Indian intellectuals, led by the famous social reformer Raja Ram Mohan Roy, had mobilized public opinion in favour of what they called 'English education'. They established a number of schools in Calcutta that had modern syllabi, modelled on the pattern of western education, where English as a language was taught, but the medium of instruction was Bengali. This was in the first quarter of the nineteenth century, much before Macaulay arrived.

Two decades or so later, Ishwar Chandra Vidyasagar, a renowned scholar of Sanskrit who had taught himself English, came to the forefront of the education movement and set up more such modern, Bengali-medium schools. It is this pattern of schooling that quickly spread all over Bengal Presidency, aided both by the government and public-minded individuals. Bhagaban C. Bose, father of Jagadish, was educated in one such school.

However, schools like the La Martiniere, no matter how few in number, made their mark. They turned out a number of Indians who proceeded to London and succeeded in qualifying for the ICS, competing with native Britishers. A few graduates of the Bengali-medium schools also competed for the ICS and qualified. Some of the ICS men aped the British as per Macaulay's prescription, so much so that they appeared as caricatures.

The British considered the ICS as the steel frame of the British empire in India, such was the loyalty and competence of the men. However, one guesses from Bhagaban's attitude and actions, that he considered the ICS as the steel chain that held the country's subjects down for economic exploitation; he viewed with disdain such men of power, Indian in blood but anglicized in culture, and forbade his son Jagadish from joining their ranks.

Bamasundari Devi, Jagadish's mother, also raised stiff objections, not to any particular profession, but to her only son's long absence, an unavoidable part of travel to Europe. She had lost her second son in his infancy and was especially attached to her only surviving son. In the end, she overcame her emotions and accepted her son's ardent wish to pursue his education abroad. She even pledged to sell all her gold ornaments to finance his trip.

After much debate, it was finally decided that Jagadish would go to England. This decision was aided by the fact, as mentioned before, that his father had by now recovered sufficiently from his bout of ill health and the mild stroke of paralysis, and could return to work; he would no longer be drawing a much-reduced salary and Bamasundari's gold would remain intact. The family would live more frugally and pool in all available resources. Jagadish decided to pursue medicine as his career of choice in England and received his father's approval.

His journey to England marked the end of the first phase of Jagadish's life. He had now reached maturity and aspired to serve his motherland while standing by his family, who were now leading a bare existence and drowning in debt. He wanted to train to be a doctor abroad and return to India to serve his country and do his filial duty. He had learnt to admire the senior Bose despite his follies. To understand Jagadish's attitude, motivation, and vision at the outset of his career, it would be appropriate to quote from what he was to say decades later:

> My father was one of the earliest to receive the impetus characteristic of the modern epoch as derived from the West. And in his case, it came to pass that the stimulus evoked the latent potentialities of his race for evolving modes of expression demanded by the period of transition in which he was placed. They found expression in great constructive work.... Every one of his efforts failed and the crash

came.... A failure? Yes, but not ignoble or altogether futile. Since it was through the witnessing of this struggle that the son learned to look on success or failure as one, to realize that some defeat was greater than victory. And if my life in any way proved to be fruitful, then that came through the realization of this lesson.... And it is on the wreck of a life like his and many such lives that will be built the Greater India yet to be.

2

EDUCATION ABROAD AND
STRUGGLE FOR HONOUR AT HOME

During a vacation from St. Xavier's College, Jagadish was invited by a wealthy landowning friend from Assam, a crack shot and a hunter himself, to spend time hunting in his forests that had wild buffalos and rhinos. On his arrival at the railway station, Jagadish found a palanquin waiting to take him to his destination. Then followed an overnight journey of over 33 kilometres into the isolated interiors of Assam, during which Jagadish dozed off, lulled by the slow and rhythmic movement of the palanquin. He spent the next day trekking and exploring his surroundings, along with his friend. However, before night fell he was overcome by a high fever. For fear that it might grow worse, it was agreed that he should return at once to Calcutta.

But the palanquin was not available then for a journey to the railway station; the only means available was a horse, a racer that was somewhat untamed and wild in spirit, his friend warned. Still, Jagadish decided to have a go at riding this horse. As he made a cautious approach, the horse reared and tried to crush him with his front hooves. He dodged the attack and quickly mounted. The horse bolted at once, allowing the rider no time to say a proper farewell. The ride for the first 22 kilometres was a tumultuous one, as the horse raced at breakneck speed and Jagadish barely managed to steer it onto the right track. Then the horse got tired and broke into a comfortable trot to the station. The long train journey delivered a young man, absolutely exhausted and shivering with high fever, to his home.

The doctors in Calcutta diagnosed him with malaria. He was repeatedly treated with quinine but it provided only temporary relief. The fever kept returning frequently and he had much difficulty in completing his bachelor's degree, which he earned in the year 1880. Before embarking on the long sea voyage to England, it was hoped that the sea air would improve his health but the reverse happened. He was quite ill for most of the journey and once even collapsed on the way to the doctor's consultation room.

On setting foot in the British Isles, the illness subsided, though it returned periodically. He enrolled for the course in medicine at the University of London and enjoyed learning zoology under the tutelage of the able Ray Lankester. Though he passed the preliminary exam without much difficulty, his worsening health became a cause for concern. He suffered increased attacks of the disease, which was aggravated by the chemicals he inhaled in the dissecting room. His physician, a professor in the medical college, Dr Ringer, who had been treating him with arsenical injections and other medications without success, advised him to leave medicine, and Jagadish took the sage advice.

He decided to pursue science at Cambridge. At the outset of his studies, he was required to learn Latin and Greek. While Greek could be replaced with Sanskrit later, he had to struggle through learning Latin. After passing the entrance examination, he managed to secure a scholarship to learn natural science at Christ's College and enrolled in January 1881. He took the bold decision to stop taking all medications, and instead took to spending long hours outdoors, particularly punting on the River Cam. Once, while on the river, his boat toppled over, taking him into the icy waters of the Cam. But Bose persisted with his sporting activities. Physical exercise and fresh air worked on his body better than medicine, and his fever started to recede.

Well into his second year at Cambridge, he got rid of the fever entirely and regained his health and vitality. The fact that he contracted the disease in Assam and it was not treatable with quinine, indicates that perhaps it was not malaria he was suffering from, but black fever or kala-azar, a disease that often proves to be fatal. He had been lucky to escape its grip; now that he was well, he could devote his full energy to his scientific studies. This was also the time when he became a member of the Natural Science Club in the university, which meant that he became a learner of science even in his leisure.

As a newcomer in Cambridge, he was first befriended by a set of boys notorious for undertaking all kinds of frivolous activities other than academics. Bose was gently advised by his watchful tutor to drop these acquaintances, following which came a phase of solitude in Bose's life. But in his second year at the university, with his health restored, he became a full-blooded undergraduate and befriended many in the halls of residence and also in the Natural Science Club.

His first summer vacation was spent in the sunbathed Isle of Wight off the coast of Hampshire. While boating far out in the Shanklin Bay, he was caught in a storm and struggled hard and long to reach back to safety. The strain brought on a relapse of the fever. He was fortunate to have a kind landlady who nursed him back to health. The next summer was spent in trekking through the Scottish Highlands with a group of friends.

Initially, Jagadish was unsure about which of the myriad subjects in science he would like to focus on. To make up his mind, he decided to attend as many lectures and laboratories as possible. This gave him a healthy width of view in science and was reflected in crucial turns he took as a researcher later in life. He savoured the papers presented and the discussions that followed at the Natural Science Club, where he acquired quite a few acquaintances. Among them were Theodore Beck, later principal of the Muhammadan Anglo-Oriental College; Fitzpatrick, the physicist; and Joseph Reynolds Green, a botanist.

Among the teachers who taught him during his first year at Cambridge and whom he always remembered with gratitude were Michael Foster for Physiology and Francis Balfour for Embryology. In the second year, he found his focus and chose Physics, Chemistry, and Botany as his subjects. He loved Professor Vines's lectures and laboratory in Botany, Professor James Dewar's lectures on Chemistry and Professor Francis Darwin's course on Vegetable Physiology. Most of all, he loved the teachings of Lord Rayleigh, whose meticulous experimentation and style of gradually uncovering the nature of physics left an indelible impression on the young scientist's psyche. His teachers too were satisfied with their student and it reflected in the ease with which he earned the Natural Science Tripos at the University of Cambridge, and at the same time a B.Sc. degree at the University of London.

Jagadish had been missing his family after a long stay of four years in a foreign land. He was always acutely aware of their frugal life and the difficulties they were facing. After graduation he could no longer resist the inner call to return home. At this point there was a fortunate turn of events. Henry Fawcett, the economist, was then the postmaster general of the United Kingdom and an old acquaintance of a Calcutta barrister Ananda Mohan Bose, who happened to be married to Jagadish's older sister. This connection now became useful. Professor Fawcett invited Jagadish to talk and followed it up by enquiring from his colleague Lord Kimberley, then secretary of state for India, about vacancies in the education department. The latter made queries and, after a while, replied that at the moment there were none.

Fawcett advised Bose to go back to India and look for a suitable job, and gave a letter of introduction for Lord Ripon, the Viceroy of India. Docking at Bombay, on the way to Calcutta, Bose made a detour and reached Shimla to present the letter to Ripon. He was given a most warm and cordial reception by the viceroy, who at once promised to nominate him to the Higher Educational Service. In the course of conversation Ripon spontaneously burst out in frustration to say, 'My life has been a failure; I wanted to serve India, and to give Indians more responsibilities. At first all seemed promising, but then came this Ilbert affair! I never thought our English liberal tradition can be thus abandoned.'

The so-called Ilbert affair, named after Courtenay Ilbert, gives an idea of the racial prejudice that existed in the British society in India. Until Ripon had taken charge, the criminal procedure code was so racially biased that a British offender could be tried only by a British judge and could under no circumstances be tried by an Indian judge or magistrate. Ripon, of liberal disposition and inclined to reform, consulted and influenced Courtenay Ilbert, who was then the legal adviser to the Council of India.

A bill to empower Indian judges to try a British accused was soon introduced by Ilbert. The proposed bill raised a storm of controversy both in India and Britain, and faced stiff opposition from the British tea and indigo planters, who were given to terrible ill-treatment of the Indian labourers and farmers. They were afraid that an Indian judge would likely not overlook their misdeeds. An overwhelming majority of the British women in India were also opposed to the bill on the specious ground that they would be unduly humiliated by Indian judges. British India had an unhealthy sex ratio, with the number of men well in excess of women, which resulted in adultery and numerous court cases which hitherto were tried by European judges; the new bill threatened to put them before judges of Indian origin.

The whole campaign was tinged by racial prejudice and Lord Ripon earned the derisive nickname 'Ripon the Good'. Finally, as a compromise, a much-diluted bill was passed having the following provision: an Indian judge facing a British offender on the dock can conduct the trial but the verdict would be delivered by a jury, at least half of which would be British nationals. Until then, trial by jury had not been the order of the day. Thus, the diluted bill became law in January 1884, precisely the year of Bose's return to India, and he walked into an atmosphere vitiated by racial tension.

On reaching Calcutta and meeting the director of public instruction, Bose found that the viceroy, true to his promise, had already nominated him; but the director, Sir Alfred Croft, did not seem pleased and blurted out, 'I am usually approached from below and not from above. There is no higher-class appointment at present available in the Imperial Educational Service. I can only offer you a place in the Provincial Service, from which you may be promoted.' In the course of the short conversation, Sir Alfred also expressed in no uncertain terms that Indians were inherently incapable of the exactitude and precision demanded by modern science.

To describe matters simply, the education service was divided into two departments, the Higher Education Service that was more or less reserved for the Britons and the Provincial Service, which was open to all. An Indian serving in the latter, and for long with distinction, was eligible for promotion to the higher service, but even then, at two-thirds the pay of a British counterpart.

In 1833, the British had thrown open the ICS to Indians because they needed competent men with knowledge of local conditions and customs. There was a qualifying examination which all the aspirants, British or Indian, had to pass. However, even here the two-thirds rule applied to the salary of the Indians vis-à-vis the English. There was no other formalized discrimination between the two, although its informal existence was easily noticeable. In the Higher Educational Service, where the appointments were only by nomination and not by qualification, discrimination was formalized and bound by regulations.

Indians, even when in possession of degrees from prestigious European universities, were never nominated directly to the higher service. Bose weighed the offer of a place in the Provincial Service, found it unsuitable, and declined. So, his name did not appear in the next gazette brought out by the government, which routinely reflected all government appointments and this was noticed by the viceroy. He called for an explanation from the Bengal government and thus the director of public instruction was pressured to act. He wrote a letter requesting Bose to appear. Bose met the man, who made no effort to conceal his irritation. He said that his hands had been forced and he could only offer the position of officiating professor in Calcutta's Presidency College with no claim to permanence; later, if Bose was found competent, he might be considered for permanence.

Jagadish also learnt that by virtue of being Indian, he was entitled to a fraction of the salary drawn by a British counterpart, and by virtue of the 'officiating' tag attached to his position, he would draw only half of the aforementioned fraction. In effect, he was offered one-third the salary of a British professor, having the same duties and responsibilities. He joined the service but refused to accept his salary until the situation was resolved in his favour.

What he had faced so far was discrimination against a subjugated people, which at its root might have been primarily the ruler's privilege, independent of race. After joining the college, he realized that there was another kind of prejudice that was purely racial in origin. In the late nineteenth century, phrenology became quite popular all across Europe. It involved a detailed study of the human skull, its shape and size and it was widely believed that this study could predict the character and ability of the human specimen under scrutiny. A defining theory in the field of phrenology was that native Europeans have a certain phrenological bump in the middle of their cranium, which other races lacked, suggesting that they were the superior race.

Very many among the British held that Indians were quite capable in the field of metaphysics, language, and literature; they were good in speculative subtleties; but they were terribly wanting when it came to matters of exact thought and precise work, as required in science.

This incapacity was said to be racial in origin, and the British colonial establishment was quite vocal about it.

It was on this ground, Bose learnt, that the principal of Presidency College, Charles H. Tawney, and the director of public instruction, Sir Alfred Croft had initially objected to his appointment until, of course, their hands were forced 'from above'. Whatever be the root cause of discrimination, he found the atmosphere in the college to be stifling. So, he resolved to struggle against it for the sake of his personal dignity as well as the status and honour of his fellow countrymen in academia.

From the outset he decided to fulfil all his assignments and go beyond the scope of his duties. At the same time, as a matter of protest, he kept refusing his monthly salary for the next three years or so. Left without any means and fully aware that his father was heavily in debt, he chose not to draw on him for sustenance. His sister Subarnaprabha and brother-in-law Dr Mohinimohan Basu came to his rescue and invited him to stay with them at their Calcutta residence.

Bose's first biographer and close friend Patrick Geddes, a British national himself, has recorded that Bose had urged him to remain silent about the discrimination he faced. But Geddes, true to his conscience, brooked no such thing and provided an objective description. Bose, as was characteristic of him, bore no bitterness afterwards towards his detractors. This magnanimity, almost to a fault, comes forth on several subsequent occasions, and at least once landed him into great trouble, almost ruining his research career.

Bose, once settled in his job, started paying attention to his father's financial affairs. He persuaded the senior Mr Bose to give him permission to sell all the ancestral properties in Rarhikhal and Bikrampur, and promptly proceeded to each location to execute the deeds. This was heart-wrenching for the entire family, for tradition has it that a Bengali Hindu never sells properties hallowed by his ancestors. His mother had some gold of her own and Jagadish prevailed upon her to part with it. Thus, a major part of the debt was settled; the overjoyed creditors exempted him of the remaining. But Jagadish never forgot what his family owed them and gradually paid them back in full. His parents did not survive to see their son's scientific success. His father died a year after the family debts were repaid and his mother two years after that.

In pursuit of his career, Bose put his heart and soul into teaching. Inspired by his teachers, Father Lafont and Lord Rayleigh, he used experimental demonstrations in the classroom to bring science alive for his students. Generally, the students of the Presidency College were drawn from among the best in Bengal. A few of his students went on to become physicists themselves and many more became successful academics and professionals in diverse fields. They confided in his biographer, Patrick Geddes, that Bose had the rare ability to present the most abstruse ideas with great lucidity and clarity. Soon, he became so popular that students competed with each other to secure the front seats in his class. Alongside this he fulfilled his other duties to the best of his abilities.

In about three years' time it became apparent to both Charles Tawney and Sir Alfred Croft that the service rendered by Bose was more than at par with his British counterparts, and they became his staunch admirers. The director understood that Bose was firm in matters of principle, and Bose realized that it was best to stand up to an Englishman and demand dignity and only then could he hope to earn his friendship. As a mark of appreciation, the director converted, by a special government order, Bose's temporary appointment as a professor to a permanent one with retroactive effects. As a result, Bose received the preceding three years' pay in lump sum and used it to settle most of his father's remaining debt. The rest he paid up over the next six years from his savings.

About four years after Bose's entry into the Imperial Service as a professor in Presidency College, another highly qualified Indian, Dr Prafulla Chandra Ray, sought appointment in the college. When Bose had been a student in Britain, Prafulla arrived in the country with his brother Dwarakanath for higher studies. Bose and another Indian student had received them on their very first day in a foreign land and made them comfortable.

After finishing school, Ray had taken admission in the First Course in Arts or F.A. in the Metropolitan Institution in Calcutta. Chemistry was compulsory but the college had no facilities for teaching the subject. So, through a special arrangement, the institution's students attended classes at Presidency College, taught by an enthusiastic British professor, Alexander Pedler. These classes proved inspirational for Ray who developed a lifelong love for the subject.

Prafulla earned a D.Sc. in Chemistry from the University of Edinburgh and returned to India in 1888, while Dwarakanath pursued a career in medicine. For about two years, Dr Prafulla Chandra Ray was denied a professorial appointment in Presidency College in spite of his excellent credentials. Finally, owing to the recommendations of Bose, the college opened its doors to Ray, but that with an offer of a position in the low-paying Provincial Service. Ray accepted the job and Bose had a fellow Indian for company in the college.

Bose had, in the meantime, married Abala Das, daughter of Durgamohan Das, also from Bikrampur, in a simple ceremony in January 1887. Durgamohan, a prominent advocate in the Calcutta high court, was a Brahmo by faith and a well-known social reformer. He had collaborated with Jagadish's father in some of his nationalistic enterprises and thus developed a close friendship with him. Durgamohan went counter to tradition to educate all his daughters.

Abala was amongst the earliest students of Banga Mahila Vidyalaya, a school for Bengali women, and later Bethune School, established by John Elliot Drinkwater Bethune, an Anglo-Indian lawyer philanthropist. She was a bright student and passed her college entrance examination with a scholarship in 1881. She used her Bengal government scholarship to secure admission in a medical college in 1882 in the city of Madras (now Chennai), because the Calcutta Medical College did not permit women's enrolment. She had just appeared for her final exam at the end of the course, when she fell ill and had to return home. Soon, at the age of twenty-two, she was married to Bose, who was twenty-nine at the time. She did not even have the chance to enquire about the result of the exam. It so turned out that she had actually passed with decent grades.

Durgamohan advised the couple to live on their own for a while and Jagadish took up a rented residence in Chandan Nagar on the western bank of the Ganga. Across the river on the eastern bank is a place called Naihati. It is said that Abala used to bring Jagadish by a boat to Naihati in the morning, wherefrom he would take public transport to the college. In the evening, she would again bring the boat across to pick him up. It seems they had a motorized boat of their own that Abala had learnt to drive from Jagadish, although a passenger ferry service was available. Perhaps, this unusual arrangement, though more expensive, was preferred by the romantic couple, who wished to enjoy the boat ride on the beautiful river in each other's company.

Later, the Boses took up residence in Calcutta. The couple had a son who died early and thereafter they remained childless. They led an extremely frugal life, almost to the point of privation, at first to save enough to pay Bose's father's creditors and then to cater to his research expenses. They also saved for another purpose—to travel during the college vacations. Jagadish had a longing to see and feel the ambience of the historic and sacred sites of India. As a nationalist he wished to feel the pulse of the ancient civilization he was heir to and which was still alive, unlike many others that had perished; Abala too was keen and knew that such travels refreshed and inspired her husband.

Years later, they continued to set aside their earnings when Bose resolved to build a private laboratory, independent of the foreign ruler, where Indians could pursue research unfettered. Tradition teaches that a married Indian woman consider the family of her husband her own, and perhaps most would cooperate to repay any outstanding debt for restoring the family honour. But saving to pay for scientific research and further to build a laboratory at the cost of personal amenities and comfort is another matter. Abala Bose certainly was an exception.

3

SUCCESS AGAINST ALL ODDS AND THE EUROPEAN SOJOURN

On his thirty-sixth birthday on 30 November 1894, Jagadish resolved that he was going to devote the rest of his life to the furtherance of knowledge. The colonial rulers and the administration of Presidency College had no interest in supporting independent research. There were, of course, laboratories for training undergraduates, which Bose had been using to prepare his classroom experiments, but there was no real infrastructure and associated paraphernalia for research. Moreover, his two well-wishers, the principal and the director, were close to retirement, and the general opinion in the department was that a professor's duty began and ended with teaching during the working hours. No funding was available for research. The only space made available to Jagadish was a small enclosure adjoining a bathroom, and he stayed on after hours to build his laboratory and work there. Though his vow of devoting his life to research was made on his birthday, Bose must have been preparing for this even earlier, for within a few short months he was already far enough into his research to be able to send wireless signals from one end of the college to the other.

His assigned workload was considerable. He had to deliver four or five lectures per day for six days a week, which he did with characteristic thoroughness; his classroom experiments took much of the rest of his time to prepare. In addition to this, his responsibilities included syllabus writing, setting question papers for examinations, correcting answer sheets, attending departmental meetings, and sundry administrative work. This was, on average, much more than what his colleagues did, and still he had to endure niggling accusations that he was neglecting his duties.

He employed the services of a semi-trained tinsmith, Barada Prasanna Ghosh, who had been running a small workshop in the neighbourhood. He paid for all the expenses of building his lab and conducting experiments from his meagre savings. It was under these trying circumstances that he dared to embark on his research career. While he dreamt of reviving the tradition of scientific research as it existed in ancient India, he had also taken to heart the prejudiced criticism that Indians were dreamy philosophers, wanting in matters of exact thought and precise work as required in science, and resolved to prove otherwise.

Bose began his scientific research in all earnest in December 1894. His success was almost immediate in difficult experiments involving what was called 'electric radiation'. The Royal Society published his first paper in its proceedings in the following year, after which his work appeared in three other publications that year. This fuelled even greater hostility from most of his British colleagues.

At this juncture, it is necessary to add some perspective to his investigations, and this will be done in a manner that would provide a bird's eye view to a lay reader and be slightly more meaningful to someone with an elementary understanding of physics, akin to what is imparted in high school science classes. The next section gives a basic introduction to the physics of waves, the wave theory of light and its properties, using just elementary arithmetics, aided by simple illustrative diagrams.

The Physics of Waves

Light and heat exhibit certain properties. They pass more or less unhindered through some mediums that are called transparent; they pass through certain other mediums, called translucent, only partially, while considerable parts get blocked; mediums that completely block light and heat are known as opaque. Light and heat exhibit another class of properties:

1. Reflection
2. Refraction
3. Diffraction
4. Polarization

Before discussing these phenomena, it is necessary to point out that there was a huge debate surrounding the nature of light—is it a wave or a corpuscle? A corpuscle refers to a packet of energy. The corpuscular theory is older and courtesy of Isaac Newton, whereas the wave theory is due to the seventeenth-century Dutch physicist Christiaan Huygens. The debate was settled in the beginning of the nineteenth century in favour of the wave theory when French physicist Augustin-Jean Fresnel showed conclusively that the phenomenon of diffraction can only be explained by the wave theory.

So, what is a wave as understood by physicists? Fortunately, it is not very different from a layperson's perception. It is a matter of common experience that if one drops a stone in a large pool of perfectly still water, one sees ripples spreading outwards in the form of concentric wave rings, as shown in Fig. 3.1. The waves propagate in all radial directions starting from point S. Fig. 3.1 shows only three such directions, 1, 2, and 3, out of the many possible. In the figure, 1, 2, and 3 are wave trains, each consisting of many waves. We get to see this picture when we view from well above the water surface.

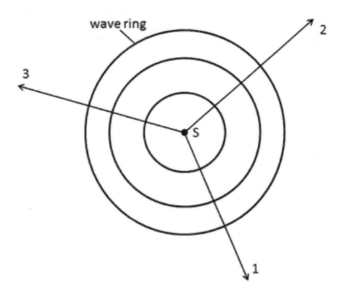

Fig. 3.1: Wave motion in water, as viewed from top when a stone is dropped into a pool.
S is the point of stone drop.

Now, if a table tennis ball is placed in water, it bobs up and down but always stays in one spot. This shows that the water particles do not move at all in the horizontal direction in which the wave is advancing. Instead, the table tennis ball and water particles oscillate vertically. This is perpendicular or transverse to the direction in which the wave is advancing. However, water is the medium in which the wave is travelling. Such a wave, in which the medium oscillates in a transverse direction relative to the wave propagation direction, is called transverse wave.

Now imagine that you are standing in neck-deep water. If you lower your eyes close to the water level and look at wave train 1, you would perceive a picture akin to what is shown in Fig. 3.2. The continuous wavy line, starting from point S at the centre of the ripple and extending to the right up to point 3, is the profile of the water surface at a certain moment. It is also a part of the wave train, which continues further beyond point 3. Of course, the picture keeps changing as the wave undulates, but that is not of importance to us. The dashed line in the middle of the wave train is where the water level had been before the waves were set into motion. It is also called the mean line of the waves, since it divides the waves into two equal halves.

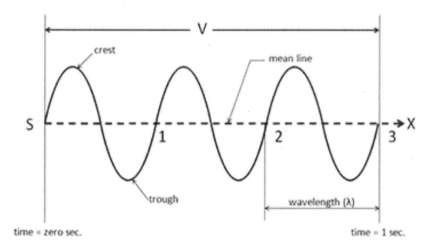

Fig. 3.2: Distance travelled by a wave train in one second.

Each wave consists of a crest and a trough as shown in the figure. The letter S marks the beginning and the numbers 1, 2, and 3 mark the ends of the successive waves. Thus, the distance between any two consecutive numbers is the wavelength, as marked between 2 and 3 and the symbol for which is λ (lambda). It is usually measured in metres and is an important parameter, as we shall see. One can produce longer waves by dropping heavier stones or increasing the depth of the pool of water; waves of different lengths can also be produced by controlled mechanical devices. The direction of wave propagation is X and is marked by an arrow in Fig. 3.2.

The wave train starts at S and reaches point 3 in one second. Let this distance be V as shown at the top of Fig. 3.2. Therefore, the speed or velocity of the wave is V metres per second or V m/s. There are three waves between S and point 3, which means the stone-drop creates three waves per second. In other words, the stone-drop creates three oscillations per second. The number of oscillations per second, contained in a wave train, is a measure of its rapidity and called frequency f. In the case of Fig. 3.2, the frequency (f) is equal to three oscillations per second or three cycles per second. It is clear that wavelength multiplied by frequency equals the velocity of a wave. This can be symbolically expressed in a simple formula (referred to as the wave-velocity formula from this point onwards):

$$\lambda \times f = V \text{ (wave-velocity formula)}$$

When water waves are obstructed by the protrusion of a wall, they can move around the obstruction and reach behind the wall (Fig. 3.3). This phenomenon is called diffraction; the waves start at point S, reach the end of the wall and bend around it to disturb the still waters behind the wall. It has been observed that waves of greater length disturb the still waters behind the wall to a greater extent. This means that the larger the value of λ, the greater the diffraction.

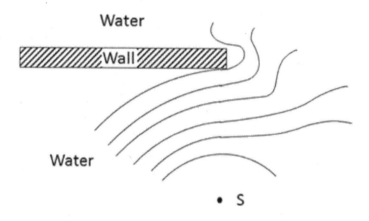

Fig 3.3: Diffraction of water waves emitting from point S.

Huygens and Fresnel, mentioned earlier, proved that light is a transverse wave like waves of water. However, they were of the opinion that light travels in a medium called ether, which is so thin that it is weightless and cannot be perceived even by the most sensitive of instruments and, of course, not by any of the five human senses. They hypothesized that ether is all pervasive and fills every bit of the apparently empty space of the universe, and that light travels from the sun to the earth through this medium.

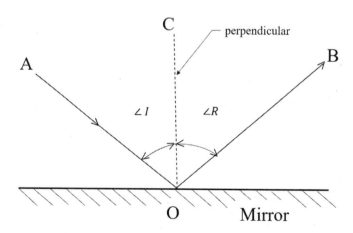

Fig. 3.4: Reflection of light from a polished surface or mirror.

It is well known that when light falls on a shiny surface, such as a mirror or polished metal, it is reflected. In Fig. 3.4, the incident ray, or the ray of light that hits the polished surface, AO is marked by an incoming arrow and the reflected ray, OB, by an outgoing arrow. The dotted line OC is at a right angle to the mirror at point O, which is the point of incidence of the ray. Physicists have determined the law of reflection by performing various experiments. The angle between AO and the perpendicular OC, called the angle of incidence, is labelled as ∠I. Likewise, angle BOC is called the angle of reflection and is given the symbol ∠R. The law of reflection says that the angle of incidence is always equal to the angle of reflection.

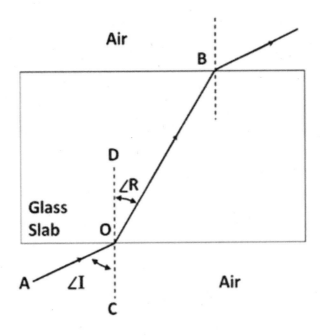

Fig. 3.5: Refraction of light.

A ray of light is known to pass from one transparent medium into another transparent one, for instance from air to glass. During this process, the ray bends by an angle while entering the other medium. This phenomenon is called refraction and is depicted in Fig. 3.5, which shows a ray of light entering a straight-edged glass slab from air. The dotted line COD is perpendicular to the glass surface at O, the point of incidence, making ∠AOC the angle of incidence. The ray bends towards COD on entering the glass, which is a denser medium. Angle BOD is called the angle of refraction and is marked ∠R (not to be confused with angle of reflection, as discussed earlier). It has been experimentally verified that ∠I and ∠R always observe a trigonometric relationship which can be expressed in a formula as:

(sine of ∠I) ÷ (sine of ∠R) = N, where N is a constant.

Here, sine represents a standard trigonometric function. If we consider a different ray having another angle of incidence ∠I, the corresponding ∠R automatically changes in such a way as to maintain the same value of N, which is called the refractive index between air and glass. While passing from a denser medium (glass) into a rarer medium (air), the ray bends away from the perpendicular, as shown at point B in Fig. 3.5.

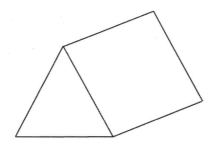

Fig. 3.6: A glass prism.

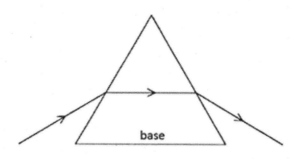

Fig. 3.7: Bending of light through a prism.

The phenomenon of refraction results in another remarkable effect—when a ray of light passes through a prism (Fig. 3.6), the ray bends towards the base of the triangle. Fig. 3.7 depicts a ray entering a prism from the left and emerging through the other side after bending twice, amounting to a bend towards the base. Using the law of refraction, it is possible to determine the angle of each turn accurately.

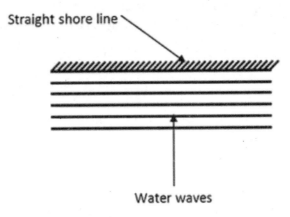

Fig. 3.8: Waves as seen from a beach.

Diffraction of light is a little more complex and is exhibited when light bends around the edge of an opaque obstruction (like waves in water bending around a wall, as shown in Fig. 3.3) and has to do with the wave-like nature of light. The phenomenon of diffraction can also produce flaring of the waves, as can be easily evinced by waves of water. While standing on a beach with a straight shoreline, one sees waves parallel to the shoreline, approaching the edge and breaking at regular intervals. The crests glisten in the sunlight and present a beautiful sight, while the troughs are dark. If a photograph is taken from above, it would look a bit like Fig. 3.8, wherein the horizontal black lines are the troughs and the vertical arrow at the bottom shows the direction of movement of the waves.

Now, if a wall with a narrow opening is constructed at a fair distance from the shore, the approaching parallel waves flare out through the opening, as shown in Fig. 3.9, provided the narrow gap is comparable to the wavelength of the ripples. The diagram shows that the distance between two adjacent troughs is λ; this is the wavelength of the water waves. The figure also shows that the opening in the wall has a width of 1.3λ. Hence, the aperture and the wavelength are comparable in size, though not necessarily equal.

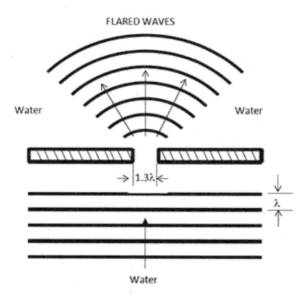

Fig. 3.9: Flaring of water waves through a narrow opening.

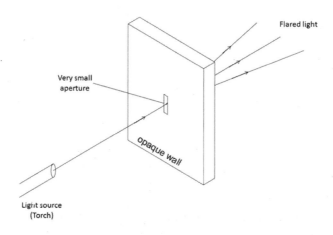

Fig. 3.10: The process of diffraction.

Similar to water, when light is allowed to pass through an extremely small aperture, whose width is comparable to the light's wavelength, it spreads out or flares, as shown in Fig. 3.10. Here, the light beam is perpendicular to the plane of the wall and the invisible wave front is parallel to the wall (similar to Fig. 3.9). In this situation, diffraction creates a spectacular phenomenon that has no parallel in the behaviour of water waves. Let the aperture mentioned above be straight-edged as in Figs. 3.10 and 3.11. If the emerging flared light is made to fall on a screen, one observes the formation of fringes of alternating bright and dark bands as shown in Fig. 3.11. The central band, aligned with the torch and aperture, is the brightest—the further you move from the centre, the more the brightness decreases. This phenomenon, in fact, could be explained only by the wave theory, and led to the wide acceptance of the idea that light is a wave, and overturned Newton's corpuscular theory of the nature of light.

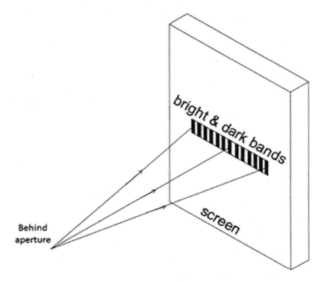

Fig. 3.11: Diffraction; flared light behind aperture creates
bright and dark bands on a screen.

It then became possible to prove that two light waves affect each other in a fashion somewhat similar to two ripples in water, crossing each other's paths; however, such comparison should not be stretched too far.

From the phenomena of diffraction and interference it became possible to determine the wavelengths of different colours of light; explanation for this is beyond the scope of this book. For instance, the red light in the sun's visible spectrum was found to have a wavelength of about 650 nanometre or 650×10^{-9} m; thus, there are about 15,000 waves lined up inside a centimetre of red light. The velocity or speed of light had earlier been measured to be 300,000 kilometres per second or 3×10^{8} m/s. We may now recall the wave-velocity formula provided earlier. Since the velocity (V) of light is 3×10^{8} m/s, we can calculate the frequency (f) of the red light (or for that matter any colour of light), if the wavelength (λ) is known, from the following expression:

$$\lambda \times f = 3 \times 10^{8}$$

Similarly, if the frequency is known and the wavelength can be found, then the speed of any kind of wave can be determined by the wave-velocity formula.

Since the wavelength of light is extremely small (measurable in nanometres, i.e. one billionth of a meter), it became obvious that our common optical reflectors (mirrors) and refractors (prisms) must be extremely large compared to the wavelength of any kind of light. From the phenomenon of diffraction seen in Fig. 3.11, it was observed that the aperture size needed for producing diffraction fringes must be very small and comparable to the wavelength of the incident ray of light. If the aperture is large, the diffraction fringes will not form. We have observed earlier in the context of water that waves of larger wavelength show greater diffraction. Thus, wavelength or, rather, its relative size with respect to a mirror, prism, or aperture was established as an important parameter that governs reflection, refraction, and diffraction. Hence, we have the following three principles:

1. The larger the value of λ, the greater is the possibility of diffraction.
2. The mirror should be extremely large compared to λ for proper reflection, without any diffraction, to occur.
3. The prism should be extremely large compared to λ for proper refraction, without any diffraction, to occur.

Light exhibits another phenomenon called polarization. There are certain materials that appear transparent, but when light passes through them it loses half of its intensity or energy. Such materials are used these days to produce Polaroid spectacles to protect the human eye from the glare of the sun. This phenomenon was not properly understood until Scottish physicist James Clerk Maxwell put forth his theory of electromagnetic waves in the 1870s. An electromagnetic wave consists of two simultaneous oscillations, one electric and the other magnetic, moving in perpendicular planes.

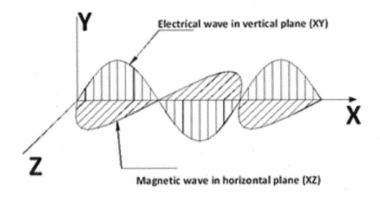

Fig. 3.12: An electromagnetic wave proceeding along the X-axis.

If you look at a point in a room where the floor meets the two walls, you see three straight lines emerging from the corner. Fig. 3.12 shows three such lines called X-axis, Y-axis, and Z-axis, which are all perpendicular to each other. Here, X and Z are horizontal and they lie in the horizontal plane (the floor), whereas Y is vertical. Fig. 3.12 shows an electromagnetic wave moving along the X-axis, having two simultaneous oscillations. The electric wave oscillates in the Y-direction and remains in the vertical plane (XY). The magnetic wave oscillates in the Z-direction and remains in the horizontal plane, the plane of the floor (XZ). Both the waves advance in the X-direction as if doing a ballroom lock-step dance move. It is to be noted that each wave oscillates in a direction transverse to the X-axis; the electromagnetic wave is also referred to as a transverse wave.

Before discussing the phenomenon of polarization as understood by Bose and his predecessor, Heinrich Hertz, we must first understand the contribution of James C. Maxwell to the theory of electromagnetism.

James Clerk Maxwell

Born in a Scottish middle-class family in 1831, James C. Maxwell possessed much curiosity about his surroundings and displayed an extraordinary memory as a child. He was a bright pupil at school and published his first scientific paper at the young age of fourteen. In 1850, he went to the University of Cambridge, where his talents were noticed. At age twenty-nine, he was appointed as a professor in King's College, London. Here, he started to formulate his theory of electromagnetism. Maxwell returned to Cambridge as a professor in 1871. He died in 1879.

Maxwell's thought process was triggered by an experiment that had to do with a conductor. Conductivity is the property by which a material conducts heat or electricity. For instance, if you hold a candle under one end of an iron bar, the other end of the bar will heat up as well. This happens because the receiving end of iron conducts heat to the remote end, in a process named heat conduction. If you do the same with a wooden bar of the same dimensions, the results will be much different. If you apply heat for long enough, the end over the candle may catch fire but the other end will remain as it was. This means that iron is a good conductor of heat and has much higher conductivity than wood, which is a very poor conductor.

Materials such as wood, sheep's wool, plastic, etc. hardly conduct any heat and are poor conductors. They are also called insulators as the act of preventing heat from being conducted is called insulation. Materials which conduct heat well are called conductors; all metals are conductors. Before Maxwell made his theory known, physicists thought a material is either a conductor or insulator—there was no third category. It was also known that, generally, materials which are good conductors of heat are also good conductors of electricity.

We have all seen sparking in a loose electric plug. The spark flies between two metal points that are connected to an electric circuit, as in a domestic electric plug. These metal points are called terminals. A spark is also called an electrical disturbance. Somewhere in the middle of the nineteenth century, Maxwell measured the speed of electrical disturbances or sparks flying between two terminals and found that it was the same as the speed of light. The speed of electricity running through a good conductor (metal) had been measured earlier, and that too had turned out to be equal to the speed of light. Hans Christian Oersted, a Danish scientist, had demonstrated that a current-carrying wire creates a magnetic field all around itself, up to a considerable distance. The French physicist André-Marie Ampère had provided the law governing this phenomenon and showed its harmonious relationship with Coulomb's law of attraction between electric charges. Thus, it had been well established that magnetism and electricity were intimately linked.

To Maxwell all this seemed something beyond a coincidence, and led him to formulate his famous generalized theory of electrodynamics. It led him to believe that light and heat are a transverse wave involving an electromagnetic oscillation. He had been working on his new formulation since the 1860s and published his magnum opus, *A Treatise on Electricity and Magnetism*, in 1873, while serving as the first Cavendish Professor of Physics in Cambridge. Unfortunately, after a prolonged illness, he died of cancer when he was only forty-eight years old.

This book did not contain Maxwell's four famous equations as they are known today. Instead, it contained a series of complex equations and abstruse mathematical development. In fact, his theory was so abstruse and voluminous that it was neither well understood nor well accepted by the physicists of his time. There were too many loose ends, obscure and latent ideas buried in his writings. Later, a small group of theoretical physicists came together to consult on Maxwell's ideas in order to offer clarifications. The group had a few British members such as G. F. FitzGerald, Oliver Lodge, J. H. Poynting, and Oliver Heaviside, along with the sole American member, H. A. Rowland. However, they soon lost their early enthusiasm; by the mid-1880s, the study of Maxwell's ideas had entered a dormant phase. Around this time they were spurred once again by the discovery of electric waves by Heinrich Hertz.

We shall now refer to electromagnetic waves as EM waves. The famous four equations, known as Maxwell's equations, emerged gradually, but after a long time, from the latent ideas in Maxwell's work, distilled by the aforesaid fraternity. Maxwell had predicted that infrared, visible, and ultraviolet light were not the only EM waves; there must be waves of lesser and higher frequencies on either side of these known radiations from the sun, the 'solar spectrum'. His ideas fired up a small number of researchers, but physicists in general were not convinced, so much so that the small group of researchers was labelled the Maxwellians.

Physicists were looking for experimental corroboration and that came in later years through the work of Heinrich Hertz and J. C. Bose. Only at the end of the nineteenth century was Maxwell's theory fully accepted—well after the death of Hertz and after several of Bose's papers had sent a wave of excitement through Europe. It is worth pointing out, however, that Bose had almost disappeared from the radar of science historians in the twentieth century in this particular context, while Hertz was given the credit for the experimental verification of Maxwell's theory.

It could be inferred from Maxwell's theory that electrical disturbances or sparks between two terminals might produce an effect at a distance by emitting radiation of invisible EM waves. The existence of these new EM waves, named electric waves to distinguish them from light waves, needed to be verified experimentally. Maxwell generally held that all kinds of EM waves should have similar properties.

It is well understood today that when a positive electric terminal is brought close to a negative electric terminal, a spark flies between the two. The terminals are separated by a gap filled with air and air is a non-conducting matter. According to Maxwell's theory, when two terminals are brought close to each other, currents are set up in the air between them, but for an extremely short duration, and this is followed by a spark, which goes back-and-forth between the two terminals. This, too, needed verification.

Berend Wilhelm Feddersen took a snapshot of the spark with the help of a rapidly revolving mirror on a single photographic plate and captured a series of streaks of varying brightness with gaps in between and appearing symmetrical between the two terminals. It became evident from the study that the spark was not continuous but intermittent. What appears as a single spark to the naked eye is really a succession of sparks, oscillating between the positive and negative terminals. A small number of physicists took note of this development and started looking at Maxwell's theory more closely. Maxwell also theorized that the energy of these sparks does not dissipate only as heat, but must also radiate in the form of EM waves.

Unfamiliar with Maxwell's thesis, an Anglo-American inventor named David Edward Hughes was conducting electric spark experiments between 1879 and 1886. His equipment could produce an effect at 460 metres (500 yards approximately). On reading his papers, some physicists attributed his discovery to induction, with which Hughes disagreed. But he had no inkling that he had been producing electric waves and did not know how to interpret his findings. This shows how unfamiliar many physicists were with Maxwell's theory even in the mid-1880s. Unfortunately, the small group of Maxwellians was not aware of Hughes's work and he was subsequently ignored by the larger scientific community.

It has been mentioned that Maxwell held light to be an EM wave. If indeed the electric waves, produced by oscillating sparks, were Maxwell's EM waves, they would travel with the same speed of light and display the same optical properties of reflection, refraction, and diffraction. Therefore, it was also necessary to ascertain through experiments whether these optical laws are obeyed by electric waves and whether these waves travel at the speed of light. In other words, conclusions drawn from Maxwell's theory about electric waves needed a most comprehensive experimental verification. This seemed essential for proving the correctness of Maxwell's ideas.

Heinrich Hertz

Now stepped into the scene Heinrich Hertz, a brilliant German experimentalist, who had studied under Hermann Von Helmholtz in Berlin. Helmholtz, though not in close touch with the British Maxwellians, was interested in Maxwell's ideas. He was familiar with Maxwell's prediction about the existence of transient electric current in a dielectric, the insulating material between two conductors. In 1879, Helmholtz suggested that Hertz put Maxwell's prediction to test. But

Hertz felt the endeavour would take much too long and turned it down, choosing to take his research in another direction.

After he was appointed as a professor at the University of Karlsruhe in 1885, he took up the challenge to verify Maxwell's theory and explore if electric waves existed well outside the known solar spectrum. What was needed was an efficient emitter or radiator of the new waves. Moreover, a receiver or detector of these waves was also necessary, first, to prove their existence and then to ascertain what laws they observed. Would these laws be the same as those for light or would they be different? Either way, the discovery would be epoch-making. For light and heat (infrared), nature has equipped us, humans, with receivers or detectors. We have eyes for perceiving light and skin for heat, but no such receivers for electric waves. Nature has also given us an efficient emitter of light and heat waves, the sun. No such emitter of electric waves was known until then.

Another important consideration was that for determining the laws of reflection and refraction, mirrors and prisms of appropriate sizes were needed. If an emitter (also called radiator) produces electrical waves that are tens of metres long, one would need reflectors and prisms that are much larger, about tens of kilometres long; to fabricate or arrange such reflectors or prisms would be well-nigh impossible.

Hertz built an apparatus that sustained steady and controlled electrical discharges. These also had to be much more rapid than what had been hitherto possible. It has earlier been mentioned that another name for rapidity is frequency, which is defined in this context as the number of spark oscillations per second or number of waves emitted per second. Hertz assumed that the waves have a constant and finite velocity, and the wave-velocity formula, relating wavelength and frequency, was applicable—the greater the rapidity or frequency, the shorter the wavelength.

Thus, in order to emit waves that are short in length, Hertz needed to devise a radiator with a very high frequency. Hertz succeeded in this endeavour, too, and the shortest waves that he could produce were about 660 millimetres long. He also needed a detector or receiver for the anticipated waves in order to prove their existence.

Developing a detector for these electric waves was not easy. After much effort and several trials, he succeeded in constructing a receiver. This was a ring detector consisting of a looped wire with a spherical knob on each end separated by a tiny spark gap (Fig. 3.13). With this apparatus, he could see discharges flying back and forth, even when the detector was placed at a significant distance from the radiator. The detected sparks had the same rapidity, that is, the same frequency as the sparks from the radiator.

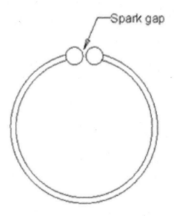

Fig. 3.13: Schematic diagram of Hertz's ring detector for electric waves.

Hertz tried to measure the speed of the electric waves but his measurements showed too wide a variation to be conclusive. However, Hertz succeeded in proving the existence of electric waves outside the solar spectrum, as predicted by Maxwell. That the detected electric waves were EM waves was yet to be proven. He now proceeded to verify the behavioural laws or the optical laws of these waves, which would certify their electromagnetic nature. These waves were soon being called Hertzian waves.

Hertz found that a sheet of water is opaque whereas glass and pitch were transparent for these waves; so, in certain respects, they were different from light. The fact that diffraction was happening too easily even when very large obstructions were placed was noticed by him. He realized that he had to construct enormous mirrors to allow reflection to occur without significant presence of diffraction. A fairly narrow beam of parallel rays, a collimated beam, was also needed for quantitative measurements of reflection, refraction, etc.; an ordinary beam contains diverging rays.

He made a few gigantic mirrors using zinc and other polished metals to observe the law of reflection, but the mirrors were not large enough. The beam he produced was neither narrow nor collimated enough, and so the observed reflection was always mixed with a significant amount of diffraction. As a result, the movement of rays along straight lines could not be ensured. The rays bent in all directions whenever confronted with an object, such as the mirror. Hence, the angle of reflection could not be measured and the law of reflection could not be verified. However, he proved that reflection did happen.

Returning to the measurement of the speed of the electric waves, the task proved much harder than measuring the speed of light, which was first accomplished by Danish astronomer Olaus Roemer in 1676. His method involved measuring the time interval between eclipses of Jupiter's moons and was not accurate because planetary distances were not accurately known.

The first direct, non-astronomical attempt was made by French physicist Armand Fizeau in 1849. The principle of speed measurement is simple. Suppose we wish to measure the speed of a car. In order to do so, we measure the time (t seconds) it takes to cover a known distance (D metres). D divided by t (D/t) is the speed of the car in metres per second (also written as m/s). Fizeau knew that light travels so fast that it takes practically no time to cover a distance of a few hundred metres. Therefore, light had to be sent over quite a long distance in order to make the travel time large enough to be measurable. The ideal location for an experiment would be a pair of hills, in clear sight of each other, separated by at least several kilometres; on one hill the source of light or emitter would be stationed and on the other hill it would be detected or received. Even so, the time interval would be so short that to measure it a very elaborate arrangement would be necessary. In Fizeau's experiment, a beam of light was sent over a distance of 8 kilometres from the source. His peer Léon Foucault improved upon his methods and measured the speed of light with an error of 2.7 per cent.

Another French physicist M. A. Cornu further improved the method in 1875 and achieved an accuracy of a fraction of a percentage. It should be emphasized that the human eye was an essential instrument, as the receiver or detector, in all these experiments. This method, however, was not feasible for the electric wave, since transmitting the wave to a distance as long as 8 kilometres was not possible in Hertz's time; nor was there a suitable receiver or detector at par with the human eye. Hertz had to use an indirect method and first needed to measure the wavelength of the electric wave and managed to do so using standing waves.

The Standing Wave

Usually, waves are always moving. However, when two waves of equal dimensions arrive at a spot from opposite directions, they interact with each other in such a way that they create a stationary wave. This wave pulsates in one spot. It does not travel at all and is thus called a standing wave. There are a few experiments that can be performed to understand the nature of this wave.

The first experiment can be easily conducted in a small garden. Suppose a rope or string is stretched and firmly tied to a peg on a wall or railing at one end. The other end is held by a person in such a way as to keep the string under some tension, as shown in Fig. 3.14 (a). The person vertically flicks the string once, causing a pulse to run through the string which looks like a half-wave and travels towards the wall, as in Fig. 3.14 (b).

On reaching the end, the pulse exerts an upward force on the wall and disappears for a moment; as a reaction the wall exerts an equal downward force on the string. Thus, an inverted pulse of the same shape is created and starts travelling from the wall towards the person holding the string. This phenomenon is the reflection of a pulse from a fixed end. The sequence of events is shown in Fig. 3.14 (c), (d), (e), and (f). It must be noted that the pulse is inverted on reflection off the wall. The same happens to a wave or a train of waves when reflected from a fixed boundary.

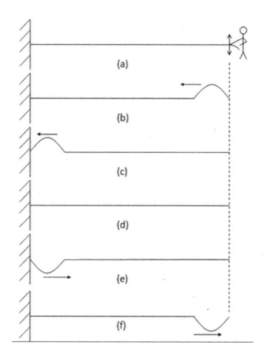

Fig. 3.14: Reflection of a half-wave pulse on a stretched string from a fixed end.

In the next experiment, we mount the string of a musical instrument such as a sitar, guitar, or violin on a wooden table between two clamps and stretch, as shown in Fig. 3.15(a). Let the length of the string be L. One of the clamps is supported on a vertical metal rod grouted on the table, with an arrangement for varying the tension of the string. When plucked in the middle, the string produces an audible twang.

We are all familiar with tuning forks which produce standard notes, used for tuning guitars and other stringed instruments. Now, let us choose a tuning fork which has a note close to that of a string. Let a trained musician modify the tension in the string until it is in unison with the tuning fork. Then, strike the tuning fork firmly on a hard surface and press its handle down on top of the metal rod at one end of the string. The vibration of the fork is conveyed to the string through the rod (a little is lost to the air) and causes the string to vibrate, producing a much louder note. Both the string and the tuning fork vibrate exactly at the same frequency and this is called resonance or sympathetic vibration.

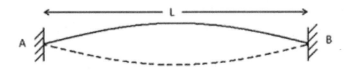

Fig. 3.15(a): A standing wave on a string.

Referring to Fig. 3.15(a), the two ends of the string, A and B, cannot vibrate or oscillate because of the clamps. The points which do not or cannot vibrate, are called nodes. The middle of the string has the maximum potential for movement and is called the anti-node. The solid line in Fig. 3.15(a) shows one extreme position of the string and the dashed line the other extreme, the string oscillating between these two.

It is obvious that the solid line is the crest of a wave and the dashed line the trough. If it is assumed that the crest is left-moving, it gets reflected at point A as a right-moving trough; this then gets reflected at point B and becomes a left-moving crest, and so on. It is as if only one half of the wave exists at any given instant. Therefore, $L = \lambda/2$. Note that this half-wave moves neither to the right nor to the left and, so, is a standing wave. This is the simplest example of such a wave. If a small paper hat (shaped like ∧) is placed on the unplucked string at the anti-node, it would be thrown off as soon as the tuning fork is pressed on the metal rod.

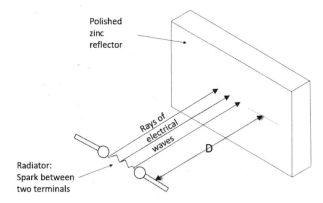

Fig. 3.15(b): Hertz's arrangement for creating a standing electric wave.

In order to create a standing wave, Hertz placed a polished zinc reflector (mirror) at right angles to the path of the electric waves at some distance (D) from the radiator. A simplified version of his arrangement is shown in Fig. 3.15(b). The mirror reflected the wave and the reflected wave interacted with the incident wave. After much testing to detect the anti-node with the help of his ring detector, when the distance was adjusted properly, a standing wave was produced.

Standing waves have been explained above with the vibration of the guitar string. The radiator at one end and the mirror at the other end at distance D are comparable to the clamps at the ends of the string. The intervening distance between them is analogous to the length of the string and therefore, equal to half the wavelength. Hertz determined the wavelength of the waves generated by his radiator by this method and found that the smallest wavelength that he could generate was approximately 660 millimetres, as mentioned earlier. The frequency of the wave, on the other hand, could be accurately estimated a priori from the circuit parameters of the radiator (also called spark oscillator or wave generator). The idea was to use the wave-velocity formula to obtain the wave speed.

Hertz also performed experiments by transmitting electric waves along a wire and creating standing waves around it. He measured the wave speed in the wire and found to his dismay that it was at variance with the speed in free space (meaning air). There was another problem—his measurements yielded a wave speed of 2,80,000 km/s in free space, which is lesser than the speed of light by as much as 7 per cent. According to the *New World Encyclopedia*,

> Hertz failed, however, to conclusively measure the speed of the waves. At first he thought the speed was infinite; another series of measurements showed a large discrepancy between the velocity of waves in a wire and through air. Later investigators resolved these differences, and showed that the waves move at the speed of light.

History has remained silent so far on who these 'later investigators' could be. Hertz had not been able to eliminate the presence of diffraction in his experiments, which means that his measurement of wavelength was not accurate. His calculation of the frequency of his radiator was accurate, which was also the frequency of the waves generated. However, his estimates of the wave speed showed a wide variation.

This notion about the failure of Hertz's speed measurement is reinforced by science historians D. J. Cichon and W. Wiesbeck who summarize Hertz's achievements but do not include any accurate measurements of wavelength or speed. Of course, Hertz's standing wave experiment and approximate measurement of wavelength are mentioned. However, they add another of Hertz's accomplishments—in the autumn of 1887, Hertz proved the existence of current in dielectric materials, the problem that had been initially put before him by Helmholtz.

Science historian John H. Bryant says that Hertz built the first transmitter and receiver and 'experienced reflection, refraction, diffraction, and polarization' of electric waves. Again, no measurement of speed is included, although Hertz's apparatus and experiments are thoroughly discussed. Bryant uses the word 'experienced' because Hertz could not make any quantitative measurements, but experienced the optical laws qualitatively. Geddes, Bose's biographer and a contemporary of Hertz, is quite effusive about Hertz's achievements but is silent on the measurement of wavelength and speed.

Hertz then made an enormous prism, casting about two tons of pitch, through which he passed the waves. The waves significantly bent towards the base, showing refraction, but again due to the heavy presence of diffraction, no precise measurement was possible and the law of refraction could not be ascertained.

He did, however, succeed in polarizing the electric waves by building an enormous metal grid like a window with parallel bars mounted on a rectangular frame. Since Hertz's waves had a wavelength (λ) of 660 millimetres, the grid consisted of rods or bars which had diameters of comparable size. The spaces between adjacent bars, too, were comparable. Hertz had to manipulate this large structure to bring it to the required alignment for polarization. It is believed that he had the assistance of many skilled workmen.

Hertz did not make much headway with his research on electric waves thereafter. He published his findings in 1888 and turned his attention to mechanics, photoelectric effect, and cathode rays, topics on which he worked until 1892, when he fell ill. He died in 1894 at the young age of thirty-six, precisely the year when Bose took a vow to pursue a career in research. As a mark of commemoration, the unit of frequency, cycles per second, was named after Hertz.

Hertz's success was partial in the sense that he compelled physicists to sit up and take note of Maxwell's theory. It is a historical fact that, except a few Maxwellians, most physicists were not convinced. There were still considerable doubts whether the electric waves, discovered by Hertz, were truly Maxwell's EM waves, because the laws of reflection and refraction could not be ascertained and the measured speed remained at variance with that of light. Even his polarization of electric waves was not entirely analogous to that of light, since the latter can only be polarized by passing through a special medium such as certain naturally occurring transparent crystals. Light, unlike the electric wave, cannot be polarized by a metal grid and a grid cannot really be called a medium.

Bose Enters the Field

Several physicists entered the field of investigation of Hertzian waves, attempting to continue from where Hertz had left off in 1888. The state of affairs in 1894 was summed up in *Heinrich Hertz and His Successors* written by a British Maxwellian, Sir Oliver Lodge. It should be recalled that Bose enrolled to study physics at Cambridge in 1881, only two years after James C. Maxwell's death. The latter had been an illustrious professor at Cambridge and in charge of the Cavendish laboratory, and was succeeded by Lord Rayleigh, who inspired Bose immensely. Either as a member of the Natural Science Club or during classroom discussions, Bose must have come across Maxwellian ideas and felt drawn to them. He eagerly read Sir Lodge's book, procured D. E. Jones's English translation of the collection of Hertz's writings and resolved to work in this field in all earnest. He became a Maxwellian, so to speak.

Bose aimed to construct a device that would produce electric waves of lengths of only a few millimetres, about a hundred times smaller than Hertz's waves. Further, Bose aimed to produce a sufficiently narrow beam of collimated rays of such waves. If such waves could be produced, then he would be able to observe the optical laws within the confines of a usual laboratory. Enormous mirrors, prisms, and metal grids as those of Hertz would not be necessary, and the properties could be verified with instruments of manageable proportions.

He hoped that he might succeed, where Hertz had failed, to verify the entire range of optical laws for the electric waves quantitatively and measure the wavelength more precisely, and thereby prove conclusively that the electric wave was Maxwell's EM wave. Even though Hertz had proved that the electric waves could be polarized, a deficiency remained, as mentioned earlier. Bose hoped to polarize electric waves by passing them through naturally occurring crystals and rendering the phenomenon more analogous to the one involving light.

Hertz and his successors had not proceeded beyond ordinary diffraction and this hardly proved affinity to light—even water waves and sound waves, which are not EM waves, diffract. Bose wished to proceed beyond ordinary diffraction.

Generally speaking, physicists in those days were generating Hertzian waves by creating sparks between two terminals or electrodes. This type of device produced a wide range of waves of different wavelengths and, therefore, of different frequencies. For reliable experiments one needed all waves to have the same frequency, as much as possible. Lodge made some improvements by inserting a metal ball in between the sparking elements, which filtered out some frequencies. However, the surface of the metal ball became rough after a being hit by a few sparks, and began producing strange waves of unwanted frequencies. Thereafter Lodge concentrated on the detection of Hertzian waves, rather than on their generation.

Bose coated a metal sphere with platinum and placed it between two hollow metallic hemispheres, as shown in Fig. 3.16. At the centre of the hollow of a hemisphere was attached a tiny platinum ball. This figure was drawn by Bose himself and gives an additional view of the radiator on the right, involving two hemispheres (shown by dashed lines) attached with tiny platinum spheres and a large platinum-coated sphere in between. Bose faced great difficulty in producing this because there was no way to melt platinum in Calcutta or its suburbs in those days. Although the city was a great mercantile hub, it was hardly industrial. The waves in Bose's apparatus were generated by sparking between the hemispheres. There was no problem of any surfaces roughening, and the device maintained a steady and quality radiation over time.

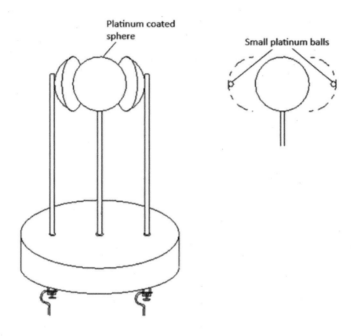

Fig. 3.16: Bose's radiator. This figure is inspired by a diagram provided by Bose.

He could produce waves ranging in length from 2.5 to 5 millimetres and with a frequency of about 60×10^9 cycles per second. These, compared to Hertz's waves, were about a hundred times shorter. In addition, Bose's waves carried much more energy. He also succeeded in producing a pencil (narrow beam) of collimated rays only a centimetre in diameter. To shield the radiator from stray electric and magnetic fields he enclosed it in a double-layered, copper-iron box. On the whole it was no mean achievement. According to Patrick Geddes,

> Further advance of the determination of the optical properties of electric (Hertzian) radiation by quantitative measurements had been retarded, since on account of the large size of the waves their strictly linear propagation could not be secured. Bose was able to

produce extremely short waves, which largely filled up the gap between the infrared rays and Hertz's long electric waves.

Bose aimed for the 'linear propagation' Geddes wrote about, and though he filled some 'gaps', some still remained. However, Bose's wave generating apparatus was much smaller and compact than the huge dimensions of those of his predecessors and could be packed in an ordinary suitcase. In performance it was superior to Lodge's and, of course, to Hertz's.

An Italian scientist, Augusto Righi, was also working with relatively short electric waves around this time and came close to Bose by producing waves ranging in length from 2.6 to 10 centimetres; these were five to ten times larger than Bose's millimetre waves. Pyotr N. Lebedev, a Russian physicist, is credited with generating waves of 6 millimetre length around the same time as Bose. He had received his PhD from Strasbourg in Germany, working under August Kundt, and then published a paper on this topic in German, a language in which he was proficient. Neither Righi nor Lebedev attempted to measure wavelength using a method different from Hertz's. It seems they assumed the speed to be the same as light's and employed the wave-velocity formula to calculate the wavelength.

Receivers Alias Coherers

Physicists were also working on improving Hertz's receiver. The first breakthrough was made by Édouard Branly, a professor at the Catholic University of Paris, who called his device a 'radio-conductor'. This was a simple device consisting of a large number of tiny metal pieces (also called filings) packed inside a slender glass tube. Each end of the glass tube had a terminal connected with the metal filings inside. These terminals were connected to a battery with a galvanometer in the circuit, as shown in Fig. 3.17(a). A galvanometer is used to measure the strength of the current in a circuit.

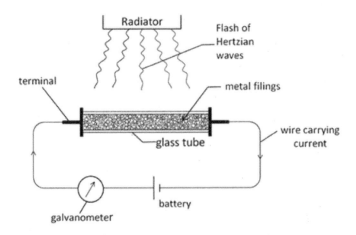

Fig. 3.17(a): Branly's receiver or detector. This is drawn from a description given by Bhattacharyya and Engineer.

Although each metal filing by itself is a good conductor, the contraption as a whole offered considerable resistance to the passage of an electric current. This was because the contact between any two metal pieces was imperfect and there were many such contacts present in the circuit through which the current had to pass. This resulted in high contact resistance. Hence, initially the galvanometer would show a reading indicating a relatively weak current.

Branly discovered that when subjected to a flash of radiation of Hertzian waves, the resistance of the metal filings fell sharply, often to a millionth, and the galvanometer needle indicated a large increase in current. This change in resistance is called conductivity-variation. Due to this property, the device could be used as a receiver of such waves and when tested it performed better than Hertz's large receiver. However, the device needed to be mechanically shaken to restore it to its original high resistance state before it could be used again as a receiver. This required human intervention between two successive operations, and proved rather inconvenient.

Lodge used variations of this apparatus extensively and put forward a theory that the metal filings sort of fused together under the action of the Hertzian waves. Contact resistance of the metal filings decreased due to this fusing or 'soldering'. This was his explanation for conductivity-variation in a stack of metal filings. On account of the soldering tendency, Lodge coined the name 'coherer' and the term became popular in the English-speaking world. The apparatuses created by both Branly and Lodge were not very consistent in their behaviour, which was attributed to the irregular nature of the contacts. Around this time, Hertzian waves began to be called 'electric waves' and this is the name Bose used in all his publications and lectures.

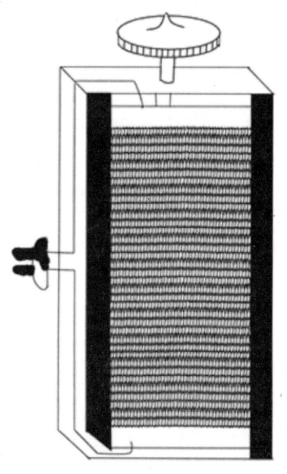

Fig. 3.17(b): Diagram of the spiral spring coherer, devised by Bose. This is inspired by a diagram provided by Bose.

Bose produced a much-improved coherer by placing a single layer of tiny spiral springs side by side inside a 2 cm by 1 cm rectangular depression excavated on a piece of ebonite, as shown in Fig. 3.17(b). He held the springs in place with a glass slide fixed to the front. The apparatus thus afforded thousands of regular contacts in the spirals of the springs instead of the irregular and much fewer contacts of the metal filings in the other coherers. The resistance of the apparatus could be varied by compressing the springs with a movable brass slider actuated by a screw, seen at the top. Every time it was subjected to a flash of electric wave radiation, its conductivity-variation remained the same and the galvanometer gave a consistent reading.

In a review dated December 1895, *The Electrician*, a London publication that carried some of Bose's early works, wrote about the possibility of replacing existing lighthouses with electromagnetic 'light'-houses. It went on to point out that the receiver on board a ship would be the most important instrument, being an electric equivalent of the human eye.

> The evolution of a suitable generating apparatus (for electrical waves) would, we thought, present little difficulty; that of a suitable receiver, on the other hand, seemed likely to give considerable trouble. In this connection, we would draw attention to the substantial and workmanlike form of 'Coherer' devised by Professor Bose and described by him at the end of his paper, 'On a new Electro-Polariscope'. The sensibility and range of this type of 'Coherer' would appear to leave little to be desired, and it is certainly more likely to withstand, with equanimity, the thousand and one shocks that the flesh is heir to at sea, than any of the forms hitherto brought about.

This was written within just a year of Bose embarking on his research and suggests that no one else could produce a receiver of such reliability and accuracy. The great possibilities of employing a suitable receiver to detect electric waves and thereby facilitate wireless communication became apparent by 1895. According to French physicist M. Poincaré[2], Bose's

----

[2]Bose's biographer Patrick Geddes attributes the quotation to M. Poincaré. A search

receiver was 'exquisite; it responds to all the radiations in the interval of an octave. One makes it sensitive to different kinds of radiations, by varying the electromotive force, which engenders the current which traverses the receiver'.

This receiver was a patentable invention, but Bose did not go down that route. In time, Bose also invented many other receivers which did not require manual tapping and recovered automatically. It is neither necessary nor possible here to go into the details of all of Bose's inventions, which are truly numerous.

Since the radiation produced by Bose was of wavelength 5 millimetres or smaller, it did not need enormous mirrors and prisms like those of Hertz and experiments could be conducted without the disturbing presence of diffraction. Bose thus could ensure linear propagation and could therefore precisely ascertain the laws of reflection and refraction, and measure accurately the refracting indices of various mediums. At this point in time, his wave generator (variously called radiator and transmitter) was the most perfect and he could produce a well-defined beam of a single frequency of half-inch diameter. Further, his receiver was also the most sensitive and steady in its performance.

To sum up, Bose improved the whole measurement system, consisting of various components, perfected it in all details, and miniaturized it from the dimensions of Hertz's and Lodge's apparatuses, so much so that it became portable and could be set up on a large table for demonstration before an audience. Hertz's comparison of the properties of electric waves and light was not complete and was, in certain respects, largely qualitative. Bose completed the endeavour by accomplishing the following tasks:

1. To show by quantitative measurements that electric waves observe the same laws of reflection and refraction as optical rays and also show that the electric waves exhibit similar total internal reflection.

---

by this author did not find a physicist, a contemporary of Bose, of the name M. Poincaré; it is likely the initial M in Geddes's estimate meant 'Monsieur'. There was, however, the famous physicist and mathematician Jules Henri Poincaré who was also a prolific writer.

2. To polarize the electric wave by passing through naturally occurring crystals.
3. To make precise measurements of refractive indices of several mediums.
4. To determine the wavelength of the radiation and thereby the wave speed.
5. To experiment with double refraction and polarization.
6. To rotate the plane of polarization.

Thus, Maxwell's predictions attained full verification through the works of Bose, which reached physicists in Europe and America through a series of publications, mostly in the Proceedings of the Royal Society.

Bose used many of his own inventions in his measuring systems. One of them was his waveguide, which took the form of a hollow metal tube with a flared end; now it is referred to as a radiator antenna. On the receiving side he used what he called a 'collecting funnel', and this was the precursor of what we now know as the pyramidal horn antenna.

The excerpt below from the introductory paragraph of Bose's very first paper brings out clearly the purpose and direction of his research.

The object of the present enquiry is to find natural substances which would polarize the transmitted electric ray. It was thought the analogy between the electric radiation and light would be rendered more complete if the classes of substance which polarize light are also found to polarize the electric ray. The two phenomena may be regarded identical if the same specimen is found to polarize both the luminous and the electric rays.

His focus was on rendering the analogy between the electric radiation and light 'more complete'. It is evident that he was looking to test Maxwell's theory of EM waves and his predictions. Hertz had polarized electric waves with a metal grid, that did not satisfactorily establish the analogy. This particular effort of Bose was eminently successful as he evinced that a large number of natural crystals polarized light and electric radiation in an identical manner. He performed double-refraction experiments with a dielectric material and measured the refractive indices of different materials and, in the process, eliminated a theoretical difficulty that had arisen in Maxwell's theory, as to the relation between the indices of refraction and the dielectric constants of insulators.

Bose's inventions were purposive—whenever he felt the need for updated technology, he invented a new instrument or improved upon an existing one. His research papers also followed one after another in quick succession. This won the admiration and goodwill of the principal, Professor Charles Tawney. There was a British colleague, Alexander Pedler, who had become a good friend of Bose's during his teaching years. A wireless experiment was performed in the college in the opening months of 1895—an electric wave signal was sent from the office of Prafulla Chandra Ray, the only other Indian professor, and it was received in Pedler's room.

Bose always encouraged his friend and junior colleague Ray to pursue his own research, apart from enlisting his cooperation in the signalling experiment inside the college. Ray, like Bose, and unlike most of their British colleagues, was not content to remain confined only to teaching. He began researching nitrite chemistry in 1895 and succeeded in preparing a new stable compound called mercurous nitrite, opening up a new field of research. His seminal papers and research in this area became well known among the chemists of the world. Later in life he was conferred the Fellowship of the Royal Society (FRS).

A Research Paper of 'Special Excellence'

Measuring the wavelength of electric waves accurately was an important task. Moreover, it would automatically result in an accurate estimation of the speed of the waves, since the frequency can be easily and accurately calculated from the known circuit parameters. Unlike Hertz, Bose did not take the standing wave route to wavelength. For the difficult experiment he embarked upon, it was necessary to first ensure that the radiation was truly monochromatic, i.e., of a single frequency. Once this was achieved, after much effort, he successfully developed a novel and ingenious method for direct measurement of wavelength by using a cylindrical optical grating for diffraction. In this way, Bose proceeded to advanced diffraction experiments well beyond Hertz's ordinary diffraction. It is to be recalled that the frequency of the electric wave could be accurately estimated from the circuit parameters of the spark oscillator (also called radiator). Since the wave speed is a product of the wavelength and frequency (as per the wave-velocity formula), an accurate measurement of the wavelength led to an accurate estimation of the wave speed almost automatically. This turned out to be the same as that of light, and the accurate measurement of the wavelength of electric waves became Bose's crowning achievement.

The merit and significance of Bose's paper on the determination of wavelength was realized by Lord Rayleigh and, on his recommendation, the University of London conferred on Bose the degree of Doctor of Science in 1896. Bose was exempted from appearing for an examination; the statutory regulations permitted this only for a paper of 'special excellence'. His thesis and research papers were examined by professors J. H. Poynting and J. J. Thompson. The former was an avowed Maxwellian and the latter followed Bose's work on electric waves closely and was usually present at most of Bose's lectures in England. Thompson later wrote a book, as did Poincaré and other continental physicists, prominently featuring Bose's achievements, particularly his apparatus. A whole generation of physicists was brought up on these books.

Sir Alfred Croft, the director of public instruction in India, wrote to the Secretary to the Government of Bengal on 16 June 1896,

> The subject dealt with has long been regarded as of very great importance, attempting as it does the complete specification of the unknown forces involved, by determining the length of the invisible wave.... The problem was attempted by Hertz and subsequently by many continental physicists but the results obtained were very contradictory. Mr Bose has recently succeeded in solving the problem with entirely satisfactory results; and a copy of the paper embodying his solution was sent to the University of London as a thesis for the degree of Doctor of Science (D.Sc). I should explain that before being admitted to the examination for that degree, a candidate has to produce a Dissertation embodying the results of original research in some branch of science. On the acceptance of the Dissertation by the university, the candidate has in general

to undergo a further examination. There is, however, a provision in the D.Sc regulations that a candidate at the discretion of the university be exempted from further examination, provided the paper submitted is of special excellence. Mr Bose received on the 27th May a telegram from the Registrar informing him that his thesis was accepted and his presence at the examination excused.[3]

This letter contains the phrase 'special excellence' and is much longer than what is quoted here. Its author, Sir Alfred Croft, held a Master's in Philosophy and was a professor of that subject before he became the director of public instruction; hence, it is obvious that he was not expressing his own opinion in this letter but quoting that of eminent physicists. The letter bears testimony to the fact that Hertz and subsequently other physicists, including Righi and Lebedev, failed in their attempts in determining the wavelength of the electric waves satisfactorily. Bose was the first to do so and, therefore, he was also the first in determining the wave speed and show that it equals the speed of light.

In summary, Bose was the one to conclusively prove that the laws of reflection, refraction, total internal reflection, and speed of travel of the electric waves were exactly the same as those of light, and that both light and electric waves were polarized by certain naturally occurring crystals in an identical manner. He thus dispelled all doubts about Maxwell's theory of electromagnetism—Maxwell's ideas found full acceptance once Bose's papers on this were published by the mid-1890s.

Life Continues: The Calcutta Townhall Experiment

We shall take a break from Bose's scientific endeavours until the next chapter and return to his life and struggle. Fortunately, he was not always alone, and often help came from people with a perceptive eye. Lord Rayleigh, who was one of his teachers at Cambridge, was one such person. He was a constant source of encouragement and communicated all of Bose's research to the Royal Society. Rayleigh found out that

---

[3]The letter is preserved in India's government archives.

Bose was funding his own research and advised Bose to apply for aid from the Government Grant Fund at the disposal of the Royal Society, of which Rayleigh was the joint secretary. So, it was easy for him to secure approval for a one-time grant. This helped and encouraged Bose immensely.

Another professor of his at Cambridge, Lord Kelvin, wrote to him that he was 'literally filled with wonder and admiration' for his achievements, congratulating him 'for so much success in the difficult and novel experimental problems which you have attacked.' This correspondence is preserved at the Bose Institute in Kolkata.

Marie Alfred Cornu, a French physicist and one-time President of the French Academy of Sciences, wrote to Bose in early 1897 with effusive praise saying, 'For my own part, I hope to take full advantage of the perfection to which you have brought your apparatus, for the benefit of Ecole Polytechnique and for the sake of further researches I wish to complete.'

Bose's predecessor, Hertz, had proved the existence of the invisible electric waves, but as for their affinity to Maxwell's electromagnetic waves, the evidence, produced by him, had not been complete and conclusive.

The dominant school among the science historians of the twentieth and twenty-first centuries asserts that the precision of these experiments was not important—Hertz's demonstration that these waves travel in space, and along a wire, at a finite speed was a step in proving the veracity of Maxwell's theory. That the speed of these waves was comparable, even if by a long shot, to that of light was a confirmation of Maxwell's predictions; it was not necessary to show the equality of the two speeds. In other words, they deliberately overlook the shortcomings of Hertz's experiments.

The history of physics has produced a certain status quo. It is but natural that many science historians of today would accept it without questioning. However, this fails to judge the perspective prevalent among physicists in Hertz's time and misses the historical context of the last quarter of the nineteenth century—in the first half of the 1890s, most physicists were not fully convinced by Hertz's qualitative experiments about the correctness of Maxwell's theory.

For instance, in 1895, seven long years after Hertz wrote his last paper on electric waves, Wilhelm Röntgen discovered the X-ray. No physicist, not even Röntgen himself, had any inkling or the slightest suspicion that it could be an EM wave, which it actually was. X-ray was proved to be an EM wave almost twenty years later. Had physicists in those days been fully convinced that the Hertzian waves were EM waves, they would have readily hit upon the idea that the X-rays might well belong to the same class.

Bose was the first to make the evidence complete and conclusive, particularly through his measurements of wavelength and wave speed, and polarization experiments with natural crystals. This was an epochal achievement. To eliminate a theoretical difficulty arising out of Maxwell's work was no mean feat for an experimental physicist.

As mentioned earlier, it was believed that all the empty space in the whole universe was filled with a massless substance called ether, which was the medium in which electromagnetic waves travelled, and this belief persisted during Bose's times. Bose, alluding to vibrations produced by sound waves, refers to the electric waves as 'notes' (of music) in ether. He then asks us to imagine an electric organ with millions of stops that can produce notes of very small to very large frequencies. In this vein he says:

> While the ethereal sea in which we are immersed is being thus agitated by these multitudinal waves, we shall remain entirely unaffected, for we possess no organs of perception to respond to these waves. As the ether note rises still higher in pitch, we shall for a brief moment perceive a sensation of warmth.... As the note rises still higher our eyes will begin to be affected, a red glimmer of light will be the first to make its appearance. From this point the few colours we see are comprised within a single octave of vibration. As the frequency of vibration rises still higher...the brief flash of light is succeeded by unbroken darkness.... We have already caught broken glimpses of invisible light; someday, perhaps not very distant, we shall be able to see light gleams, visible or invisible, merging one into the other in unbroken sequence.

The passage is remarkable for its literary flourish, and also for a prediction that the gap in experimental evidence between the electric waves and optical waves would be closed in a continuous fashion. This prediction was fulfilled in the future.

Bose's system of tabletop apparatus and procedures became popular and were used by scientists for nearly a generation. The facilities at the Presidency College were primitive, the time available to Bose for research was limited to the evenings after the college hours, and he was constantly overworked and had to fund his research from his own salary. Under these circumstances, the feats he achieved within just two years of the commencement of his research were astonishing.

ſ

As was his wont, Bose arranged classroom demonstrations of the transmission and reception of electrical waves and other such simple experiments, attracting students as well as colleagues. In the beginning of 1895, an event was organized: a signal was sent from Ray's room and received in Pedler's office in the college.

The news of this wireless signalling came to the notice of the authorities, who decided to stage a well-publicized show for the lieutenant governor of Bengal, Sir Alexander Mackenzie. The demonstration took place in the Townhall of Calcutta in early 1895, a few months before May, the month his first publication would appear in the journal of the Royal Asiatic Society, Calcutta.

Several British officials, as part of the entourage of the lieutenant governor, many newspaper reporters, and a motley crowd of curious onlookers were present in the Townhall. Emulating Father Lafont, who taught him at St. Xavier's College, Bose had made it a practice to deliver lectures for the masses, and on this occasion, he had created an astonishing spectacle for exciting the popular imagination. He generated the electric wave in one room and had it pass through the body of the lieutenant governor and three thick walls and then trigger a receiver in a different room, at a distance of nearly 23 metres. This, in turn, actuated a relay circuit to ring an electric bell, trigger an apparatus to catapult an iron ball, fire a pistol, and explode some gunpowder.

Bose himself has given a vivid description of this event in a book titled *Abyakta*[4] written in his mother tongue, Bengali. This public demonstration was reported on in numerous newspapers and journals around the world, and found mention in the annual presidential address of the Royal Asiatic Society in 1895; Alexander Pedler was its President then. Bose had performed such an experiment even earlier according to a statement by Father Lafont, which appeared in a Calcutta newspaper. This experiment might have been performed in late 1894.

This experimental demonstration introduced the concept of the elevated aerial and showed the penetrative capacity of electric waves, which could go through three brick and mortar walls, each 45 centimetres thick. This was the first example in the world of the wireless transmission of a man-made signal sent across barriers over a distance to activate a mechanical device.

In May 1895, Russian scientist Alexander Popov successfully captured a signal from natural lightning on a stormy evening in Saint Petersburg that rang an electric bell. He did not generate his own electric waves and used a Branly coherer in this experiment. In a paper published in 1997, D. T. Emerson discussed the efforts of Marconi and Popov, and unambiguously gave priority to Bose. While the entire gamut of Bose's research in radio physics cannot be discussed here, it should be noted that he made many inventions which remained buried in the pages of the *Proceedings of the Royal Society* and did not attract immediate attention, only to be re-invented later in the West. Emerson quotes Sir Nevill Mott, winner of the 1977 Nobel Prize for Physics: 'J. C. Bose was at least sixty years ahead of his times. In fact, he had anticipated the existence of P-type and N-type semiconductors.'

Returning to the introduction of the elevated aerial, Bose had connected a circular metal plate to the top of a six-metre-tall vertical pole attached to the radiator and a similar device to the receiver at the other end. This metal plate was a precursor to the modern elevated aerial or antenna. His transmitter and receiver were of his own design. This event made headlines in newspapers in Calcutta and other major cities across India, Europe, and America. It must have been sensational; in an interview with an American journalist in London over two years

---

[4]This was an essay titled 'Adrishya Aalok' (Invisible Light) in *Abyakta*, first edition, p. 58.

after the Calcutta Townhall experiment, Bose was still being asked about this particular event.

Bose often signalled wirelessly from the college to his residence, a distance of about a mile, using a pair of aerials. He had planned a public demonstration, but could not arrange the event due to heavy workload in the college; and then he had to leave for England.

During the course of his research, so far, Bose had made a series of inventions, including a receiver, many of which were patentable. His inventions and findings were published in *The Electrician* and the *Proceedings of the Royal Society*. But Bose steadfastly refused to apply for any patents, in spite of much coaxing by his friends, teachers, and well-wishers. He would respond to every query from India or abroad, and give out information freely.

His arguments for not seeking any patents were two-fold. In ancient India, knowledge was never limited or restricted but available for all, and he wished to live up to that lofty ideal of Indian sages. In his opinion, in the context of the modern world, it was unethical for scientists to restrict knowledge for the sake of personal pecuniary gains. Many of his friends and acquaintances found his attitude in this regard to be quixotic and warned him that he would have to pay a heavy price someday.

Around this time, Bose was made a fellow of the Calcutta University, an honorary position with no emoluments; the university, although receiving grants from the government, was an autonomous body and his work as a fellow was not linked to his duties in the college.

Unsung in Modern Times

Modern books on physics present a linear description of events of the last quarter of the nineteenth century. Their narrative runs as follows: Maxwell developed his theory of electromagnetism by the mid-1870s; his theory predicted the existence of EM waves well outside the solar spectrum of infrared, visible, and ultra-violet rays; Hertz started his experiments in the early 1880s and discovered the electric waves that were well outside the solar spectrum and proved that they have all the properties of Maxwell's EM waves by 1888. This is quite far from the truth, as we have just seen in previous sections.

The above narrative gives the impression that when Hertz began his work, Maxwell's theory was universally accepted. The real history is non-linear in character, involving much back and forth, the reformulation of ideas, removal of obscurities by the Maxwellians, and interaction of theoreticians and experimentalists towards reaching a consensus. According to science historian Bruce Hunt, Maxwell's theory found full acceptance only after the mid-1890s, well after Hertz had completed his research into the subject. This was when Bose published his first series of papers and proved quantitatively that electric waves obey all the optical laws and have the same speed as that of light. The quantitative nature of Bose's experiments cannot be over-emphasized, as opposed to Hertz's qualitative experiments.

It has been mentioned earlier that the unit of frequency was named after Hertz for his research on verifying Maxwell's predictions. For an electromagnetic wave, the rate of energy transport per unit area is described by a term called Poynting Vector, after physicist John Henry Poynting, who first discussed its properties. Even a small contribution—a discussion—was considered due for commemoration. The publication of Bose's papers on EM waves coincided with his year-long travel in Europe, where he visited England, France, and Germany. From 1895 to 1900, Bose received high praise from his European counterparts. But it was never thought fit to accord him a mark of commemoration, as done for Hertz, Poynting, and many other well-known physicists.

Back home in Calcutta, as the news of the award of the D. Sc. degree and Bose's research success featured in the newspapers, his seniors at Presidency College became more hostile. However, Sir Alexander Mackenzie was most impressed by all the admiration expressed by the leading men of science in Europe and took due notice.

Sir Mackenzie, who had been sympathetic to Bose, having presided over the Calcutta Townhall experiment earlier, floated a scheme to give Bose a new post with higher emoluments, which would also afford him more time for research. Moreover, his new duties would be to develop the college's research laboratories, including his own, under the aegis of the government. The scheme, forwarded through the education department, was sanctioned and Bose was informed that a formal letter would reach him in a few days.

At this time, a meeting of the senate of the Calcutta University was convened and Bose, a fellow of the university, was called upon to participate, and he expressed his opinion on a particular question in a frank and forthright fashion. Unfortunately, this was contrary to the view of the chairman and disagreeable to the officials present, most of whom were British. At their behest, the sanction of the new post for Bose was cancelled. Thus, what the lieutenant governor had proposed, his subordinates collectively disposed of.

Sir Mackenzie then offered to compensate Bose for his research expenses thus far; the latter expressed gratitude but declined to accept. The government then arranged to give an annual grant of 2,500 rupees for his future research, which was promptly accepted with thanks. Bose's financial situation improved but the heavy burden of work remained as usual. There was, however, one event that gave him some encouragement. Lord Rayleigh, his teacher at Cambridge and a well-wisher, was so intrigued by Bose's waveguide that he arranged an official trip to Calcutta in order to see Bose's laboratory. He was quite impressed by what he saw and advised Bose to occasionally visit Europe, which would be of great benefit to his work. Later, Rayleigh developed and published his theory of wave propagation through waveguides.

Rayleigh's visit did nothing to change the hostile attitude of most of Bose's colleagues. Soon, he was at the end of his tether and realized that overworking was sapping his energy as never before. He took his teacher's sage advice and applied for a year's furlough, which was his due, to visit Europe and get in touch with other scientists.

He met Sir Mackenzie who asked if Bose could afford such a costly trip. Bose realized at once that he could not, and enquired if he could be sent on a scientific deputation by the government. The lieutenant governor, fully aware that the imperial government would permit no such thing, hesitated and, finally, on his own personal responsibility, decided to send Bose on deputation for six months, instead of the requested one year. The director of public instruction, Sir Alfred Croft, now found courage to break ranks with the mass of officials and expressed his full support. Decisions were conveyed to the Government of India and the secretary of state in London telegraphically and Jagadish and Abala Bose were soon on a long sea voyage to Europe. They boarded SS *Caledonia* from Bombay on 24 July 1896.

It is worth mentioning a strange but significant event that had occurred before his meeting with the lieutenant governor. The Education Board met in Shimla, a hill station in the Himalayas, and passed a resolution expressing regret that India had never taken to scientific pursuits in spite of the government's best efforts. Quite naturally, Bose felt hurt that all his achievements, the acclaim and publicity he received in Europe and India were ignored, and the same old prejudice against his countrymen had been reflected in this new official resolution. He brought this up with the lieutenant governor, who seemed embarrassed but also irritated with this plain-speaking scientist.

It is this author's belief that the resolution in question was not just prejudiced, it was meant to be a political statement. There had been signs of an Indian nationalist awakening and a demand for independence gaining momentum. The imperial rulers perhaps reckoned that an overt recognition of Bose and the acknowledgement of scientific prowess in Indians would add to their confidence and give a boost to the nascent independence movement. Sir Mackenzie, the second most powerful official in the British Raj, did not object to the resolution because he was aware of its purpose. To his credit he did not defend the Education Board before Bose, and to his generosity he still proceeded to grant the aforementioned deputation, but only on his personal responsibility. To a British administrator, long-term relentless policies in the interest of keeping a hold on the Indian empire was one thing and a personal sense of fair play was another, and never the twain did mix.

Bose's publications on electric waves and, in particular, his inventions, had been making waves in England and Europe. Well before his arrival in England, *The Electrician*, as mentioned earlier, had taken note of his publications, and attracted attention to its practicability in wireless communication.

First Scientific Mission to Europe

His first public appearance after arriving in England was in Liverpool on 21 September 1896. The occasion was a conference of the British Association for the Advancement of Science. The speaker was a curiosity to the attendees—he was the first Indian to speak before a learned European audience on scientific advances and the hall was full.

The demonstration of the properties of the electrical waves with his tabletop compact equipment created a tremendous impact. His presentation was titled 'Complete Apparatus for Studying the Properties of Electric Waves', and after he finished, the hall echoed with the sound of loud applause. Lord Kelvin was so overcome with admiration that he limped upstairs to the gallery, leaning on his walking stick, and shook Abala's hands, congratulating her on her husband's achievements.

A special correspondent of the *Daily Chronicle*, London, interviewed Bose and wrote on 28 November 1896:

> The inventor has transmitted signals to a distance of nearly a mile and herein lies the first and obvious and exceedingly valuable application of this new theoretical marvel. It is telegraphy without any kind of intervening conductor. ...If all this be true the great problem of transmitting signals from ship to ship or lighthouse to ship through a fog, has been solved and this alone will be a priceless benefit to the human race.

It is apparent that the correspondent had learnt about crossing this 'milestone' from Bose himself, during the interview. As mentioned earlier, Bose often sent signals to his home from the college over 'a distance of nearly a mile'.

About this, Geddes writes, 'Our inventor not only went on signalling through the college but planned to fix one of these poles on the roof of his house and the other on the Presidency College one mile away; but he left for England before effecting this.'

Geddes was writing Bose's biography twenty-five years after this event, and his only source of information was Bose himself. Obviously, there was a memory lapse or misunderstanding on Geddes's part. In reality, Bose had already achieved this feat and been planning a public demonstration of this achievement, but could not arrange the event because he had to leave for England. What is noteworthy in the quote is the use of the phrase 'one of these poles'. It is obvious that Geddes used the term 'pole' to mean the elevated aerial.

After the great success of his Liverpool lecture, Bose was invited to deliver a Friday Evening Discourse at the Royal Institution, London. Here it is necessary to point out that in the scientific community in Britain, there was no honour greater than an invitation to lecture at the Royal Institution. It had a reputation for providing a platform for the presentation of new and impactful scientific investigations. Though lectures were held throughout the week, the Friday Evening Discourses were a hallowed series known for their quality and prestige, wherein the lecturer would enter the historic hall and begin his discourse without an introduction, for it is assumed that he is too well known to need one. He does not address the president or the audience, since it is assumed that his message is not for a particular assemblage, but for the whole world. So, he has to begin abruptly and this custom at first appears jarring to a newcomer.

This invitation so impressed the India Office that they extended Bose's deputation by three months. His presentation at the Royal Institution on 29 January 1897, 'The Polarization of the Electric Ray', was as well received as his lecture in Liverpool. An excerpt from his paper reads:

> The parallel pencil of electric radiation, used in many of the experiments to be described below, is only about 1 cm in diameter. The production of such a narrow pencil became absolutely necessary for a certain class of investigations. Merely qualitative results for reflection and refraction may no doubt be obtained with gigantic mirrors or prisms, but when we come to study the phenomena of polarization as exhibited by crystals, Nature imposes a limit, and this limitation of the size of the crystals has to be accepted in conducting any investigation on their polarizing properties.

Bose succeeded in polarizing electric waves by passing them through crystals in order to establish complete similarity with the process of polarization of light; it should be recalled that Hertz had polarized electric waves by passing them through a grid of parallel bars, though light could never be polarized by this method. Reporting on this, *The Electric Engineer* wrote about his 'coherer' expressing 'surprise that no secret was made as to its construction so that it has been open to all the world to adopt it for practical and possibly money-making purposes.'

We have already spoken about Bose's distaste for patents. Sometime before this trip to England, he and his wife had resolved to set up a research institute in Calcutta, dedicated to research, where Indian scientists would get an opportunity to work in peace, unhindered by racial discrimination. Years later, in 1917, he succeeded in founding this institute and said at its inauguration:

> Through regular publication of the Transactions of the Institute these Indian contributions will reach the whole world. The discoveries made will thus become public property. No patents will ever be taken. The spirit of our national culture demands that we should forever be free from the desecration of utilizing knowledge for personal gain.

It seems that this was a matter of faith for him. Knowledge was sacred and a patent, which is necessarily for personal gain, desecrates knowledge. He weakened only once on this principle and very quickly restored himself thereafter; but that moment of weakness turned out to be historic.

After the Friday Evening Discourse at the Royal Institution, the *Times* paid a different kind of tribute by commenting on his work environment:

> The originality of the achievement is enhanced by the fact that Dr Bose had to do the work in addition to his incessant duties as Professor of Physical Science in Calcutta, and with apparatus and appliances which in this country would be deemed altogether inadequate. He had to construct himself his instruments as he went along. His work forms the outcome of his two-fold lines of labour— construction and research.

Yet another kind of tribute was paid by *The Spectator* and reads as follows:

> The people of the East have just the burning imagination which could extort a truth out of a mass of apparently disconnected facts, a habit of meditation without allowing the mind to dissipate itself and a power of persistence—it is something a little different from patience—such as hardly belong to any European. ...We do not know Professor Bose, but we venture to say...[n]othing would seem to him laborious in his enquiry, nothing insignificant, nothing

painful, any more than it would seem to a true *Sannyasi* in the pursuit of his inquiry into the ultimate relation between his own spirits to that of the Divine.

It is amusing to find that, even during the closing years of the nineteenth century, some in the West were stereotyping an extraordinary and thoughtful Indian scientist as a yogi or sannyasi. Bose certainly did not have the personality of a yogi. He keenly felt hurt if he was discriminated against and was frustrated by the constant struggles he had to wage. He often got violently swayed by the vicissitudes of life. He was a believer and had certain religious convictions, but was not seeking any spiritual ecstasy or fulfilment through scientific research. If he had any motives other than the purely academic, they were far from spiritual; he only wished to establish his country, India, in the scientific comity of the world.

The stir his lectures created in England radiated throughout the continent of Europe, and he soon received invitations to visit from prominent physicists in Paris and Berlin. In the first quarter of 1897, he demonstrated his apparatus before a gathering of the Société Française de Physique in Paris. The meeting was chaired by Marie Alfred Cornu, who expressed glowing admiration after Bose finished. Also in attendance were Gabriel Lippmann, who had become famous for inventions on colour photography, and Louis-Paul Cailletet, who was a pioneer in liquefying gas. Lippmann and other prominent physicists were so impressed that they persuaded Bose to repeat his lecture at the University of Sorbonne. An honorary membership of the Société Française de Physique was soon conferred upon him.

On 5 March 1897, he spoke at a meeting of the Physikalische Gesellschaft in Berlin, which later published a summary of his work in German. Georg Hermann Quincke, who had attempted to duplicate Bose's apparatus, came all the way from Heidelberg to hear him speak and extend an invitation to travel to his town in southwestern Germany. Bose also visited the University of Kiel before arriving in Heidelberg. Bose's apparatus and findings were rapidly popularized and included in contemporary science textbooks in Britain and the rest of Europe. In May 1897 the period of his deputation ended, and the Boses set sail homewards from the port city of Marseilles in the south of France.

4

HELP OUT OF THE BLUE: RABINDRANATH TAGORE, SISTER NIVEDITA, AND THE VEDANTA CIRCLE

Lord Rayleigh had seen for himself Bose's laboratory in a small annexe adjacent to a washroom in Presidency College. He must have aired his impressions to colleagues on returning to England. Lord Kelvin could see the all but impossible conditions under which Bose had been working, and wrote to Lord G. Hamilton, then secretary of state for India, stating, 'It would be conducive to the credit of India and the science education in Calcutta, if a well-equipped Physical Laboratory is added to the resources of the University of Calcutta in connection with the Professorship held by Dr Bose.'

Lord Lister, then president of the Royal Society, led a galaxy of professors and scientists to write a memorandum to Lord G. Hamilton about the

> great importance we attach to the establishment in the Indian Empire of a Central Laboratory for advanced teaching and research in connection with the Presidency College, Calcutta. We believe that it would be not only beneficial in respect to higher education, but also that it would largely promote the material interest of the country; and we venture to urge on you the desirability of establishing in India a Physical Laboratory worthy of that great empire.

Hostility of the Bureaucrats

The Secretary of State Lord Hamilton, forwarded the memo to the Government of India with favourable recommendations. Lord Elgin, then the viceroy, assured Bose of his support to the project, and wrote to the Government of Bengal enclosing the memo. It climbed up the chain of bureaucratic command, attracting comments on its journey, and finally reaching a conclusion to the effect that although the project was eminently desirable, the time was not opportune. Therefore, the project had to be postponed. Bose knew exactly what that meant as he had become all too familiar with the British colonial administration and the individuals who worked within it.

After returning to Calcutta in April 1897, Bose had doubled down and started his work anew. His friends in England often wrote to him to know of any progress on his project and asked what the cause for delay was. He knew that he would have to devote considerable time to trace, through the labyrinthine layers of colonial bureaucracy, the point of the obstruction. He considered this a futile pursuit and ignored his friends' entreaties, instead choosing to concentrate all his energy in continuing his research in the harsh circumstances he was used to. His biographer Geddes sarcastically wrote in this connection, 'It is worthy of remark that the cog wheels suddenly became mobile when Bose had neared the period of retirement from government service. Then the scheme for which he had striven for many years resulted in the recent foundation[5] of a fully equipped physical laboratory.'

This reinforces one's belief that the British colonial administration considered a talented Indian scientist and any indigenous scientific progress a threat to the Raj. Once the threat was past his prime, the administration could afford to shower amenities on the institution. Fortunately, the colonial education policy evolved for the better in the 1910s. Regarding the policy in the late 1890s, the following two episodes are illustrative.

Soon after returning from Europe, Bose had appealed on his own to the Government of Bengal for improving his financial situation in the interest of aiding his research. This appeal is today preserved as a historic document in the national archives. The finance member of the advisory council of the viceroy, wrote on the appeal on 7 September 1897,

> He is now drawing Rs 500 and it is simple nonsense on the part
> of a native gentleman in the service of the Government to talk,

---

[5]In the year 1914.

under such circumstances of 'difficulty in maintaining himself on his small means.' I wonder what any of the universities in England would say to any of its staff who said, 'I am a distinguished man, and you must agree to give me, on that account, more than the allowances of my offices.' I think Mr Bose has got his head a bit turned and he can wait a bit for his distinctions and records.

The comment reflects malice and tries to divert attention from the real issue. Fortunately, Sir John Woodburn, a member of the home department and a distinguished scholar of philosophy, who was to become the lieutenant governor of Bengal later, made a more positive comment: 'Mr Bose's distinction is not ordinary distinction, and as to the adequacy of his salary, I am personally aware that it has not been sufficient to meet the expenses of his experiments and tours.'

It becomes apparent from this comment that the government was aware that Bose was bearing much of the cost of his research from his own salary, notwithstanding the small annual sum granted earlier. Negotiating between the two conflicting comments, the government granted a modest sum of 2,000 rupees per annum to Bose.

The other episode revolves around the second visit of Lord Rayleigh to Presidency College on 27 December 1897. Charles Tawney had just retired from service, and a new principal had taken charge. Lord Rayleigh was on an official trip to Calcutta and Bose availed of this opportunity to invite his ex-teacher to his laboratory. Rayleigh expressed much appreciation, but the event did not end on a happy note. That afternoon, the principal wrote the following on official stationery and sent to Bose: 'I hear from Lord Rayleigh that he visited the Presidency College this morning and inspected the laboratory over which he was shown by you. I should be glad to hear by what authority you have received outsiders into the laboratory.'

Bose's reply was caustic and conveyed his surprise at the idea that the president of the Royal Society could be considered an outsider in an academic institution like the Presidency College. He was so incensed that he considered handing in his resignation, only to be persuaded against taking such a step by close friends.

Freedom Movement and the Vedanta Circle

It has been made clear how British officials showed a kind of lethargy when it came to offering due recognition and facilities to Bose. However, to understand the policy and style of the British government at the turn of the century, we need to trace India's political development. In the closing decades of the nineteenth century, there were signs of a national awakening, particularly around Bombay and Calcutta. The Indian National Congress was founded in Bombay in 1885 and its first president was W. C. Banerjee, a fellow of the Calcutta University. The Congress took the path of moderation and attempted to negotiate with the British government. It initially asked for self-rule, only demanding full freedom after a few decades.

But there was also a violence endemic in the freedom movement in the Bengal and Bombay presidencies. In 1897, the Chapekar brothers from Pune fatally shot a British official, Walter C. Rand, and his military escort, Lieutenant Ayerst; the brothers were arrested and sentenced to death. Some years later, a Bengali youth named Khudiram Basu threw a bomb, intended to assassinate an oppressive magistrate named Douglas Kingsford, but ended up killing two innocent British women. He was soon caught and tried and gallantly went to the gallows. His martyrdom fuelled more violent struggle. The fact was that since the 1890s, the government had been receiving disturbing intelligence reports of underground revolutionary activities. Several search and seizure operations carried out at the beginning of the twentieth century by the police and the intelligence wing, in and around Calcutta, discovered that many of these revolutionary conspirators had Swami Vivekananda's writings in their personal effects.

Who was this Swami Vivekananda? Swami Vivekananda, a graduate of the Calcutta University, was a wandering Hindu monk and preacher; his British and American disciples were to play a remarkable role in Bose's life. He was leading an order of monks, in which every monk's name ended with 'ananda', the Sanskrit word for blissful joy. The word 'Swami' means 'master', or according to the Sanskrit root, 'he who is one with the self', and has a spiritual connotation. It is an honorific usually placed before or after the name of a monk such as Swami Vivekananda, where Vivekananda is the actual name. For the purposes of our text, we will refer to Swami Vivekananda as 'the Swami', while using 'swami' as a postfix for other Hindu monks.

In 1893, the Swami travelled to America to attend the Parliament of Religions in Chicago. He spoke at this convention, and also from other platforms, to preach the Advaita Vedanta philosophy, referred to as the Vedanta, in short.

His personality, eloquence, and message of universal acceptance of all religions created such a stir that the American newspapers called him 'the cyclonic monk'. He visited England, too, and became a sensation due to his style of oratory and his unique message of spiritual unity of all humankind. His method of applying the Vedanta to day-to-day life, which he called 'practical Vedanta', was no less stirring. Although not a specialist, the Swami was well versed in the sciences of physics and chemistry. He showed that unlike the revealed religions, the Vedanta had no conflict and was fully compatible with science.

During his first trip to London, Swami Vivekananda was invited to lecture at the Princes' Hall. The next day newspapers came emblazoned with headlines stating that a great Indian yogi had come to London. During his second trip he gave a few lectures in private gatherings, but soon the small halls started to overflow. The gallery of the Royal Institute of Painters in Water Colours was booked and a series of Sunday evening lectures was arranged. Swami Vivekananda carried no notes and always spoke extemporaneously, which made his speeches seem spontaneous and made them all the more interesting.

Present in these lectures were famous personalities such as the dramatist George Bernard Shaw, biologist-cum-sociologist Patrick Geddes, poet William Butler Yeats, and many others. Later, Geddes would meet the Swami in Paris, spend several years in India, become a close friend of the Boses, and write the first biography of Jagadish Chandra Bose. In the audience were the Swami's American disciple Josephine MacLeod, British disciple Margaret Noble, and his stenographer, Josiah Goodwin. Margaret and Josephine were to become very intimate with another one of the Swami's American disciples, Sara Chapman Bull, and all three were destined to facilitate Bose's research in various ways and stand by him in times of distress. Josephine became a lifelong friend of both Geddes and G. Bernard Shaw. This was the beginning of the formation of the Vedanta circle that, though never formalized, would grow in strength and influence. The Boses and their associates were destined to receive succour from this loose fraternity.

Startling news reports about the Swami's exploits in America and England reached the shores of India too and pushed the cause of Indian freedom further into the national discourse. Around the same time, Bose was being applauded in Europe as a scientist, and attracted much public attention. Going by newspaper reports, Swami Vivekananda's triumphant return to India in 1897, after his first sojourn abroad, created a mass frenzy first in the city of Madras and then in Calcutta. In both cities, there were tremendous receptions organized by his students and intellectuals.

Even before going to America, the Swami had set up a monastery with other monk-disciples of his guru, Sri Ramakrishna. Their order was named Ramakrishna Math (Math means a monastic order in Sanskrit) and they had been living in a rented home, on donations from other disciples of their guru. After returning from abroad, the Swami made the Math a legal entity by executing a deed of trust, purchased a large piece of land in Belur on the western bank of the river Ganga several miles upstream of Calcutta. Here, he built a temple and some housing and shifted the monastery to its new home. This was mainly financed through the fees he collected for his lectures in the West; the rest was covered by donations from American disciples. Additionally, he added a mission of service, called Ramakrishna Mission, to the monastery.

All this made the British rulers quite uncomfortable—the memory of the Sannyasi revolt, which had taken place in eastern India in the late eighteenth century, was still fresh in their minds. A Bengali novel named *Anandamath* (*The Abbey of Bliss*), based on this rebellion and written by Bankim Chandra Chatterji, had been published in 1882. It contained 'Vande Mataram', a poem that had been gaining currency as a nationalist slogan among the youth. This is what was part of the backdrop when the literature of Swami Vivekananda was found in the possession of the revolutionary youth mentioned earlier.

The intelligence officers pored over the seized literature. All they found were exhortations to serve the poor and downtrodden and a call to build character and sacrifice the self for serving the society, but not a word against British rule. In any case, they had already noticed that the recognition and appreciation of an eminent Indian abroad acted as a great boost to the nationalistic spirit. To curb this nationalist fervour that was taking over the youth of the country, they decided to employ certain subtle methods as a matter of policy. As their actions were interlaced with instances of individual generosity and liberalism, their methods served their purpose of containment far better than a purely dictatorial stranglehold over the subjugated people.

The British Government was a parliamentary democracy at its cosmopolitan centre in England, while practicing imperialism in its colonies. It was natural that it would have internal contradictions, something with which Bose was familiar by now. It offered a boon with the right hand and denied the same with the left, and it is the left hand that prevailed most often.

Bose was a Brahmo by faith and belonged to the religious movement of Brahmoism. They were, in general, a socially and politically conscious, patriotic people. It is likely that Bose had heard about the Swami's impact; the Swami, too, was sure to have heard of Bose's success in England. There is evidence that they met in Calcutta at least once before they were destined to meet in Europe.

The Poet and the Maharaja

Returning to India in 1897 from his Europe trip, Bose quietly settled into his daily routine and started to plough a lonely furrow in his laboratory, determined more than ever to persist against all hurdles. Little did he know that solace and sympathy were soon to arrive in the person of an eminent poet and writer—Rabindranath Tagore called on him to felicitate him at his residence. At that time, Tagore was already a well-known poet, composer, and litterateur, and a prominent figure in the Brahmo society of Calcutta. Not finding Jagadish at home, Tagore left a magnolia blossom on his table as a token of his appreciation.

Since then, a strong but unusual camaraderie gradually developed between the scientist and the poet, two apparently unlike personalities. It often happens that a famous physicist has a flare for some form of art, which he pursues for recreation. Albert Einstein was an able violinist, Robert Oppenheimer was a scholar of classical Sanskrit texts, and Richard Feynman was a percussionist. Likewise, Bose had a flare for literature. Even a few samples of his English prose that have been quoted in this book have a marked literary quality, although English was not his mother tongue. His popular science articles in Bengali were a pleasure to read. The first work of science fiction in Bengali, 'Niruddesher Kahini', was penned by him in 1896, a scientific satire which has the reader in splits. Bose later translated it into English as 'The Story of the Missing One'.[6]

About the common ground between poetry and science, Bose wrote in English:

> The poet seeing, by the heart, realizes the inexpressible and strives to give it expression. His imagination soars, where the sight of others fails, and his news of realms unknown finds voice in rhyme and meter. The path of the scientific man may be different, yet there is some likeness between the two pursuits. Where visible light ends, he still follows the invisible. Where the note of the audible reaches the unheard, even there he gathers the tremulous message. That mystery, which is behind the expressed, is the object of his questioning also, and he in his scientific way, attempts to render its abstruse discoveries into human speech.

About their introductory meeting, Tagore wrote decades later,

> Years ago, when Jagadish, in his militant exuberance of youthfulness, was contemptuously defying all obstacles to the progress of his endeavour, I came into intimate contact with him, and became infected with his vigorous hopefulness. There was every chance of his frightening me away into a respectful distance, making me aware of the airy nothingness of my imaginings. But to my relief, I found in him a dreamer, and it seemed to me, what surely was a half-truth, that it was more his magical instinct than the probing of

---

[6]More than two decades later, in 1921, Bose rewrote the story and renamed it 'Palatak Tufan', the English translation being renamed 'Runaway Cyclone'.

his reason that startled out secrets of nature before sudden flashes of his imagination. In this I felt our mutual affinity but at the same time our difference, for to my mind he appeared to be the poet of the world of facts that waited to be proved by the scientist for their final triumph, whereas my own world of visions had their value, not in their absolute probability but in their significance of delightfulness. All the same, I believe that a part of my nature is logical which not only enjoys making playthings of facts, but seeks pleasure in an analytical view of objective reality. I remember often having been assured by my friend that I only lacked the opportunity of training to be a scientist but not the temperament. Thus, in the prime of my youth I was strangely attracted by the personality of this remarkable man and found his mind sensitively alert in the poetical atmosphere of enjoyment which belonged to me.

At this time, he was busy detecting in the behaviour of the non-living the hidden impulses of life. This aroused a keen enthusiasm in me who had ever been familiar with the utterance of the Upanishad which proclaims that whatever there is in this moving world vibrates with life.

Bose was always ready to explain his work before an audience and often during a visit, Tagore would be regaled with an experimental demonstration. Bose would write about his experimental findings to the latter, who replied with a description of his own latest literary work. Bose's letters were often aided by sketches; they also shared their personal concerns, and thus grew a volume of correspondence between them in their shared mother tongue. The letters often expressed Bose's moods, high and low, his frustrations and more often, joyous discoveries. His Bengali prose often read like free verse. This book shall frequently quote from these letters, in translation of course, from the original Bengali.

The poet wrote thus about his relationship with his physicist friend:

He was busy in employing his marvellous inventiveness in coaxing Nature to yield her hidden language.... I had the rare privilege of sharing the daily delight of his constant surprises.... At this early stage of his adventure when obstacles were powerfully numerous and jealousy largely predominated over appreciation, friendly companionship and sympathy must have had some needful value for him even from one who to maintain intellectual communion with him lacked special competency.

During his second trip to Europe, Bose regularly corresponded with Tagore and his letters contained a fair amount of scientific matter, accompanied with sketches. His style was so lucid and clear that the poet could follow the scientific themes fairly well. The upshot was that Tagore himself wrote a series of popular science articles in a journal called *Banga Darshan*, acquainting the common Bengali reader with Bose's current work.

The Tagore family had a zamindari[7] on the bank of river Padma in a place called Silaidaha. Jagadish and Abala were occasionally invited by Rabindranath to spend a few days there. The vast river, with its other bank somewhere beyond the horizon, the long river trips on the bajra houseboats, and the lush greenery of the east Bengal countryside rejuvenated the tired nerves of the overworked and ever-struggling scientist.

On one such trip, Jagadish imposed a condition that on every day of his stay his host would have to write a short story and read it out to him in the evening. This was to encourage his writer friend to be more creative and thus were born a series of memorable short stories, part of the collection *Galpaguccha*.

At the start of the twentieth century, although famous at home, Rabindranath Tagore was not known in Europe. Jagadish was pained at this lack of recognition for his friend. Once during his stay in England, he had one of Tagore's short stories 'Kabuliwallah' translated and sent to the *Harper's Magazine*; the magazine declined to publish the story. Years later, after Tagore had received the Nobel Prize for Literature, Bose sarcastically reminded the Harper brothers about this short story and their refusal. This pathos-filled short story is now quite famous and has been translated into many languages and has a number of film adaptations as well. It is obvious that there was an inner affinity between these two apparently unlike souls, both geniuses in their own separate spheres.

---

[7]Vast land and real estate with the responsibility, on behalf of the government, to collect land revenue from the farmers and peasantry.

Tagore had another extraordinary friendship. It was with the maharaja of the princely state of Tripura, geographically adjacent to Bengal. Maharaja Radha Kishore Manikya, in addition to being a benevolent ruler and an able administrator, was a great connoisseur of literature. He was one of the first to recognize the literary genius in Tagore when the latter was a young and fledgling poet. Usually, it is the poet, scholar, or mathematician who arrives at the durbar of a king in search of a patron. But in this case, it was the king who sought out the relatively unknown poet. Bose became acquainted with the king through Tagore and this trio of a scientist, poet, and a king embarked on an interesting relationship.

A colourful description of the first meeting of the maharaja and the scientist has been provided by Colonel Thakur Mahimchandra Debbarma, in his book *Deshiya Rajya* (Indian Principalities). They had not been invited, yet Colonel Debbarma had escorted the maharaja to Bose's laboratory. He recorded the meeting in first person; a free translation of an excerpt is given below:

We arrived at the denoted hour at the laboratory of the Presidency College to find an assembly of many learned people. Rabindranath was surprised and delighted to see the Maharaja and introduced him to Professor Jagadish Bose. The Maharaja spoke in Bengali to Mr Bose in a sweetly worded complaint,

'Why don't you consider me your student? Why not let me also watch these interesting demonstrations? I read *Sanjivani*[8] regularly and thus I am somewhat familiar with your novel discoveries.'

Then he took a seat in the gathering and watched the experiments which took about two hours. Dr Bose asked him, 'I have spoken in English. Have you been able to follow?' The Maharaja replied, 'I do not know English. However, if you let me close to your instrument, I may be able to tell how far I have understood. '

Thereafter he was taken near the apparatus. He picked up a book and held it in front of an equipment and told Bose to turn on

---

[8]A Bengali journal that often carried popular science articles.

the electricity. There was no response. Now the Maharaja changed the orientation of the book, and asked Bose to repeat the action. There was an immediate response, as expected. Jagadish Babu was absolutely delighted and said,

'Maharaj, I am convinced that you have followed. I explained to Lord Elgin[9] but he could not understand. My Master's students too have much difficulty. You truly surprise me.'

Polarization of Electric Waves

In the demonstration the maharaja attended, Bose performed an experiment on polarization using a thick book as the polarizer. Bose intuitively felt that a book was likely to be a good polarizer and his experiments proved him right. Working on a shoestring budget, he chose the thickest and cheapest book available—a railway timetable.

Having experimented with simple polarization earlier—his first publication was on that topic—he now concentrated on the more advanced aspects of polarization of electric waves. What has been shown in Fig. 3.12 on p. 38 is a single ray of an electromagnetic (EM) wave, which may either be a light or electric wave. A beam of light (or electric waves) usually consists of thousands of rays, all with different orientations of their planes of oscillations.

Fig. 4.1 illustrates this point by choosing to show an extremely thin beam that consists of only five rays. The first ray has e_1 as its plane of electric oscillations, the second has e_2, and so on. All of them are shown radially distributed on an imaginary circular disc; the beam of light advances in the X-direction which is horizontal and perpendicular to the plane of the disc starting at its centre. This means that the face of the disc, which is visible to us, lies in the plane of Y and Z axes, and this plane is a vertical plane. Hence, all planes of oscillations are at right angles to the X-axis.

---

[9]Then Viceroy of India.

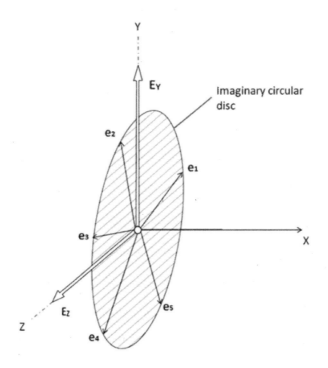

Fig. 4.1: A beam of five rays advancing in X-direction; e_1, e_2, ... e_5 are electric oscillations of the rays; E_Y and E_Z are net effects along Y, Z directions.

The magnetic oscillation for each ray is also present, but not shown in this figure. For now, we shall pay attention to only the electric oscillation of the EM wave. In order to show the face of the imaginary disc and all three axes we have had to take an angled view in which the imaginary circular disc appears as an ellipse and many of the angles do not appear as they should.

If these five rays are added up, the resultant effect would have two components. Each component is an electric oscillation, stronger than that of any individual ray, shown by a longer double-lined arrow; one component is along the Y-axis and marked E_Y, and the other component is along the Z-axis and marked E_Z, as shown in the figure. To summarize, Fig. 4.1 shows a thin beam of five rays and their resultant effect in the form of two components of electric oscillations: E_Y and E_Z. The resultant effect is alternatively called net effect.

In practice, such a thin beam is impossible to produce as, usually, there are thousands of rays in a beam. Their net effect can be found likewise by adding up the vectors, and again it would amount to two very strong components of electric oscillations: E_Y and E_Z. Hence, we can represent a beam of thousands of rays with an arrow along the X-axis showing the direction of propagation, and two arrows along Y and Z axes, as shown in Fig. 4.2.

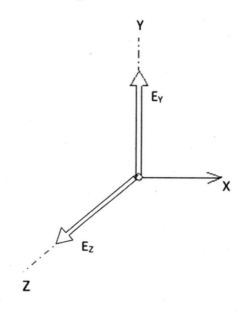

Fig. 4.2: Net effect of a beam of thousands of rays.

Now, we may proceed to understand the principle of polarization. Fig. 4.3 shows a crane and a tortoise in front of a window with a grid of vertical rods. The crane can easily wiggle through because its body is tall and narrow, whereas the tortoise, whose body is flat and wide, cannot pass. Bose himself drew such a diagram to explain polarization in a popular science article written in Bengali. The message is that a grid of parallel bars may allow passage to one kind of ray, and not to the other.

If we attempt to pass a beam of electric waves through a grid of horizontal bars as in Fig. 4.4, where the gap between two adjacent rods and the rod diameter are comparable to the wavelength λ, the horizontal component E_z is prevented while the vertical component E_Y is able to pass. The beam crosses the grid at point P and emerges on the other side with its intensity diminished by half. This phenomenon is called polarization.

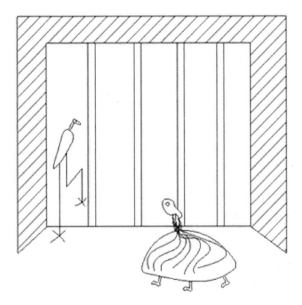

Fig. 4.3: The crane can pass through a window with narrow vertical grid, while the tortoise cannot.

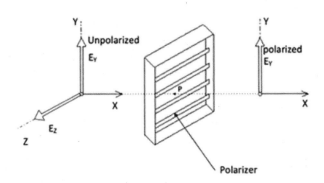

Fig. 4.4: Polarization of a beam of electric waves by a horizontal grid.

We note that a polarized beam has only one component (E_Y) of the net effect. The other component (E_Z) is absorbed by the horizontal bars. Now if a second grid with vertical bars (not shown in Fig. 4.4) was to be placed before the polarized light, even the vertical component E_Y would be absorbed. The electric wave would disappear altogether and nothing more than an extremely feeble beam would emerge on the other side.

In contrast to the large grid Hertz had utilized for his experiment, the dimensions of Bose's grid were about sixty to seventy times smaller, measured in millimetres, since he had much smaller waves at his disposal. Additionally, Bose put forth a novel explanation about the mechanism of polarization. This chiefly depended on the differential conductivity or selective conductivity of a material or a polarizing grid. As discussed earlier, conductivity is the property by which a material conducts heat or electricity; highly conductive materials are conductors, while those with low conductivity are insulators. Bose explained the process of polarization in his grid as follows:

> In a grating we have a structure which is not isotropic, for the electric conductivity parallel to the bars is very great, whereas the conductivity across the bars, owing to the interruptions due to spaces [between bars], is practically zero. We may therefore expect electric vibrations parallel to the bars to produce local induction currents which would ultimately be dissipated as heat. There would thus be no transmission of vibrations parallel to the grating, all such vibrations being absorbed.

The main point of the explanation is that the bars conduct heat and electricity very well lengthwise, but very poorly across, because of the breaks in material continuity, and hence, the grid is said to possess differential conductivity in two perpendicular directions. Therefore, they conduct and absorb the energy of the vibration that is parallel to the bars and prevent the transmission of this component. The vibrations across the bars are not absorbed and allowed to pass through.

Bose held that materials, which polarize electric waves and light, generally have the property of differential conductivity. He supported his theory with substantial experimental evidence by showing that a large number of natural crystals—beryl, apatite, nemalite, chrysotile, barytes, microcline, tourmaline, and Iceland spar, all known polarizers of light—were good polarizers of electric waves as well; and all these have much greater conductivity along one particular direction than in the direction perpendicular to the first. So, it is the same mechanism that is at work whether it is a polarizer grid or a crystal.

Bose measured the conductivity of all the aforementioned crystals in the two perpendicular directions meticulously; it was shown that conductivity in one direction, say Y, may be more than ten times that in the other direction, say Z. Note the two perpendicular directions, Y and Z, cannot be chosen at random but must be determined on the basis of the crystal's structure by a trained physicist.

He further showed that ordinary jute is a good polarizer of electric waves and has a similar property—it has much greater conductivity along its fibres than across it. He demonstrated that a bundle of jute is transparent to the electric wave although it is absolutely opaque to light. Additionally, a bundle of parallel fibres of jute can polarize the electric wave; Fig. 4.5 illustrates this. An ordinary (unpolarized) beam of electric waves enters the bundle from the left. The E_Z component, which is parallel to the jute fibres, is absorbed and the E_Y component is allowed to pass. The polarized wave can be seen emerging on the right.

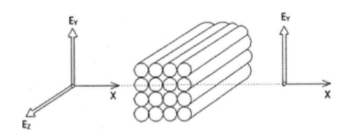

Fig. 4.5: Polarization of electric waves by a bundle of horizontal jute fibres.

Bose also demonstrated that a thick book could polarize electric waves, owing to the fact that it has much better conductivity in a direction that lies in the plane of the pages than in a direction perpendicular to the pages. Here, too, the property of differential conductivity is at work. Let us now recall the meeting between the maharaja and Bose where the book was being used in an experiment to show polarization. We can summarize Bose's explanation as follows:

If a material or a device is transparent to electric or light waves, and has different conductivity in two perpendicular directions, say, along Y and Z, then it can polarize the wave, provided the wave propagates in the third perpendicular direction, that is, along X.

To find an explanation for the process of polarization, and why certain crystals can polarize whereas others cannot, is no mean achievement. Bose was the first to discover that these crystals have a rate of conductivity that falls halfway between conductors and insulators. He was the first to measure the conductivity of these materials and discover that they fall in a third category and that they have differential conductivity in two perpendicular directions.

These discoveries by themselves are quite significant, because these are the properties of what we now know as semiconductors. However, the term semiconductor had not been coined then, nor its theory developed, because it depended on the quantum theory of physics that first saw the light of day with Max Planck's seminal paper in 1900. Within a couple of years into the new century, Bose would leave the field of electric radiation and turn his attention to physiology. Unknowingly, he had reached the boundary between classical physics and quantum physics.

Rotation of Plane of Polarization

Scientists knew that certain crystals, such as quartz, can rotate the plane of polarization (POP) of light. Each molecule in these crystals is made up of atoms arranged in a twisted lattice structure. Further, the molecules are organized in a certain formation. This complicated array is what causes the rotation of the POP. This principle is illustrated in Fig. 4.6 for a fictitious crystal whose molecule has a simple box-like structure. The box-like structure, however, is twisted and placed in the middle of Fig. 4.6. At each corner of the box is an atom. So, there are eight atoms in this molecule, though only four of them are labelled—A, B and A', B'.

The roof and floor of the box are shaded. A polarized beam of light which is about to enter the box is shown to the left. Looking along the direction of advancement of the beam (OX), the box appears twisted to the left. The beam goes through the crystal and exits through the right side. The diagonal connecting atoms A and B is shown by a dashed line; the diagonal at the right-hand face A'B' is shown likewise. The angle between A'B' and a line parallel to AB is the angle of the twist, marked by θ. Note the E_Y vibration of the entering beam is vertical, while the E_Y of the exiting beam is rotated to the left by the same angle θ. Thus, passing through a twisted crystal rotates the POP of light.

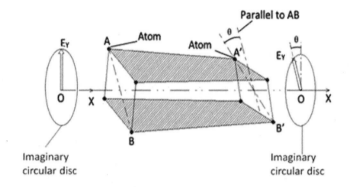

Fig. 4.6: Rotation of plane of polarization of light while passing through the twisted structure of a crystal.

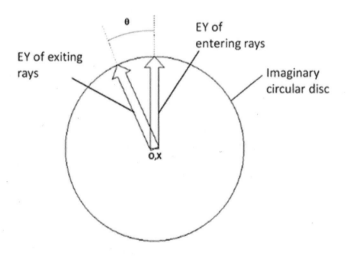

Fig. 4.7: A view of the light beam while looking along OX.

Fig. 4.7 shows a view of the same beam while looking in the direction of its advancement, OX. Notice that O and X coincide at the same point. The 'disc', which indicates the plane of E_Y and appeared elliptical in Fig. 4.6, appears as a perfect circle here; this is the true shape. The angle of rotation of the POP also appears in its true value in this figure.

The Paradox of the Sugar Solution

There was another problem before the scientific community that defied resolution. It was known that certain organic compounds such as sugar and lactic acid, when in a solution of water, can also rotate the POP of light. Sugar molecules generally consist of a large number of atoms. The structure of each molecule is twisted—some to the right, called Dextrose, and some to the left called, Laevulose.[10] Usually, a commonly available sample of sugar is an uneven mixture of both. If the sugar solution had a greater fraction of Dextrose, the POP of the light beam was rotated to the right. When the amount of Laevulose was greater, the rotation was to the left. In a solution with an equal mixture of both, there was no rotation at all.

However, what was puzzling physicists was that sugar molecules move about randomly in water and there is no question of their being ordered into a certain formation like in a solid quartz crystal. Yet, the solution was able to rotate the POP. Moreover, the solution could accept light from any direction and still rotate the POP, whereas a crystal could only do that when approached from one particular direction. Bose quoted the following from a well-known book, *The Theory of Light* by Thomas Preston, in 1898:

> It is perhaps not surprising that crystalline substances should, on account of some special molecular arrangement, possess rotatory power, and affect the propagation of light within the mass in a manner depending on the direction of transmission. [B]ut the possession of it in all directions by fluids and solutions, in which

---

[10]Dextrose is chemically same as glucose. Laevulose is an older name for what is now called fructose.

there cannot be any special internal arrangement of the mass...is not a thing which one would have been led to expect beforehand. To Faraday it appeared to be a matter of no ordinary difficulty; it is just possible that the light, in traversing a solution in which the molecules are free to move, may, on account of some peculiarity of structure, cause the molecules to take up some special arrangement, so that the fluid becomes as it were polarized by the transmission of light....

It seems that Michael Faraday had tried to resolve this difficulty by a speculation that light, on entering the solution, on account of some peculiarity of structure, induces a special arrangement or formation in the molecules, and in the process gets its own POP rotated.

Bose applied his intuitive genius and offered arguments that are best described as given below; the reader will recall that Bose was also producing millimetre waves at this point:

1. The size of the sugar molecule (known to be twisted) is comparable to the wavelength of ordinary light. So, light on passing through a sugar molecule gets its POP rotated.
2. The electric millimetre waves (called microwaves in modern times) are about a million times larger than normal light waves. Likewise, a jute fibre is also enormously larger than a sugar molecule.
3. Therefore, the size of the jute fibre may be comparable to the wavelength of millimetre waves.
4. Hence, the millimetre waves may undergo similar rotation of POP, when passed through twisted jute fibres.

These ideas are schematically represented in Fig. 4.8. A molecule of sugar is represented by a twisted rope-like object. Note that the purpose here is to emphasize the twist; in reality, a sugar molecule is twisted but looks very different.

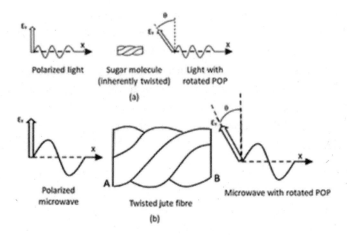

Fig. 4.8: Analogous relationships of following pairs: (a) Light and inherently-twisted sugar molecule, and (b) Microwave and twisted jute fibre.

In this representation of polarized light or microwave, the X-axis is shown by a dashed line with an arrow at the end. On this line a wave is depicted in order to indicate the size and wavelength. Light is shown to have a small wavelength, whereas the microwave has a much larger one. What is truly depicted in Fig. 4.8 is Bose's expectation of the outcome of his experimentation. Bose wrote in the same paper quoted from above:

> In order to imitate the rotation produced by liquids like sugar solutions, I made small elements or 'molecules' of twisted jute, of two varieties, one kind being twisted to the right (positive) and the other twisted to the left (negative). ...In the above we have electro-optic analogues of two varieties of sugar—dextrose and laevulose.

The term 'electro-optic analogue' pertains to the equivalence that exists between electric waves and optical (light) waves.

Through a series of carefully crafted and difficult experiments, Bose proved that his intuition was correct. When he passed a beam of polarized microwave through a bundle of twisted jute fibre, it emerged with a rotated POP. This turned out to be exactly as anticipated in Fig. 4.8. Note the rotation in this figure is similar to the rotation of POP in Fig. 4.6, although the 'imaginary circular disc' is not shown.

Bose further showed that reversing the ends of the jute bundle (i.e., putting the B-end in front and A-end at the rear in Fig. 4.8) makes no difference; in either orientation, the bundle appears twisted to the left in relation to the microwave, and leads to the same result. Hence, the fact that the sugar molecules in the solution are not in any formation does not matter.

Light travels much faster than the speed of movement of the molecules in the solution. Hence, the sugar molecules act more or less stationary for a light beam passing through the solution. The beam encounters many molecules in the appropriate orientation which can rotate the POP and since the molecules move about and change orientation randomly in the solution, the phenomenon is independent of the direction of the beam.

Further, he demonstrated that a jute bundle twisted to the left rotates the POP of the microwave to the left; and the right-twisted one rotates the POP to the right. Bose then placed a left-twisted bundle and a right-twisted bundle one after the other before the microwave; the result was no rotation at all. This explains why a solution of equal mixture of dextrose and laevulose does not produce any rotation in the microwave at all. Thus, he comprehensively explained the paradox of the sugar solution and dispensed with the need for any kind of speculation.

Physicists did not appreciate the merit and ingenuity of this experiment and remained indifferent to this piece of brilliant research for a long time. Microwaves and their applications have received renewed attention recently—a special branch of physics has sprung up called Microwave Analogue Physics. It aims to study the internal structure of a crystal first by X-ray imaging and then by looking at its much larger artificial analogue by means of microwaves. The process is explained below.

The X-ray has been proved to be an electromagnetic wave with a wavelength even smaller than light. It is known that if an X-ray is made to pass through a natural crystal, it undergoes diffraction. The emerging X-ray creates a certain diffraction pattern on a screen, from which information can be extracted about the internal structure of the molecule of the crystal, through a method that has a fair amount of ambiguity attached to it.

For confirmation, a larger but geometrically similar model of the molecule can be constructed artificially. This will be referred to as the 'model molecule'. The microwave is likewise much larger in size than a wave of the X-ray. The model molecule is subjected to a beam of microwaves. The latter undergoes diffraction while passing through the model molecule. If the diffraction pattern turns out to be similar to that of the crystal subjected to X-ray, the findings about the crystal's molecular structure are confirmed. If the patterns are not similar, then more investigation is due. This is known as microwave analogue crystallography.

It should now be apparent that the sugar molecule-jute fibre experiment (see Fig. 4.8) of Bose is quite similar to microwave analogue crystallography in modern times, making him the pioneer of this method. The enormously larger jute molecule, subjected to the microwaves, was called the electro-optic analogue of the sugar molecule by him. John F. Ramsay and Ian K. Snook acknowledge Bose in this regard in their work.

It has been mentioned that there is no mark of commemoration for Bose in physics in spite of his substantial contributions. It may be worthwhile to consider if the subject of microwave analogue crystallography should be called Bose crystallography or Bose analogue crystallography. It is for the physicists of the world to take a call and undo a historical wrong.

Auto-recovering Receivers

Another important task undertaken by Bose was devising a better receiver or detector (also called coherer) for electric waves. His receiver, which featured a stack of tiny steel springs[11], had won high praise worldwide. He now perfected it by coating the springs with cobalt to prevent oxidation and altering the receivers so that they no longer needed to be manually tapped after each receiving event and recovered automatically. In 1899, he published a paper with his findings in the *Proceedings of the Royal Society*. In this paper, he made a systematic study of the behaviour of different metals in response to electric radiation. Three methods were

---

[11]See Fig. 3.17(b) on p. 56.

used to sense variation in their contact resistance. For certain metals such as silver, tiny spiral springs, as in the case of the steel receiver in Fig. 3.17(b), were found suitable. For certain other metals, their filings were used as in the experiments of Branly (see Fig. 3.17(a)). For the rest, two pieces of the same metal were brought into contact under graduated pressure. For increasing the pressure gradually, he used a mercury-filled U-tube with a plunger, the invention of which will be described later.

To his surprise, Bose found that alkali metals, such as potassium and sodium, exhibited properties quite contrary to expectations. Their contact resistance increased when exposed to a spell of electric radiation. This also resulted in considerable movement of the galvanometer needle; hence, this property could also be used for the detection of electric waves. Even more remarkably, they recovered automatically and were ready to receive another wave of radiation—no manual input was necessary at all.

We have seen earlier that, from Branly's iron filing receiver to Bose's spiral spring receiver, the contact resistance of the metal pieces always decreased after an exposure to radiation. Lodge had proposed a theory that on being exposed to radiation, the metal pieces sort of fused with each other resulting in a fall in contact resistance. Hence, he coined the name coherer, which hints at this property of sticking together. His theory for conductivity-variation now seemed untenable.

Bose repeated his experiments and was convinced that something else, quite different from the fusing action of Lodge's theory, was happening. Bose offered a theory of 'molecular strain' to explain conductivity-variation. This theory states that a flash of radiation induces a rearrangement of the molecules, that is to say, causes a strain in the molecules; hence the name 'molecular strain'. Today, we know that what is responsible is a phenomenon at the subatomic level, explained by quantum physics. But quantum physics had not been developed until then. Since a molecule is a larger entity consisting of many atoms, Bose's theory to explain conductivity-variation, at least, seems to point in the right direction.

Artificial Eye

Bose invented another very versatile auto-recovering receiver which he called the artificial eye, because it could detect visible light as well as invisible electric waves. The key material for this device was the galena crystal. On 6 March 1900, before his second trip to Europe, he wrote to his friend Rabindranath Tagore, 'Very recently I have been able to make a marvellous artificial eye. This eye can see many invisible radiations. It can also see red and blue visible light very clearly.'[12]

This device could actually detect infrared and ultraviolet rays as well which are not visible to the human eye, and turned out to be the world's first solid state diode detector. It was also the world's first photovoltaic cell. The two detectors described above—one with a mercury-filled U-tube, and the other a galena crystal—use conductivity-variation. They are important for our historical narrative. The one made of galena crystal, called the artificial eye, although made of inert non-living matter, was more versatile than a human eye.

On this particular phase of Bose's work on electric waves, a more time-tested assessment came two decades later from Jacob Kunz of the University of Illinois, USA. Kunz, a theoretical physicist, famous for his lectures on the theory of relativity and pioneering work on the development and applications of photoelectric cell, made the following comments in a review:

> Bose showed that these short electric waves have the same properties as a beam of light, exhibiting reflection, refraction, even total reflection, double refraction, polarization, and rotation of the plane of polarization. ...He found a special crystal, Nemalite, which exhibits polarization of electric waves in the very same manner a beam of light is polarized by selective absorption in crystals like Tourmaline which Bose found to be due to their different electric conductivity in two directions. The rotation of the plane of polarization was demonstrated by means of a contrivance twisted like a rope, and the rotation could be produced to the left and right. ...The index of refraction of these electric waves was determined for

---

[12]This is a translation from Bengali to English.

different materials; and a difficulty was eliminated which presented itself in Maxwell's theory, as to the relation between the index of refraction and the dielectric constant of insulators. ...He had to invent a large number of new apparatus[es]...distinguished by simplicity, directness, and ingenuity.

One of the large number of inventions, discussed by Kunz in the quotation above, was the artificial eye. It was demonstrated during a lecture in England but never written about and published in a research paper, contrary to Bose's usual practice. He was prevailed upon by Sister Nivedita and Sara Chapman Bull, two disciples of Swami Vivekananda, to take out a patent for this invention. The patent was applied for, at Sara's initiative, on American soil.

It should be recalled that the business of taking out patents had been against the existential principles of the inventor. He deviated just this once, and never again. Even this straying occurred soon after he fell seriously ill and had to undergo a surgical procedure, which took place in England. Perhaps he gave in to the pleadings of Sister Nivedita and Mrs Sara Bull during this period of vulnerability.

Every patent is required to be renewed once a year, and a fee paid, in order to maintain ownership of the invention. Unsurprisingly, Bose refused to renew his patent and it lay dormant for nearly a century until it was discovered by some members of the IEEE[13], who were researching the history of science and technology. One of the researchers, Probir K. Bandyopadhyay wrote in 1998,

With the rapid progresses in the semiconductor revolution in the second half of this century, the history of the true origin of the solid-state diode detectors has been attracting intense interest. [A]ttention has been focused on the seventeen-year time period from January 1888 through December 1904, during which the research and development work was very intense. The intense search led to the *Proceedings of the Royal Society*—the most prestigious scientific publication of the Victorian British Empire. Attention comes to a

[13]Institute of Electrical and Electronic Engineers, an American non-profit association of engineers and scientists, headquartered in New York.

focus on a revolutionary research work done 100 years ago that dealt with propagation of millimeter waves through certain polarizing crystals, leading to the creation of solid-state contact detectors. The paper was by Prof. J. C. Bose. An exhaustive search of the U. S. patent system finds the world's first patent on a solid-state detector device, invented by Bose.

The patent served the purpose of reinforcing the evidence contained in the paper published in the *Proceedings of the Royal Society*; both had been forgotten for a long time. When researchers discovered US Patent No. 755840, dated 29 March 1904, for a 'Detector for Electrical Disturbances' by J. C. Bose, they realized that they had found what they were looking for, which was not what they had been expecting. The patent application had been filed in 14 September 1901. However, there is evidence to suggest that the invention had been created in 1898, or even earlier. So far, the scientific community had believed that the American H. M. C. Dunwoody was the inventor of the solid-state diode detector, who held Patent No. 837616, dated 4 December 1906.

Many historians were likely astonished to discover Bose as the rightful inventor of the solid-state diode detector, and this event triggered a renewed interest in the West in the Indian scientist. Further, this induced some science historians to revisit history and they made many new discoveries.

Margaret Noble and the Two Americans

The true mover and motivator behind the aforesaid patent were, of course, Ms Margaret Noble, alias Sister Nivedita, and Mrs Sara Chapman Bull. Ms Noble arrived in Calcutta in January 1898 at the invitation of her guru Swami Vivekananda. Two American disciples, Mrs Sara Bull and Miss Josephine MacLeod, also arrived about the same time. Margaret was not aware of their arrival till she met them, and the three soon became fast friends. It was a friendship cemented by spiritualism and the bond was strong. The Swami's message to them came in two parts. One was about renunciation as a means to spirituality and the other was very simple—'Love India and do for her all you can'. The

trio understood what it meant—an
all-round rejuvenation of India; the
revival of education, art, science,
culture, all led by spirituality. They
resolved to follow the lead of their
revered and beloved prophet.

Margaret had the spirit of
renunciation within her in ample
measure. She alighted from the ship
at the Calcutta port in an unknown
country with only two rupees in
her possession. She carried nothing
from her previous life into this
new world. Sarada Devi, the wife
of Swami Vivekananda's guru Shri
Ramakrishna, was still alive and was
considered the holy mother of the

Sister Nivedita (Margaret Noble)

Ramakrishna order set up by the Swami. 'Mother, I have brought a sky-
flower for you,' said the Swami (in Bengali) while introducing Margaret
to the holy mother. 'She is not touched by the worldly meanness and
vanity'.

Among the three, Margaret was special because she was to be
ordained as a Hindu nun by the Swami and had been tasked with
promoting women's education in India. Besides, she was to play a
prominent role, that of a versatile facilitator of research, in Bose's life.
To understand the kind of versatility and assistance she brought to the
table, it is necessary to present a brief description of her upbringing
and training.[14]

Margaret Elizabeth Noble was a few years younger to the Swami
and born into a Protestant family in Northern Ireland in 1867. Both her
grandfather and father were ordained priests. In spite of their Protestant
faiths, they sided with the Irish nationalists, who were mostly Catholic,
and struggling against British rule. Margaret not only inherited the

[14]The story of Margaret Noble's early life has been taken from *The Dedicated* by Lizelle
Reymond.

rebellious spirit of her forefathers, but was also spiritually inclined and introspective from her very childhood. Her father died young and as he breathed his last, reportedly whispered to his wife, 'When God calls her, let her go. She will spread her wings. She will do great things.'

Soon, Margaret and her younger sister, May, were sent to a residential school in Halifax in England, run by the local Protestant Church. She was most probably in her early teens and had been placed in a dormitory of ten, all daughters of ministers. Botany, physics, mechanics, literature, and theology were prominent among the subjects taught. She excelled in all of them, although literature was her favourite. Her head mistress in high school, Miss Collins, was of an intellectual disposition. In addition to botany and physics, she taught her little charge the rudiments of religious art. Margaret was introduced to the world of form, colour, and aesthetics through a few well-chosen books. She passed all her subjects with flying colours and left school when she was eighteen, determined to make her own living.

She chose to be a teacher and her first appointment was at an excellent private boarding school for girls in Keswick in northern England. Here, she was at once gripped by the spirit of renunciation and wished to embrace Catholicism to become a nun, there being no similar institution in Protestantism. The head mistress dissuaded her from taking such a step. Later, as she wished to live an austere life, she gave up her well-paying job to become a teacher at an orphanage where pupils were trained to become domestic servants. After this, she moved again to become a mistress at a school in Wrexham, a dreary mining town. Here, she became romantically involved with a Welshman, an engineer with a love for literature. In the evenings, they would read Thoreau, Emerson, and Ruskin together. Just as they became engaged to be married, he fell ill with tuberculosis. In the face of death, he remained supremely calm in his submission to God and quietly slipped away, much like Margaret's father who had been stricken by the same disease. He left behind a grieving mother and fiancé.

Weeks later, the restless and inconsolable Margaret moved again and began experimenting with teaching methods. In her fifth year as a teacher, she arrived at a school in Liverpool and soon joined a group who were introducing something called the 'new education'. Following in the footsteps of a close friend, who was more experienced in these new teaching methods, Margaret moved to a small school in Wimbledon in the suburbs of London. After school hours were over, she engaged in writing political columns in newspapers and occasionally penned articles for a science periodical, named *Research*. She wrote also, but less frequently, for a more specialized scientific journal called *Review of Reviews*.

In 1895, she opened her own school, named Ruskin School, in another part of Wimbledon. Here, teaching became pure joy and the conventional teacher transformed into an educator who led her pupils step by step through a series of discoveries. Soon, she was famed as a wonderful educator throughout London. Next, an extraordinary new teacher by the name of Ebenezer Cooke was hired by the school. He was the first in the country to advocate introducing small children to the world of colour and form. In his company, Margaret further honed her own artistic skills and acquired a higher sense aesthetic appreciation.

Now, Margaret gave free rein to her journalistic and literary spirits. She became a prolific writer of articles on diverse subjects such as education, politics, and science. Gradually, she was becoming a prominent figure in the intellectual and literary circles of London. Ebenezer Cooke was a friend of Lady Ripon and introduced Margaret to the esteemed gentlewoman, who had an exclusive reception hall, where notable persons regularly gathered to discuss literature, art, and science, among other subjects.

The group soon developed into the famous Sesame Club, with Margaret as its Secretary. George Bernard Shaw, Thomas H. Huxley, William B. Yeats, Patrick Geddes, and other famous figures were frequent visitors. She became well known as a versatile and cerebral personality. In spite of her busy schedule and numerous activities, Margaret remained deeply spiritual. However, there remained a sense of disquiet in her mind, because she could no longer reconcile the rigid dogmas of her native religion with modern science. She came across Edwin Arnold's *The Light of Asia*, a book on the life and teachings of the Buddha, and found some solace. She was seeking but knew not where to seek, and sensed that there was something amiss in her life.

At this time, she was invited to a private gathering arranged by one of her acquaintances, Lady Isabel Margesson, to hear a Hindu monk named Swami Vivekananda. She wrote later that upon entering the sitting hall, she saw a tan-complexioned man, a monk in 'strange orange attire and a yellow turban, sitting cross-legged on the floor—silhouetted against the glow of the fireplace—who uttered new ideas in beautiful English in a mellifluous but deep voice.' She further wrote that the monk was 'wearing a look of mingled gentleness and loftiness that one sees on the faces of those who live much in meditation, that look, perhaps, that Raphael has painted for us on the brow of the Sistine Child.'

This meeting happened during the Swami's first visit to London in 1896. His speech struck a chord with her and she became his disciple. He invited her to India and asked her to start a school for girls. She reached Calcutta in January 1898 and was received at the docks by the venerable Swami himself. Within the next three days, the Swami had requested Mahendranath Gupta, a reputed school teacher and a guru-brother[15] of his, to teach her Bengali. The lessons started immediately. The Swami also instructed his first disciple, Sadananda-swami, to help Nivedita in every possible way.

It has been mentioned that two American disciples of the Swami arrived in Calcutta about the same time. The second among these was Mrs Sara Chapman Bull, an elderly widow who had inherited much wealth and many properties in America and Norway, from her father, Joseph G. Thorp, and her Norwegian husband, Ole Bull. The latter was a celebrated musician, composer, and violinist. Sara herself was an accomplished pianist and often accompanied Ole as he performed all over Europe and America. Ole was quite famous, but cared little for money and fame on account of his spiritual nature. He had told her that India was the home of the violin[16] and India's philosophy, poetry, and music were unsurpassed. Sara imbibed some of her husband's spiritualism and esteem for India.

---

[15]Two men having the same spiritual guru call each other gurubhai, which translates into guru-brother.

[16]There is some truth to Ole Bull's assertion. There are several traditional musical instruments in India which use a bow on a string, like the violin, the most well-known being the esraj. During the reign of the Buddhist king Kanishka (127–150 CE), such instruments spread to Central Asia.

An influential figure in the Cambridge circle of the American east coast, she was known for her liberal patronage of art and science. During the Swami's very first visit to her home, she told him that he was like her son. Her biographer writes, 'Sara's entire life's aim was to realize herself as the mother.' This idea of motherhood perhaps sprang from Sara's interest in Indian philosophies, an interest which existed even before she met the Swami.

She was about fourteen years older than the Swami and started mothering him in a gentle manner; he reciprocated the sentiment and often called her 'mother'. He even gave her an Indian name, Dheera Mata, a steady mother. When asked for his definition of a saint in a large gathering, the Swami instantly replied that Mrs Sara Bull was a saint.[17]

Josephine MacLeod was about five years older than the Swami, and much older than Margaret. She never called herself a disciple but a friend of the Swami, although she did receive a mantra from him. She inherited some money from her father, was financially comfortable, and belonged to an influential social circle in New York. A confirmed spinster all her life, Josephine was the only sister of Betty Leggett, who was married to a millionaire businessman, named Frank Leggett. Betty was also a disciple of the Swami, while Frank remained an affectionate admirer.[18]

Josephine usually lived in the Leggett household where the Swami was often a guest. Betty was fond of throwing grand parties and entertaining the important and the

Josephine Macleod (Joe)

famous, and was dependent on Josephine for the day-to-day running of

[17]The story of Mrs Sara Chapman Bull's life has been taken from *Saint Sara* (2014).
[18]The story of Josephine MacLeod's life has been taken from *The Life of Josephine MacLeod* (1994).

the household. The two sisters were of very different temperaments yet got on well. Often when a dinner party was in full swing in Betty's salon, Josephine would spend a solitary evening in her room, surviving on bread and milk. Josephine, or Joe in short, had accompanied the Swami to England and was a friend of Lady Margesson. She was, therefore, present in her drawing room on the fateful evening when Margaret met the Swami for the first time. She often helped all of Margaret's causes in various ways.

For a while, all three disciples stayed in an old and abandoned house that stood on the land and had been acquired for building the monastery. Both Joe and Sara grew very fond of Margaret, often affectionately referring to her as Margot. Sara started looking upon her as her daughter. They were witness to the feverish preparations that were going on to construct the monastery—several houses and a temple were to be constructed within a year.

Intrigued by Bose's reputation, Margaret and Sara visited his laboratory on 30 March 1898, and were received cordially by the scientist. On the same day, Sara immediately recorded her impression in a letter[19] to her daughter Olea, 'The fact that metals grow tired and require rest for readjustment of their molecules is as true of the mind. When the electric eye requires the same care that is given the human eye, it also gets fatigued and requires rest, we are told, and sometimes complete rest.'

This is evidence that the electric eye, which Bose called the artificial eye, had been invented before March 1898. It seems that the ladies' guided tour around the laboratory was not superficial, but included actual performance of experiments. Bose loved to demonstrate his research for laypersons and his enthusiasm was contagious and Sara carried a lasting memory of this meeting.

Margaret did not record her experience of this visit; instead, she took the initiative of involving Sara and Josephine in helping Bose in his many endeavours. Mrs Bull financed the publishing of some of Bose's books and all of them aided his research work in various ways.

---

[19]The primary source of this letter is the Sara Chapman Bull Collection under the care of the Vedanta Society of Northern California.

On 11 March 1898, during the inaugural meeting of the Ramakrishna Mission, held at the Star Theatre, a public lecture was arranged by Margaret where she spoke on 'The Influence of Indian Spiritual Thought in England'; the meeting was presided over by the Swami. He was extremely pleased with her speech and remarked that she could be a real asset as a platform speaker for the Ramakrishna Mission. This prophecy was fulfilled for the Ramakrishna Mission, and then many times furthermore—she was to use her oratory and pen for the cause of setting up 'independent' institutions of higher learning for Indians, by Indians.

On 18 March, a lecture by another monk of the order, Saradananda-swami, was presided over by the Swami; Jagadish C. Bose, Margaret, and Sara were present on the stage. Bose had long been a member of the Brahmo religious movement and, following its fundamental precepts, had given up idol worship. Though he knew that Swami Vivekananda and his organization practiced that mode of worship, he had no qualms with sharing a stage with the Swami. This was perhaps the second time that Margaret and Sara met Bose. The Swami and Bose were both renowned personalities by then and knew each other.

Margaret Becomes Nivedita

On 25 March 1898, Margaret was provisionally initiated into the order by the Swami in a simple ceremony. She was made a novice nun, a brahmacharini and named Nivedita, which means 'the dedicated' in Sanskrit. She had to take a vow of abstinence and renunciation and considered herself a dedicated seeker of the ultimate truth. She also knew that her guru had dedicated her to the service of the god Shiva. No special colour was prescribed for her to wear, although she learnt that white was to be preferred. She resolved to make the country her home for the rest of her life. Sister Nivedita wrote to Joe on a later date, 'I do for India everything that comes my way.'

In early April of the year of Sister Nivedita's initiation, Swami Vivekananda had a near physical breakdown. As a young man, he had been in possession of a very stout constitution. However, his days of wandering around India as a penniless mendicant, and his many arduous journeys abroad, had ruined his health, perhaps beyond repair. The doctors advised him rest and a change of climate. Knowing that if he stayed in Calcutta, he would not rest, his well-wishers and fellow monks arranged a retreat in picturesque Darjeeling.

A few days into his retreat, he received the news that bubonic plague had broken out in Calcutta—people were dying in droves and fleeing in thousands. There was panic all around, and the troops had to be called to maintain order. The plague regulations were promulgated by the government and their nature created great mistrust among the people who were generally suspicious of the authorities.

The Swami immediately returned from the mountain resort and started to organize relief work on a large scale. He drafted a plague manifesto in Bengali and Hindi, which explained the purpose of the plague regulations, and distributed it widely. It emphasized the need for sanitation and raised public awareness of the prophylactic measures. The Swami worked tirelessly in spite of his failing health, ably assisted by his disciple, Sadananda-swami, and other monks of the order. They set up a segregation camp where the afflicted were quarantined and given treatment. The young monks and a few volunteers worked with brooms and shovels in hand to sanitize the lanes at great risk to themselves. The three ladies watched the goings-on with admiration from their little house on the river.

The plague raged through the city for about a month but was brought under control, and before autumn the plague regulations had been withdrawn. The admirable role of the Ramakrishna Mission led by Swami Vivekananda did not escape the notice of the government.

In the autumn, the Swami took Sister Nivedita, Sara, and Joe on a long educational trip across northern India, from Calcutta to Kashmir. On the way, they spent a few days each in Bodh Gaya and Benares; then proceeded to the Himalayan town of Almora, where the Swami created a mystical atmosphere for Nivedita. She wrote about it later to Joe, and drew inspiration from this hallowed memory as long as she lived.

Josephine MacLeod, Sara Bull, Swami Vivekananda, and Sister Nivedita in Kashmir.

After reaching Punjab, they travelled by boat up the Jhelum River to reach Srinagar, the capital of Kashmir. Mrs Patterson, who had known the Swami in America and whose husband was the American consul in Calcutta, accompanied them part of the way. Everywhere they received a cordial welcome because of the fame of the Swami. They had an audience with the Maharaja of Kashmir.

Then the party, leaving behind Mrs Patterson, embarked upon a pilgrimage to the famous cave temple of Amarnath, situated high on the Himalayas. Only Margaret and the Swami reached the cave and offered obeisance, the other two chose to remain behind in the base camp. Following his return to the Kashmir valley, the Swami faced another bout of illness after a few days, and had to hurry back to Calcutta escorted by a monk. The three women returned at a slower pace and after much educative sightseeing in the company of another monk of the order. When the party arrived in Benares, the ladies were put up in Hotel Paris. The party moved to Calcutta after a few days.

Soon after returning to Calcutta, Nivedita doubled her efforts to learn Bengali. The other two ladies spent a few weeks in a suburban area near Belur and then sailed home in January 1899. Nivedita started her girls' school in Bosepara Lane in the Baghbazar locality, deep inside the Indian quarters of Calcutta. It was inaugurated on 13 December 1898 by the holy mother, Sarada Devi. Nivedita chose this location because it was inexpensive to rent; on the flip side, it was damp and unhealthy. The school also doubled up as her residence.

In those days, a sort of apartheid was practised in Calcutta. The British lived in the well-planned townships in the centre of the city where native Indians were not allowed to live. These exclusive zones were dotted with tree-lined parks, promenades with fountains, and beautiful commercial and residential houses. Towards the west was the wide, meandering Ganga, guarded by the imposing Fort William. The eastern ill-defined boundary was the Upper Circular Road where the colonial residences mingled a bit with Anglo–Indian and Indian ones. Baghbazar, where Nivedita chose to live and work, was in the far north, also on the bank of the river, and mostly populated by Indians.

Nivedita's ideas on education were shaped by the principles formulated by Swiss educationist Johann Heinrich Pestalozzi and his German follower Friedrich Fröbel. While starting her school in Bosepara Lane, there was no radical change in her views; she merely adapted them to suit the women of the land. The Swami introduced a new principle to his followers which stated that to teach against the aspirations of the taught was counterproductive.

She was of the opinion that education should be in the medium of the mother tongue. In addition to reading, writing, and arithmetic, a complete education should draw from the cultural roots of society, and sustain them. Adhering to the Swami's principle meant that she started looking at the world through the eyes of her Indian pupils. Hers was the first school that looked to awaken a national spirit in its pupils and all this distinguished her work from the schools opened by Christian missionaries.

Her pupils were young girls and even child widows, mostly drawn from middle- and lower-class families. They brought their own religious lives, taught by their elders, into the school, which Nivedita was determined to nurture and blend with modern, progressive ideas. Alongside this, vocational training in sewing, knitting, embroidery, etc. had to be imparted. Initially, hardly any subscriptions were brought in by her students and for the first few months, the school was sustained by a donation of 800 rupees from the Maharaja of Kashmir. On the whole, this was a new and daring experiment.

Women were being educated in the towns of Bengal before this, but this was done in typical English fashion and confined to the progressive elite. The Swami had asked Nivedita to start a school for girls belonging to the vast conservative segment of society that had remained untouched.

As funding ran out, Nivedita began looking towards her two friends for assistance. Josephine MacLeod was one of the first visitors to her school. She stayed and played with the girls for one whole day. Her penetrating eyes could see that beneath the merry atmosphere, there was dire poverty; the children were malnourished and Nivedita was depriving herself. The next day she returned with tins of biscuits, grapes, jam, condensed milk, butter, and sugar. She brought slates, exercise books, chalks for the classroom and for tailoring lessons, rolls of fabric, and sewing items such as bobbins, thimbles, and scissors. Joe remained forever ready to help and sent clothes to Nivedita regularly as long as she lived. The other friend, the elderly Mrs Bull, arranged for a modest annual grant for Nivedita's personal sustenance.

Once her school became fully functional, Nivedita plunged into what she knew best—writing, journalism, and public speaking. She rapidly learnt about Hindu religious life, its epics and cradle tales, and started to write about them in English magazines and newspapers. Her favourites were the *Calcutta Statesman* and *Modern Review*. Her articles afforded discerning members of the British society a glimpse, for the first time, into the inner life of Hindu society, particularly its women.

Nivedita's perception of education, her austere lifestyle, and writing prowess afforded her much fame but she generally refrained from socially mingling with the British residents of Calcutta. However, her renown and good looks attracted a young English suitor who was persistent and would sometimes pursue her even into the monastery at Belur, where the Swami was staying.

She was already a brahmacharini. But now, to get rid of the keen suitor, she urged Swami Vivekananda to confirm her position as a nun. A fairly elaborate ceremony followed wherein she received a white robe and a rosary of holy rudraksha beads; it had the desired effect on her tenacious suitor. This took place on 25 March 1899, exactly one year after her first initiation and about four months after her school was founded.

Nivedita and the Tagores

In the meanwhile, Sister Nivedita's writing continued apace. Her spreading fame now started attracting the right kind of people— the public-spirited Brahmo elite of Calcutta. Bose's younger sister Labanyaprabha, and Sarola Ghosal and Surendranath Tagore, niece and nephew to poet Rabindranath Tagore, were the first to arrive at Nivedita's school and became frequent visitors. For a while, every Saturday Nivedita spoke about teachers' training before her female friends from the Brahmo Samaj, among whom were Indira Devi Chaudhurani and Sarola Ghosal, both members of the prominent Tagore family, Labanyaprabha Bose, and the two daughters of famous Brahmo preacher Keshab Chandra Sen. Sarola observed, with great interest, the school's workings, and reported what she saw, in glowing terms, to her family at home. Soon, others of the Tagore clan became interested in Sister Nivedita's work and she became an oft invited visitor to the Tagore mansion. Usually, a religious discussion ensued once she arrived.

The twenty-six-year old Surendranath was noticed by Nivedita for his militant patriotism and passionate desire to improve India's agriculture. He had first-hand knowledge of the problems faced by the Indian peasantry, and Nivedita was keen to learn from him. Later, he was to get involved in the violent independence movement and to draw her into its vortex.

Sarola and Surendranath drew their uncle Rabindranath towards the school. Rabindranath had earlier been introduced to Nivedita by Bose. On 16 June 1899, she wrote to Rabindranath Tagore, 'I really want to add a new friend to those with which India has already blessed me, and you are so dear to my friend Dr Bose, that I could not help hoping that you should be my friend too.'

Rabindranath found in Nivedita a person of great literary appreciation and empathy. Once, he asked her to teach English to his youngest daughter and take charge of her education. Nivedita was taken aback and roused to indignation.

> What! Do you want me to play the part of transforming a Tagore into a little girl of the West End? ...What is the good in imposing foreign ideals and standards? The proper education is to draw out that which lies latent as one's individual potentiality, as also the national skill.[20]

On matters of principle, she was inflexible and combative. She lectured Tagore against westernization and education in the medium of a foreign language.

Rabindranath[21] himself wrote about this episode years later that initially he had the notion that Nivedita was like the usual kind of English missionary, and

> It was this notion which made me propose that she take charge of my daughter's education.
>
> 'What kind of education would you like to give her?' She asked.
>
> My reply was 'A good grounding in English and English-based education would do'.
>
> She asked, 'What good is it to force education down the throat? For me real education is to draw out and develop the knowledge and skill which tradition has handed down, and the aptitudes acquired by the child. Not to subject them to the steam-roller of regimentation which goes by the name of English-based education in India.'

Nivedita's outburst compelled Tagore to rethink his ideas about education. Later, when he founded a residential school in Shantiniketan in the Bengal countryside, he tried to blend traditional education, taught in the mother tongue, with modernity and progressive thought.

In January 1899, Nivedita arranged a tea for her Brahmo friends, many of them Tagores, and Swami Vivekananda.

---

[20]This quotation is sourced from *The Dedicated: A Biography of Nivedita* by Lizelle Reymond and *Nivedita of India* edited by Swami Prabhananda. This conversation has been talked about by many authors—this is the gist of what they say.
[21]Originally published in a Bengali journal called *Prabasi* in 1911.

In the meeting, the Swami reminisced vividly about the benediction he had once received at the age of eighteen from Rabindranath's father, Debendranath Tagore. So, he was delighted when Nivedita brought a message that the Tagore patriarch wanted to see him. Soon an audience was arranged and Nivedita and the Swami were received cordially in the Tagore household. They were shown up immediately by a few members of the family and the Swami said, 'Pranaam', greeting the old saintly man seated in an armchair, who asked him to take a seat. She wrote later that the old gentleman took ten minutes to recount,

> ...in Bengali, the Swami's various success with the doctrines he had preached at each point and said that he had watched and heard it all with intense pride and pleasure. The Tagores were astonished. I ought to have known why Swami-ji looked so curiously unresponsive, almost disagreeable. It was shyness! Then the old man paused and waited and Swami very humbly asked for his blessing. It was given and with the same salutation as before we came downstairs.

It might be possible that Sister Nivedita did not quite understand the conversation in its entirety, which was in Bengali. There might have been some muted reprimand, mixed in with the praise, which the Swami recognized. He wanted to leave for the Belur monastery at once but the Tagores would not let him. They sat around him, eager to talk, and offered him tea and a hookah; he accepted the latter. They exchanged pleasantries and then the Swami paid a most wholesome tribute to Raja Ram Mohan Roy, the founder of the Brahmo movement. Then the discussion inevitably shifted to symbol and idol worship, especially the worship of Kali. The Swami said in a soft conciliatory tone, that the Brahmo position was the true Hindu doctrine, but they should also acknowledge the option of symbol worship. The Tagores seemed pleased. When the Swami took his leave, invitations for each to visit the other were exchanged.

Later, when Sarola and Surendranath visited the Belur monastery, they were shown around with great hospitality. In the temple of his departed guru Shri Ramakrishna, the Swami prostrated himself before the statue, while Sarola wore a look of studied indifference. Nivedita felt that Sarola was beginning to appreciate his position. Later, the Swami remarked about Sarola, 'She is a jewel of a girl and will do great things.' The hopes of reconciliation were shattered when a letter arrived two days later from Sarola. She thanked Swamiji for his hospitality but made it very clear that the Tagore family's cooperation would flow only if he gave up the cult of Shri Ramakrishna. If he did that, they would help him in his work and join forces with him. Thereafter, the Tagores including Rabindranath became entirely aloof of Nivedita's school and the endeavours of the Swami and his monastery.

Although a Brahmo now, Bose must have perceived in Sister Nivedita's school a reflection, however remote, of his childhood pathshala. Of course, there were some stark dissimilarities too. The pathshala, for example, would not permit any play, or focus on teaching any drawing or painting. However, on the whole it seemed to him that there existed some kinship, however remote, between Nivedita's and his own father's views on primary education. He helped Nivedita whenever possible and even prevailed upon his wife, Abala, and his younger sister to teach in Nivedita's school for free. It should, however, be noted that the Boses never visited the Swami's monastery at Belur, not even for the sake of curiosity.

The Swami's health deteriorated again in the winter of 1898–1899 and he was again advised rest and change of climate. He was taken to Deoghar, a place of pilgrimage for its famous Shiva temple. However, it did not suit the Swami at all who suffered a vicious attack of asthma there. He was brought back to Calcutta post-haste by a fellow monk.

By this time, Sister Nivedita had started receiving invitations from different schools and colleges to speak, some from outside Calcutta also. Usually, Sadananda-swami accompanied her during her sojourns. The Swami and the senior monks of the order were convinced about Nivedita's erudition and versatility. In January 1899, she was requested to give talks twice a week to the novice monks on physiology, botany, and the kindergarten system, and, surprisingly for many, also on the arts including painting.

Later, Nivedita and her friends were to play a role in inspiring a school of young Indian artists. Her friends, Sara and Joe, were instrumental in initiating contacts with an art school in Japan. Several years hence, and long after Nivedita's passing away, when Bose began to build his independent research institute, these Indian artists became the architects, landscapers, and interior and exterior decorators for the structure, which bore an unmistakeable imprint of Nivedita.

In late March 1899, the plague visited Calcutta once more. A committee was formed with Nivedita acting as the secretary and the Swami's first disciple, monk Sadananda-swami, as its supervisor, and three other monks as members. A group of monks plunged into relief work under their leadership. Nivedita put her heart into cleaning up and sanitizing her locality, Baghbazar, which was quite a large area. She was perhaps overdoing things and taking undue risks in the process; something that is hinted at in the following letter that Josephine wrote to Sara Bull on 11 May 1899. She addressed her friend as 'St Sara' and shortened Margaret to 'Margot'; the Swami is referred to as the 'Prophet'.

Dearest St Sara,

I received back the packet of Margot's letters, also the Prophet's. Bless him! His criticism of Margot and the plague sanitation is very like the time on the Amarnath pilgrimage, when she gave her dandy to a poor, weak pilgrim, which he thought a bit of sentiment, but which brought more glory than her any one act in Kashmir!

And now this intense interest in the sanitation of Baghbazar and her appeal to the English has been a common ground on which they may unite. And you can see by her letter the exhilaration and joy that has come into her life by the knowledge that her countrymen want to do the right thing.

Her methods may sometimes antagonize, but on the whole, she is wonderfully gentle. And it is evident that she did not find any response in the Tagore element to help her cause or rather theirs. And so, she turned to the monks for help....

Yours, Jo Jo.

In the context of plague relief, a touching episode has been described in *The Life of Josephine MacLeod* by Dr R. G. Kar, an eminent physician. After visiting his patients, he had returned home to find Nivedita sitting on a dusty chair near the door. She enquired about the arrangements made for a plague-stricken child in her neighbourhood and was informed that his condition was critical. When he went to see the patient later in the day, he was astonished to find Nivedita sitting with the child on her lap in that damp, unclean hut, as the mother of the child had died earlier of plague. She nursed the child day and night, ignoring all warnings issued by the doctor until he died on her lap.

The plague affected the life of the Bose couple, too. Since the plague regulations were in force, large gatherings were prohibited, and so teaching in schools and colleges had been interrupted. In the following year, the plague visited Calcutta again. In June 1900, one of Bose's domestic servants contracted the disease and died. To keep themselves safe from the illness, the Boses had to escape to a different house and Jagadish's research documentation work, which he used to do at home, was disrupted. They continued to live in their new residence until they sailed again for Jagadish's second trip to Europe.

Bose Turns to Physiology: The Vedantic Inspiration

As mentioned earlier, after his return from Europe, Bose had plunged into work with renewed vigour. But within two years, he became frustrated with his constant struggle against the administration. His recognition as a scientist in Europe brought out the darker side of the character of the new principal and director of Presidency College, who had taken charge after the retirement of Charles Tawney and Sir Alfred Croft.

There was some discussion among college officials to close down Bose's research facilities altogether. The reason offered always remained the same—his research was a private activity; even if pursued after college hours, it was being done using college facilities—an irrefutable argument. Bose's resolution to build a separate research institute for the nation's scientists became firmer. This conspiracy to put a stop to Bose's research came to the knowledge of Rabindranath Tagore. In this atmosphere of constant friction, Bose summoned all his will and carried on with his research.

In 1899, while working with a coherer, Bose noticed a curious phenomenon. After being subjected to electric radiation repeatedly, the coherer started responding lesser and lesser. The strength of its response kept declining, as if it was getting fatigued by its exertions. When he rested the coherer for a while, it began behaving normally again. It appeared to him that this thing made of inorganic matter was behaving like living matter. Was it the same for other forms of inorganic matter as well?

The artificial eye device invented by him, which was to be patented later in America, behaved much like the living eye and reinforced his impression. This invention turned out to be a watershed event in his career and his line of research took a sharp turn towards biology. It should be recalled that he was always drawn to animals and plants. He had been born in the lap of nature and grew up in a semi-rural setting in the verdant land of Bengal.

During his schooling in the city of Calcutta, he had taken to gardening and caring for a number of pet animals. In England, he had taken up medicine as his subject at first and had some understanding of human anatomy and physiology. In Cambridge, he had admired his physiology and embryology professors and in his second year had unusually chosen botany as his minor subject, with the major being physics. He had thoroughly enjoyed Professor Vines's lectures and laboratory in botany and Professor Francis Darwin's course on vegetable physiology.

It was his interest in both physics and the biological sciences that made him study physics with physiology. In this specific instance, he became interested in comparing the responses of living and non-living, inert matter, such as metals, to outside stimuli. He discovered that muscle tissue and tin foil gave almost identical responses when subjected to electric radiation. Even a mechanical stimulus, such as a twist or a strike with an object, drew similar responses from each.

Like all discoverers, Bose became restless to publish his astonishing findings. In March 1900, maybe a little earlier, an opportunity arrived in the form of an invitation from the International Congress of Physics. This congress was being planned as a part of the Paris International Exposition 1900, which was to be held beginning from August that year. At this time, Bose came across an editorial in a scientific journal praising one of his papers, published in the *Proceedings of the Royal*

Society. What he wrote in his diary, on his birthday on 30 November 1899, gives us a glimpse of his fluctuating mood,

> 'Blessed is the infinite power of human fellowship'; and this appreciation from a source unknown to me has removed the mood of depression; working in isolation and want of sympathy, I grew despondent and the paper which has excited so much interest, was in danger of being consigned to the waste paper basket. I shall take up the work once more; I see clearly a clue to many things which were regarded as anomalies. Anomalies! There is no anomaly in creation, it is we whose sights are dim, and who will not see.

In the meantime, Sir John Woodburn had become the lieutenant governor of Bengal. He was aware of Bose's work and was kindly disposed towards him. Bose felt the hostility of the college authorities and so, decided to approach him directly.

Bose met Sir Woodburn at his residence, the Belvedere, towards the end of February in 1900, and gave a brief description of his ongoing research. Sir Woodburn expressed great satisfaction and the desire to visit his lab to see his experiments and interact with his students. Bose brought up his invitation to speak at the International Congress of Physics. The lieutenant governor promised to do his best to advance Bose's case for deputation but with the caveat that the final decision rested with the secretary of state. Next week, Bose received a letter from the new director of public instruction, 'I am informed you had an interview with the Lt. Governor and have asked to be deputed to the Paris Exhibition to attend a meeting of the European scientists. May I ask you to inform me of the reason for making your request to His Honour?'

The sheer callousness of this letter struck Bose. In great despair, he wrote to his friend, Rabindranath Tagore, about the incident,

> I know you will suffer much on learning this, but could not help writing. Even then please keep these things under wraps.
>
> There is another matter I wish to bring up. I would rather not be informed about your initiative in building a laboratory [for me]. If the authorities call for an explanation, I shall be at a loss. After all, it is a slight for the Government if a laboratory is commissioned

by private endeavour, when there is already one in a Government College.

This event sharply shows up the college administration's attitude towards Bose and his research. The poet had realized that without a laboratory facility, the scientist's talent would find no avenue for expression and be suppressed for good. Unknown to Bose, Tagore collected a sum of 10,000 rupees from members of his family and friends. He approached the Maharaja Radha Kishore Manikya, who happened to be in Calcutta at the time, for an additional sum of 20,000 rupees.

The maharaja of Tripura was taken aback to hear the honoured poet speaking like a humble supplicant and replied in Bengali, 'Sir, the pose of an alms-seeking mendicant is not meant for you. You should command me instead.' The maharaja was then busy preparing for the marriage of his son, Prince Birendra Kishore. He added, 'The heavens will not fall if I buy my would-be daughter-in-law fewer sets of jewellery. In fact, if Jagadish Babu wins more laurels abroad to adorn our motherland, it would be incomparably more gratifying.'

Once a decent sum had been collected, the scientist was informed. In the meantime, the lieutenant governor visited Bose's laboratory. He not only expressed great satisfaction but also promised to institute three scholarships of 100 rupees for Bose's students. The cordial relationship between Bose and Sir Woodcomb made the college authorities a bit more conciliatory, though Bose understood that, sooner or later, the situation would change again. For the time being, Bose could carry on his research after work, as he had done before. Building the private laboratory, therefore, was not immediately necessary, but a part of the sum collected helped to mitigate his burden in purchasing and engineering research equipment.

Nonetheless, the possibility of a complete close-down of facilities had been hovering over Bose for more than two years and this had shattered his nerves. At this juncture, Sister Nivedita walked into his life. Attracted by his reputation, she had visited him earlier in 1898. The acquaintance was likely renewed due to Jagadish's sister Labanyaprabha, a member of a group of young Brahmo women teachers who were interested in Nivedita's 'new education' and had invited her for a few lectures.

Nivedita understood the agony he was going through and admired his nationalist ideals that made him persist against tremendous odds with the sole purpose of putting India on the scientific map of the world. That Abala Bose was giving her unflinching support to her husband and accepting a life of frugality was appreciated by Nivedita, too. She and the Boses became good friends in no time. Hers was a calming and energizing influence on him as she started playing the role of an assistant in his scientific activities.

Nivedita's crowning achievement was to persuade Bose to apply for a patent in America for one of his inventions, the artificial eye. This went entirely undetected by the British Raj. Of course, she was aided by Sara all the way in this endeavour. As mentioned before, this patent was later discovered in the 1990s and brought back focus on Bose. He has now been rediscovered as the scientist who pioneered the work on millimetre waves, a subclass of radio waves. In 2012, the IEEE named him as one of the fathers of radio science, after his contribution to the fundamentals of physics had long been consigned to oblivion. Such are the twists and turns in the history of an unprivileged scientist!

It has been mentioned that Bose was steeped in the religious philosophy of the Brahmo Samaj since his childhood; his faith was further deepened while living in a hostel run by that society. Raja Ram Mohan Roy propagated Brahmoism as a religious and social reform movement in the early nineteenth century. One of the central tenets of the religion was the strict prohibition of idol worship. Nivedita, like her guru, believed in worshipping the formless as well as the symbolic, often anthropomorphic, form of the divine. Both ignored this difference of ideologies and cooperated for the sake of the progress of science in India.

She discovered that he had the attitude of a seeker and broached the Vedantic concept of essential unity of all existence with Bose. He replied

—You ask science for the proof of unity?

Nivedita—Exactly.

Bose—Do you believe that spiritualism and scientific experience lead to the same unity?

Nivedita—The Upanishads seem to assume they should.

Here, there was a meeting of the two minds. Nivedita assisted Bose in every possible way. She helped him in writing books, often composing his ideas in her own language, writing the manuscripts by hand and then proofreading them. Nivedita knew that Mrs Bull could help him financially, and wrote to her on 26 March 1899, 'I wish you knew how I love the Boses. And I do hope you will take Dr Bose into your heart as a son—for he always talks of you.'

Nivedita wrote to Sara again,

> You know how to inspire a great man to do great work.... You must protect [Bose]. Become a second mother for him as you are for Swami-ji. Bose is sick of life, yet honestly anxious to hold on and on just to prove to his countrymen that their chances of success in experimental science are as great as that of any other European.

She then advised Bose to write to Mrs Bull and they began corresponding.

The Swami and Nivedita in the West Again

Mrs Bull received Nivedita's letter in Cambridge, Massachusetts. She was a mother to the Swami and then to Nivedita, and now resolved to be one to Bose as well, who was about ten years younger than her. The Vedanta societies set up by the Swami in America were of great concern to Mrs Bull and Joe as they were nascent organizations and needed further nurturing. Both of them had been urging the Swami to come to America once more. In the spring of 1899, he felt sufficiently strengthened and decided to travel again. The doctors were of the opinion that the long restful sea voyage would restore him further.

On the eve of his departure, the Swami gave a fiery speech to the monks on 'Sannyasa: Its Ideal and Practice'. In the speech, he emphasized that Sannyasa means being rid of the fear of death. A monk was to love death; he was to hold his life as a sacrifice to the welfare of the world. This speech left a firm impression on Nivedita's mind. She realized that her guru was a personification of this principle—he had been sacrificing himself bit by bit for the welfare of others.

All who came to know her, Jagadish and Abala included, perceived that she too had been emulating the path of her guru and working herself to the bone and depriving herself of proper nutrition when there was a paucity of funds at the school. The Boses made it a point to invite her to their residence from time to time and arranged sumptuous meals. Sometimes, when Nivedita fell ill, they had her shifted to their home and cared for her as they would a member of their own family.

On 10 June 1899, when the Swami and a monk of the order sailed for England, Nivedita decided to accompany them. She had for long been missing her family, and also thought this trip could be used for the purpose of fundraising for her school. The Swami spent a fortnight in London renewing old contacts but did no public work; since it was holiday season, many of his usual circle were away. He set out for America with a fellow monk while leaving Nivedita behind, and reached America later by the end of August.

The Swami, during his first sojourn in America, had set up two Vedanta societies, one in New York and the other in Chicago. During his second trip, he found the New York society flourishing, with its membership increased manifold. The Chicago society was also doing well, he was happy to observe.

He spent about a year preaching across America and set up Vedanta societies in Los Angeles, Pasadena, and San Francisco with the help of his enthusiastic followers. A good part of the Swami's stay in America was spent in the company of Josephine and the Leggetts. Early in 1900, he received an invitation from the Paris International Exposition to speak at the Congress of the History of Religions.

Nivedita stayed back in Wimbledon with her family for a while and then reached America on 20 September 1899. She was received by her friend Josephine MacLeod and later, was a guest of the Leggetts at their home, Ridgely Manor, located in the Catskill Mountains. Here, Betty Leggett, Joe's sister, had arranged a gathering—the Swami, Mrs Bull and her young daughter Olea, and Patrick Geddes and his wife were among the guests. Josephine had become friends with Geddes, a regular at Swami's lectures, in London.

Geddes was an eminent biologist as well as a sociologist, and had been appointed as one of the secretaries of the upcoming Paris International Exposition. Nivedita was greatly interested to learn sociology and European history under his guidance, and agreed to assist him in writing summaries of the presentations that were to be given during the Exposition. He too was looking to work in India. It was Geddes who sent out the invitation to Bose to contribute a paper for the Exposition; it is possible that Nivedita had a hand in the matter.

Betty Leggett revelled in entertaining important people and she and her husband wished to do so in Paris during the summer of 1900. With the Exposition taking place in the city, Paris would be filled with all kinds of extraordinary personages. The Leggetts, along with Josephine, arrived in Paris in June and rented a huge mansion. The Swami arrived in Paris from New York in early August. Nivedita and Geddes travelled separately and reached Paris before the grand inauguration of the Exposition.

The Swami spoke at the congress on 7 September and garnered much attention, with newspapers in Europe and India carrying eye-catching headlines about his speech.

Bose's Second Scientific Mission to Europe

In the meantime, there were favourable developments in Bose's life. The director of public instruction was informed that Sir John Woodburn was keen on sending Bose on deputation to the Paris Congress. When he asked for the letter of invitation that Bose had received so that he could send a report to Sir John, Bose discovered that the letter, which he had been carrying around in his pocket, had been misplaced. However, apart from the huge embarrassment this caused him, no real harm was done. A duplicate of the invitation letter had to be requisitioned from Paris.

The new letter took a long time to arrive and Bose received the approval for deputation at the eleventh hour. He immediately sent a wire to Paris. A delay of a few more days and there would have been no point in going to the congress, as the list of participants and the schedule of lectures were to be fixed one month in advance. Then, to his despair, Bose discovered that he hadn't enough money to book his sea fare to Paris. His all-weather friend Rabindranath Tagore came to the rescue and offered him the remaining part of the fund that had been initially collected to fund the making of a private lab for the scientist.

On the eve of his departure for Paris, Bose wrote to Tagore (in Bengali):

I feel sad and low because I shall be away, for quite some time, from my beloved motherland. At such times, small selfish considerations disappear. I hear the consenting voice of the mother; this son of hers will touch her feet and set sail. May you all bless me so that I can serve her wholeheartedly.

He sailed in early July and reached Paris in August 1900, just in time for the congress, where he presented a paper titled 'On the Similarity of Effect of Electric Stimulus on Inorganic and Living Matter'. He showed that the response curves of muscle tissue and metal were almost identical. As per the prevailing belief among physiologists, only living tissues could give this kind of electric response, and such a response from a piece of a tin foil, therefore, seemed unbelievable. That it was similar to a living matter's response was even more astonishing. Bose's paper created a sensation and the news reflected that in full measure the next day.

On 31 August, Bose wrote to Tagore,

I reached the Congress late and then I was hesitant to speak about my findings, already submitted to the Royal Society but not yet published. However, one day, all of a sudden, the president requested me to speak. I presented some selected portions of my research and that seemed to astonish many. One of the secretaries of the congress, who knew English, wanted a full account of the subject, stating he would like to translate it into French. ...He met me in this connection and after an hour of discussion he exclaimed, 'But Monsieur, this is very beautiful'. We discussed my work for three more days; everyday he was getting more and more excited. On the last day he became ebullient and started speaking to the president and other secretaries of the congress about my work breathlessly, only pausing to say that it was 'très jolie magnifique' etc.

In the end he told me, 'Your subject is truly novel and will take time to be accepted.... Physiologists do not know physics and vice versa. On top of that, if you bring in psychology, memory, and the like, most people will not understand.... They would consider you dreamy. Hence, at first the purely physical aspects should be

published. He added that my paper would be published in the very
first volume of the *Transactions of the Congress.*

In the same letter but in a different context Bose wrote,

> On the one hand, I have been truly happy in seeing the influence
> of new age science in Paris. On the other, whenever I think of
> my own country in this respect, I descend into despair.... What
> eagerness I see here! As soon as there is an invention, it is put to
> good use. Those who could master its application first, defeated
> other nations in business and manufacture.

Bose's anguish, as a citizen of an impoverished, subjugated country,
comes through in this passage.

Patrick Geddes and Sister Nivedita may have been present during
Bose's lecture; there is no evidence to support or refute this. However,
another eminent personality was present and observing. It was Swami
Vivekananda, who himself was a delegate to the Exposition. In one of his
letters, published in the form of a collection, *The Wanderer,* he wrote,

> Here in Paris have assembled the great of every land, each to
> proclaim the glory of his country. Savants will be acclaimed here;
> and its reverberations will glorify their countries. Among these
> peerless men gathered from all parts of the world, where is thy
> representative, o thou the country of my birth? Out of this vast
> assembly a young man stood for thee, one of thy heroic sons,
> whose words have electrified the audience, and will thrill all his
> countrymen. Blessed be this heroic son; and blessed be his devoted
> and peerless helpmate who stands by him always.

Abala was always present for all of Bose's lectures away from Calcutta.
After his lecture, the couple went to climb the Eiffel Tower, as is the wont
of all tourists in Paris. As a delegate of the congress, he was entitled to
a free pass in the elevator. But his wife was not and a fee of five francs
was charged. Bose wrote in a letter to Tagore,

> During the exchange with the ticket vendor, I had been struggling
> with my French when one English-speaking French gentleman
> offered to help and gave me his own card. When he saw my delegate

card, he exclaimed, 'Bose! Surely not Jagadish Bose!' ...When he learnt that I was indeed the same person, he started reprimanding the poor ticket vendor for charging my wife—'Our guest is a famous scientist and a foreigner; collecting the fee from him is mean shop-keeping, etc.' Soon, others gathered around and began chiding the ticket seller.

What the final outcome of all this commotion was has not been written about. Knowing his generous nature, one may guess that he intervened on behalf of the poor vendor who had merely been doing his job. The Bose couple then climbed the Eiffel and enjoyed the view of beautiful Paris from atop the tower.

In Paris, the Boses often met Swami Vivekananda at the Leggetts residence. The Swami wrote in a letter about his host and hostess and the parties they threw,

> Mr Leggett brought about an enormous expense in his Parisian mansion, by inviting them to at-homes. All types of distinguished personages—poets, philosophers, scientists, moralists, politicians, singers, professors, painters...of both sexes—used to be assembled in Mr Leggett's residence, attracted by hospitality and kindness. That incessant flow of words, clear and limpid like a mountain-fall, that expressions of sentiments emanating from all sides like sparks of fire, bewitching music, the magic currents of thoughts from master-minds coming into conflicts with one another—which used to hold all spell-bound, making them forgetful of time and space....

The Leggetts arranged such gatherings almost every day; Joe usually remained in the background but was still a constant presence. Jagadish Bose and Patrick Geddes were some of the oft-invited guests. Nivedita, too, would often be present. When the conversation turned to Bose's experiments on the growth of a stunted lily, the Swami, proud of his countryman, exclaimed in an allusion to Bose's experiments on the response of the non-living, 'Oh, that's nothing! Bose will make the very pot in which the lily grows respond!'

Now that the Paris Exposition was in full swing, Patrick Geddes would often lead a party consisting of members of the Leggett household, the Swami, Nivedita, and the Boses, among others, to the exhibition where he would explain the exhibits. Jagadish was a keen observer of French engineering and science.

While in Paris, the Boses and Sara Bull grew more closely acquainted. Sara was invited to the Leggett house by Joe, but soon became tired of the boisterous parties. Once the Exposition was over, Sara moved to a rented home in the quiet and scenic environs of Brittany.

After the Paris conference, Bose was invited to speak at the University of Sorbonne, Société de' Physique, and Société de' Zoologique, all in Paris. In Brittany, Sara invited the Swami, Nivedita, the Boses, and a few others. Bose, as usual, was happy to find a peaceful corner and busied himself with writing his research papers.[22] After a week, the Swami returned to Paris, and then accompanied by Joe and a few other friends, went homewards. Nivedita went ahead to London via Paris to look for accommodation; the Boses and Sara Bull followed her separately in late August and September of that year.

---

[22]The Boses's trip to Brittany on the west coast of France, as Sara's guest, was uncovered for the first time in *Saint Sara: The Life of Sara Chapman Bull.*

5

FALL FROM GRACE AND REDEMPTION

It was to be a lasting friendship between Bose and Nivedita—but such an unusual one! What contrast! One, a scientist, born Hindu, turned Bramho, a believer in iconoclasm, while the other a Protestant Christian, turned a Hindu idolater, and in love with an alien land and its culture. She had followed her guru to India in search of spiritual fulfilment. Her attitude, reflected in her statement, 'I do for India all that comes my way', was also a part of that spiritual quest. Bose had admired Swami Vivekananda's mission to bring 'manliness' to subjugated Indians, only to be disappointed when the Swami set up a monastic order engaged in idolatry. These two remarkable personalities, however, were united in their love for India and faith in the Vedanta philosophy of the Upanishads.

Bose believed, like all Bramhos, that idol worship was nothing but superstition and the root cause of India's ailments. How could an idolater exert much influence in the West, steeped in monism, praying to a formless God? It was natural for those belonging to the Brahmo Samaj to underestimate the impact of Swami Vivekananda's preaching on Western society. Many orthodox Hindus too were aghast that a man born outside the Brahmin caste like the Swami could preach at all and hoped that his influence would not be too great at home or abroad.

However, an article written by Bipin Chandra Pal, a noted orator and leader of the Indian National Congress, set the record straight. It appeared in London's the *Indian Mirror* on 15 February 1899, and reads,

> Some people in India think that very little fruit has come of the lectures that Swami Vivekananda delivered in England, and that his friends and admirers exaggerate his work. But on coming here I see that he has exerted a marked influence everywhere. In many parts of England I have met with men who deeply regard and venerate

Vivekananda. Though I do not belong to his sect and though it is true that I have differences of opinion with him, I must say that Vivekananda has opened the eyes of a great many here and broadened their hearts. Owing to his teaching, most people here now believe firmly that wonderful spiritual truths lie hidden in the ancient Hindu scriptures.

Bipin Chandra Pal was not only a Bramho, but also a good friend of the Boses; Jagadish occasionally corresponded with him. Both Jagadish and Abala were readers of the *Indian Mirror* and kept up with the current affairs. Pal's article might have softened their attitude towards the Swami's monastic order, for we later find them travelling to one of the Ramakrishna Math monasteries set in the high Himalayas. They undertook another journey in the company of a few monks of the order to Bodh Gaya. From there, Nivedita brought back the figure of a vajra; Bose learnt to venerate the vajra symbol from Nivedita.

Nivedita leaves us many accounts of her trips—some of them taken with the Boses—to different parts of the country. She was a prolific writer and her numerous letters are a valuable record of events that transpired around her and in her life. Her biographer had Nivedita's writings at her disposal and gave us the following dramatized account. When she heard Bose asserting that life is present everywhere, even in inorganic matter, and that he would capture it first in metals and then in plants, she said, 'You must write down all that you are telling me. It's important. It's necessary.'

'How do you expect me to seize on the idea that passes like a flash? It eludes me.'

'But I am here. My pen is an obedient servant; it will serve you well. It is yours.'

This conversation is significant, because quite a few manuscripts of Bose's books and papers were found to be in her handwriting. Nivedita had earlier written to Mrs Bull, trying to draw her affection towards the Boses, 'It is on your heart, I know, as it is on mine, and you and Yum [Josephine MacLeod] and I will make these two people feel a warm circle of love and strength about them while there is still time to make the world feel like home....'

To spare the Boses the trouble of searching for an accommodation in London, Nivedita had travelled ahead of them after the Paris Exposition. Initially, Nivedita wanted to put the Boses up in her mother's home but the elderly lady was too feeble to entertain guests. So, she found an alternative before they arrived, and then helped Bose with his work and tried to surround the couple, as far as possible, with an atmosphere of peace and tranquillity. Mrs Bull remained in Europe for a little while and then joined them. She often helped them financially, in this case by bearing the house rent.

While in Europe, Bose kept up a steady correspondence with his friend Rabindranath Tagore. Their correspondence gives us a valuable record and chronology of events. Tagore wrote to Bose, 'I keep the Maharaja of Tripura well informed about your sojourn. I became delighted to learn that he holds you in very high esteem. A messenger has brought word that he is now prepared to contribute much more than what he had promised for aiding your work.'

This undated letter was most probably written within a month or two of the Boses reaching England. In another letter, dated 20 November 1900, Tagore wrote,

> The Maharaja of Tripura is now in Calcutta. I can hardly express in words how happy and joyous he is at your success. ...I shall show him your letter today—he would be very glad. On receiving your last letter some time ago, he felt highly honoured and expressed his delight in no uncertain terms. Now, he seems eager for an opportunity to come to your aid.

Both Bose and Tagore were extremely grateful to the maharaja and tried to keep him informed of all developments. Bose's research, in the meanwhile, was reaching a turning point. For about a year Bose had been following two distinct but overlapping lines of research—one on the physics of electric waves and the other on the responses of the living and the non-living to stimuli. The latter obviously had much to do with the subject of physiology. These two lines converged in the artificial eye, the galena crystal receiver, his latest creation. The lectures he gave in England were on both aspects, often running side by side. However, for the convenience of the reader, we shall trace the trajectory of the former first. While going over both facets of Bose's research, we may refer to the same letter multiple times.

The Physical Phase: I

Bose's first presentation was at Bradford before the physical branch of the British Association, on 10 September 1900. The subject matter included the working of the coherer (discussed in the earlier chapter) and his initial physiological research. Bose had published two new papers in 1899 and 1900 on electric waves and their receivers and also proposed a theory of 'molecular strain' in explaining conductivity-variation in receivers, which was in opposition to Lodge's theory of 'soldering' action. He was so pleased after the Bradford lecture that he immediately wrote to Tagore from the lecture hall's reception room,

> There were reasons for apprehension. There was praise about my research in a scientific journal and criticism of Prof. Lodge's theory. He was not pleased and came with his friends, determined to contradict my proposition.... Right at the outset there was debate about the two theories—Lodge right in front of me—what could I do?...
>
> I began by saying, 'From the results of previous experiments Prof. Lodge was led to suppose etc....but these new investigations seem to point to the theory of molecular strain.'...
>
> Everyone was looking at Lodge; I too stole a look once in a while. John Bull's[23] face does not show up his emotions. However, when I concluded, there was much applause. The president said, 'Chandra Bose of Calcutta is well known to us etc.' and invited questions and comments.
>
> No, there was no adverse comment. Lodge stood up and praised and walked over to my wife to say, 'Let me heartily congratulate you on your husband's splendid work.'
>
> Thereafter I was seated quietly in my corner. Lodge came over to me and asked a few clarifications. I understood that

---

[23]By John Bull, Bose meant an archetypal Englishman.

he is gradually seeing it my way. John Bull's love of fair play is extraordinary indeed! Then Lodge said something to the President. The latter said,

'Many are eager to hear about Prof. Bose's remarkable discovery about vision. We shall be very happy if he says a few words.'

I spoke and the audience seemed quite convinced. After the lecture Lodge and his friends looked into my Stereoscope and were quite marvelled. He said to me,

'You have a very fine research in hand, go on with it'; then abruptly asked, 'Are you a man with plenty of means?—All these are very expensive and you have many years before you; your work will give rise to many others—all very important.'

I evaded the question (on my means). The next day Prof. Barret[24] spoke to me,

'We had a talk last night. Lodge was with us. We thought your time is being wasted in India, and you are hampered there. Can't you come over to England? Suitable chairs fall seldom vacant here, and there are many candidates. But there is just now a very good appointment (a newly created professorship in a renowned university) and should you care to accept it, no one else will get it.'

Now tell me what should I do? On one hand, I have only touched the outskirts of the investigation that has far-reaching implications and which cannot be done in an amateurish way. Hard work and favourable conditions are necessary. On the other hand, my inner being cannot withstand severing of the connection with my motherland—so neglected and impoverished. I am in a state of terrible dilemma and cannot decide. My inspiration at the root is the love and affection I get from my people—if that bond is broken then what am I left with? Let me end here today, etc.

Tagore replied upon receiving this letter. The letter emphasized that Bose's success in the scientific arena would bring glory to the motherland; therefore, Tagore advised,

'You must not hesitate even for a moment. If your country comes

---

[24]William F. Barret was Professor of Experimental Physics at the Royal College of Science for Ireland.

in the way of your success, you have to bid farewell even to her.'

Bose had another friend, Ramesh Chandra Dutt, a retired ICS officer, who had been living in England for quite some time. He too urged Bose, again and again, to accept the offer. At this time his work on the whole was being well received by fellow physicists. However, his second line of research produced a mixed reaction in the rest; some thought it was esoteric and magical, others were perplexed. A section of physiologists even became hostile because they thought he was as an intruder in their domain.

Further, as luck would have it, Bose was diagnosed with an affliction that needed surgery. The illness had surfaced in Calcutta, brought on by excessive fatigue and prolonged standing while doing experiments; then neglected, it now took a serious turn. To add to his misery, the period of deputation was drawing to a close (it would end in March 1901) and he had to return to India. While these hurdles were being dealt with, he became a victim of plagiarism. There were aspersions cast on his character and competence. He realized that he needed time, a few years, to stay on in England to gather more evidence in order to vindicate himself.

These events unfolded one after another in quick succession, with Bose hanging on in the grip of indecision for months. He was agonizing over his situation and subsequently becoming more depressed. Abala, Nivedita, and Mrs Bull tried their best to cheer him up; Tagore's letters also helped immensely.

Finally, the pull of the motherland prevailed. He decided to reject the excellent offer he had received and applied for an extension of the deputation for two years. The authorities granted his request, but the deputation was only extended for six months, that is, until September 1901.

We recall that the president of the Bradford meeting had talked about a 'remarkable discovery' about human vision due to Bose, who had demonstrated there an instrument called a stereoscope. The link between Bose's research on electric waves and human vision was again the artificial eye, that is, the galena crystal receiver. It was also instrumental in drawing him into non-optical photography, i.e., photography without light.

The retina of an eye is where an inverted image of the object is formed. The retina then sends an electric signal via the optic nerve to the brain where the image is interpreted; and only then do we 'see' the image. Bose likened his galena crystal receiver to the retina, the wire of the circuit to the optic nerve and the galvanometer, which is used to register the electric response of the receiver, to the brain. This had led him to do certain experiments with human vision and photography before he sailed for Paris, which led to the birth of the stereoscope.

It is common experience that vision lingers for a fraction of a second even after the object is removed or changes position. That is why we see a blur when an object moves very fast. Bose wished to test how this lingering or persistence of vision in one eye combines with that of the other. When we look at an object, one eye has a slightly different point of view that the other. So, what they see are also not the same. The brain combines these two visions to judge the distance or depth of the object and this is called binocular vision.

Bose placed on a table two parallel tubes, 38 millimetres in diameter, a certain distance apart and connected them in the middle by a short bar. If this contraption was to be looked at from the top, it would look like an 'H'. A circular glass was fitted with each tube. The distance between the glasses equalled what separates the two eyes of an adult, much like a pair of spectacles. So, one can think of the device as a special pair of spectacles, in which one glass had a horizontal line marked on it, and the other had a vertical line, as shown in Fig. 5.1(a). This device was named stereoscope by Bose.

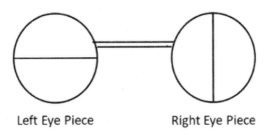

Left Eye Piece   Right Eye Piece

Fig. 5.1(a): The stereoscope.

If one holds the device close to the eyes and looks at a blank wall, one sees a cross. This proves that the brain combines the two visions. Moreover, the horizontal line becomes dim one moment while the vertical remains as is, and the vertical dims the next, just as the horizontal becomes clearly visible. This alternation continues as long as one looks through the stereoscope. Bose explained that the signals from the two eyes are not processed simultaneously by the brain, but alternately at short intervals. This he called alternating binocular vision of humans.

His theory of molecular strain provided another interesting lead and this was in the realm of photography. Bose argued that light produces a similar molecular strain in the photographic plate as electric radiation produces in the receivers he had created. What was most interesting is that his artificial eye, the most versatile of his receivers, experienced molecular strain with electric radiation as well as light. This led him to attempt photography without light but with the help of electric radiation; and then compare the result with optical photography.

At this time, various radioactive substances were being discovered whose radiation affected the photographic plate. But Bose wanted to photograph substances that were not ordinarily radioactive. It is well known that the cross section of a tree trunk shows concentric rings of a kind, as in Fig. 5.1(b).

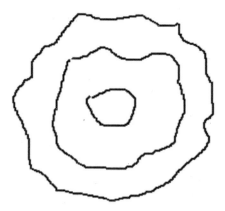

Fig. 5.1(b): Cross section of a tree trunk.

A section of a dried-up log also shows this pattern. Bose argued that these rings should emit radioactive rays at different rates, because they grew in successive seasons and therefore had different ages.

A section of a stem was enclosed in a box with a photoplate in front of it, but at a short distance. There were two metal plates on either side of the box, connected to an instrument and circuitry, to produce rapid electric oscillation for stimulating the stem inside the box. The wood, thus treated, left an extraordinarily clear impression on the photoplate.[25] Fig 5.1(c) is a photograph of a leaf of a Bodhi tree, taken by this method.

Fig. 5.1(c): Photograph of a leaf of the Bodhi tree, taken by Bose.

Bose employed this method to photograph various stones and crystals, which revealed information about their structures. But he did not pursue this new field of experimental investigation, instead swiftly moving on to another branch of study. He was, perhaps, the first to take photographs without light. It remains for historians to investigate and verify this.

The Physical Phase: II

After arriving in England, Bose quickly settled down in Maida Vale

---

[25]This photograph is no longer available.

and began busily preparing for his lecture to the British Association at Bradford. After the experimental demonstration, he had noticed that while his fellow physicists were quite appreciative, the physiologists present looked perplexed and were unusually quiet. He reasoned that his physics-styled experiments were not understood by the physiologists; so he planned to restructure some experiments so as to not alienate them. Nivedita helped him with his preparations and writings.

On 5 October, a few weeks after his Bradford lecture, Bose wrote to Tagore,

> I had planned to do some experiments in the Royal Institution for a few days. For this I had been making some new instruments. Unfortunately, now I am stricken by a disease that is coming in the way. I consulted a famous surgeon named Dr Cromby and he said that there is some internal affliction, which if left untreated may pose danger. A difficult operation is necessary soon. It is not really life-threatening but would keep me in bed for about five weeks. I have to give up experiments for the time being.

It was Mrs Sara Bull who engaged the best surgeon in London and financed Bose's treatment. The operation was slated for mid-December 1900. Bose had written to Mrs Bull in early September,

> My paper will probably come next week. Then too I feel some restraint, as some of the important things which I recently did with crude homely apparatus are capable of much more improvement and far-reaching development with proper apparatus. If I give out the idea of my method, and do not continue the work myself, better results will be brought forward and my work will appear ridiculous and crude.

Mrs Bull promised to meet him ahead of his lecture. As for the crudeness of some of his instruments: the reader may remember the polarizer Bose fashioned out of a cheap railway timetable. Mrs Bull did come to see him. She attended his lecture and stayed on for quite some time in London, right through Bose's post-surgery convalescence.

On 2 November 1900, Bose wrote to Rabindranath Tagore,

Yesterday I heard from Sir William Crookes. He writes, 'I have read the most interesting account of your researches with extreme interest. I wonder whether I could induce you to deliver a lecture on these or kindred subject of research before the Royal Institution. If you could do so, I shall be very glad to put your name down for a Friday Evening Discourse after Easter of 1901'.

[There] was a meeting with Dr Waller, the great physiologist. ...Dr Waller initially was much opposed to my ideas, but in the end, he came round somewhat and said with much excitement, 'It appears that your work will probably upset mine. Truth is Truth and I don't care a d-, if I am proved to be the wrong. So, come and work; I will place my laboratory at your disposal. Teach me or let us work together.'

Yours, Jagadish.

This Dr Waller, who appeared so generous then, became some kind of a nemesis for Bose later. A prolonged phase of harassment was about to begin, all through which Mrs Bull and Sister Nivedita stood by him. Nivedita soon left for Scotland for a fortnight, and visited Patrick Geddes on her tour. Thereafter, she was back in London.

In May 1901, accompanied by Nivedita, Sara left for Norway to attend the unveiling of a statue of her late husband Ole Bull, in his home town of Bergen. The ceremony was scheduled for 17 May, the Norwegian Independence Day. After the event they spent a few solitary weeks living by the sea, in deep introspection. They returned to London together and Mrs Bull went homewards while Nivedita busied herself in assisting Bose to write *Response in the Living and Non-living*.

Dr Muirhead, an academically accomplished person and the proprietor of a famous electrical company, was known to Bose, and occasionally consulted him informally; he requested Bose to keep his inventions confidential in the interests of taking out patents. We shall see a mention of this in one of his letters to Tagore.

Intimately associated with Bose's research, Nivedita must have known about Dr Muirhead's suggestion to Bose to apply for patents for his inventions. Sara, on the other hand, had learnt the ways of the real world from her father, and had applied them in managing the wealth

and contractual dealings of her musician husband, who had a distaste
for such things. She understood well enough the importance of patents
for an inventor. While Nivedita and Sara were staying with Bose in
London, during the months of his convalescence, the two persuaded
Bose to begin applying for patents.

In July 1901, Sara took Bose to America to initiate the patenting
process. It is not known if Abala accompanied Bose on this trip, though
knowing of their history, she might have. On 23 July 1901, Nivedita
wrote to Sara, enquiring about the possibility of taking out patents. The
necessary documents had been under preparation for some time, with
Bose as one of the signatories and Sara as the other.

Two patent applications were filed, one on 'Improvements in and
Connected with Wireless Telegraphy and other Signaling', dated 30 July
1901 (Application No. 15467) and the other on 'Improved Method or
Apparatus for Detecting or Indicating Light Waves', 'Hertzian Waves and
Other Radiations', dated 14 September 1901 (Application No. 18480).
The latter came to fruition as Patent No. 755840, titled 'Detector for
Electrical Disturbances', on 29 March 1904. The fate of the former is
unknown. In *Saint Sara*, Pravrajika Prabuddhaprana has given facsimiles
of the front pages of the applications for these two patents, in which
the application number, date, and other details are clearly visible.[26]

Sara paid for the to-and-fro travel and the patent fee. They returned
to London after a brief stay in America. At this stage, if Bose had
informed Dr Muirhead about the patent application and given him
the related know-how, Dr Muirhead would have taken over the entire
responsibility of maintaining the patent and applying it for the benefit
of his company. Muirhead would have left his competitors far behind,
and Bose would have derived a handsome royalty. It was not as if he

---

[26]Bose's short visit to America, his first, in the middle of July in 1901, had remained
unknown for a long time, perhaps, because of his reluctance to talk about patents. His
first biographer, Geddes, who learnt about Bose's life from the man himself, was also
in the dark. The story of the successful patent (No. 755840) only came to light in the
late twentieth century. Bose's trip to America, as Sara's guest, and the application for
the other patent have been discovered very recently by Pravrajika Prabuddhaprana.
However, most evidence remains buried in the letters and diaries of Sister Nivedita
and Mrs Sara Bull, and also in the records of the patent office.

did not need money. But he did no such thing! One is tempted to say that his attitude in this regard was entirely impractical.

Sara stayed with Nivedita in her mother's house until they sailed together for India on 4 January 1902, while the Boses stayed back in England. Having expected their brief sojourn to Norway, then Nivedita's trip to Scotland, and Sara's to America, the two had stayed busy all this while assisting Bose in preparing the manuscript of his book, which was to be published later that year; the cost of publication would be borne entirely by Sara.

The duo reached Calcutta in February. Joe had already arrived from Japan, where she had stayed for about a year, and was accompanied by a well-known Japanese artist and author, Okakura Kakuzō, and a student named Hori who wanted to learn Sanskrit. A Japanese Buddhist priest, Reverend Oda, joined them later. They stayed either in the guest house of the Belur Math, or in the American consulate, as per individual conveniences. The Consul, Mr Patterson, who had known the Swami in America and become his admirer, offered his hospitality; his wife had travelled with the Swami and the three western disciples in Kashmir, for a part of the tour, three years ago. The three women found their prophet, Swami Vivekananda, in very poor health.

Okakura and Oda came to India to meet the Swami and invite him to the Parliament of Religions, to be held in Japan later the same year. The Swami initially accepted the invitation but could not travel due to his health issues. Oda returned to Japan; Okakura, however, stayed back because he had another purpose—to study Indian art—for which he needed to visit the country's holy sites and monuments. Sara sensed that he possessed talent and had a noble cause, and decided to help him as far as she could.

Hori was immediately directed by the Swami to Tagore's school at Shantiniketan, where he started to learn Sanskrit. Okakura was put in touch with artists from the Government School of Arts, Calcutta, including Abanindranath Tagore and Nandalal Basu, who told him about Shantiniketan's Kala Bhavan. However, at first, he travelled with Nivedita and Christine to Mayawati; later he visited Bodh Gaya, Rajgir, and Nalanda, sites made famous by the Buddha, and other historic places known for ancient Indian art.

In the winter of 1900, both Mrs Bull and Nivedita were in London when Bose had his surgery. He was operated upon by Dr Cromby in his Cavendish Street Hospital on 11 December. Before the operation, he had concentrated on improving his apparatus for recording reactions of plants. Nivedita wrote on 3 November, 'He has devised self-recording and self-stimulating instruments, which can take a plant and go on working with it *alone*, for hours.'

Simultaneously, Bose was in the process of writing up his recent experiments. Nivedita noted down the essential points of these experiments, lest he forget anything due to the ensuing long interruption caused by the operation. She performed this task voluntarily, which was normally something a trained research assistant would do under instruction. Nivedita wrote to Sara's intimate friend Emma Thursby[27] that these papers consisted of, 'the most wonderful things you ever knew—actually verifying the Vedanta doctrine of unity for many departments of physical science, one of the greatest generalizations of the century.'

Bose recovered from his surgery in time for Christmas and moved back into his London residence. Nivedita and Sara were staying in a house (29 Wompole Street) that was a minute's walk from the Boses's home. They came over to see Jagadish every day during his convalescence and were constantly ministering to his needs, alongside Abala. In January 1901, they all moved to Nivedita's mother's house in Wimbledon, as she had gone away on a trip. They had all their meals in the kitchen, so that the relatively large dining room could be made into a laboratory for Bose. When his strength returned, he became busy in this laboratory, where Nivedita often lent him a helping hand.

In his first letter after the operation, dated 3 January 1901, he wrote to Tagore:

> Friend...I know that lady luck is more kind to me than she was to Caesar. When Brutus stabbed him in the stomach, the great Caesar was felled at once, whereas three doctors knifed my stomach for one and a half hour and still I am alive. When the effect of

---

[27]The primary source of this letter is Emma Thursby Papers of the New York Historical Society.

anaesthesia wore off, I lost all interest in life and gave up on food. Then your friend's wife held before me a plateful of typical Bengali fish curry with gravy and rice. She had deceived me by cutting up a foreign fish Indian style. Indian food appeared dearer than even dear life. Thus, it took nearly four weeks before I got back strength little by little. I have to rest for four more weeks before I start work.

...You ask for a report of my work. That is adding insult to injury, as the parrot said when they not only brought him from his native country, but also made him speak English! You should have yourself come to observe or sent a special news reporter.

...Following my suggestions, the famous Electrical Company Messrs. Muirhead & Co. obtained remarkably good results in their work with wireless telegraphy. ...I have written a new paper that should bring much benefit to practical wireless telegraphy.[28] Dr Muirhead, however, is requesting me not to disclose the new inventions. My time here is limited and I have to accomplish much. Once I get drawn into making money there is not much else I can do.

Dr Waller, who is investigating the frog's eye, invited me to see his laboratory. I have been smitten by jealousy on seeing his facilities.

His two assistants, one of them a doctorate in science, his wife and himself—all four work from early morning to late evening. There is a good stock of food and drinks in one corner, so that no time is lost while eating. He finds it unbearable that he has to deliver five lectures a week and is thinking of resigning.... Experimental results are recorded automatically by photography. The advanced state of his laboratory I can hardly describe in words...! Now think of the conditions under which I have to work!...

A point to note is that I have been obstructed by the lower rung of officials in India, but the Lieutenant Governor has been especially kind to me. But people on the outside would not understand the

[28]He was referring to his paper, 'On a self-recovering coherer and the study of the cohering action of different metals', published by the Royal Society in 1899, much of which would be presented in the Friday Evening Discourse in May 1901.

difference between these two kinds of rulers. No matter what, I do not wish to appear ungrateful.

I shall have to speak on 'Science in Ancient and Modern India' at the Society of Arts. Please send me whatever historical accounts you can gather about Medicine, Astronomy, Chemistry, and universities in ancient India.

Yours, Jagadish.

This letter shows an interesting side of Bose's personality. It also has Dr Muirhead's request regarding patents. It is also noteworthy that in spite of his busy schedule, illness, and his worrying financial situation, he still wishes to showcase his country's scientific past before a learned audience and hence asks Tagore for his input.

Even before the operation, Bose had accepted what had been a standing invitation from his well-wishers, Lord Rayleigh and Sir James Dewar, and begun working in the Davy-Faraday laboratory, attached to the Royal Institution. An assistant by the name of Mr Bull[29] had been hired and the construction of certain instruments started. In Sister Nivedita's biography as well as in Bose's letters to Tagore, there are references to this lab. Geddes, who learnt about Mr Bull from Bose himself, devotes a commendatory paragraph to Mr Bull. The Boses were not of enough means to employ a hand; therefore, they had to curtail living expenses to be able to pay the assistant's salary. Jagadish even had to turn down invitations for lecturing because they could not afford to travel.

Bose's talk for the Friday Evening Discourse at the Royal Institution was scheduled on 10 May 1901, after the Easter holidays. As per the request of Sir William Crookes, he was to speak more or less on the same subject as the one he had earlier at the Bradford British Association. Here, the topic was 'The Response of Inorganic Matter to Mechanical and Electrical Stimulus'. He had been working very hard to acquire newer evidence for this lecture, since his post-operation convalescence. Exhaustion started weighing on his health.

---

[29]Mr Bull's first name remains unknown.

An Inspiring Vision and a 'Commercial' Theft

A few days before the all-important Friday Evening Discourse, Bose was assailed by self-doubt, and felt extremely depressed. A week after the event, on 17 May 1901, he wrote to Tagore,

> Even on the Thursday, the day before the lecture, I could not decide on what to speak. Different leads from physics, physiology, and chemistry had to be brought together. How could I do that in one hour? Besides, the experiments that I had to perform were very difficult. Some of the instruments could be readied only at the last hour. In the afternoon I was stretched out in bed in great despair. An unspeakable agony began to wring my heart. All hopes of my friends and countrymen would be dashed because of my weakness, physical and mental. Then an event that cannot be explained by science took place; and even a mere recollection of that gives me goose pimples. All on a sudden I had the vision of a shadowy female figure, in the attire of an Indian widow. I could see the face only in profile. The slender sad-looking woman whispered, 'I have come to offer my holy embrace and acceptance,' and the next moment she disappeared.
>
> In that moment all my self-doubt and depression vanished. Since then I thought not about what to say or what would happen. Next day when I was standing before the audience, I was enveloped by an unspeakable ecstasy but only for little while. Then all darkness dissolved, everything became light and I do not know who or what made me speak....
>
> A few hours before my lecture, I had received a wire from the millionaire proprietor of a very famous telegraph company for an urgent meeting. I wired back, 'There is no time'. He replied, 'I am coming myself'. He arrived with a patent form in hand. He pleaded with all sincerity, 'Please, do not disclose everything in your lecture. There is money in it—let me take out patents for you. You do not know what money you are throwing away, etc. Of course, I shall take half share in the profit—I will finance it etc.'
>
> This millionaire had come to me like a beggar to earn a few more

pounds. Friend, you would be astonished to see the love for lucre in this country—money, money, money—what an all-pervasive greed! Once I get trapped by this money-making grinder, there is no escape for me...I did not agree.

My Friday Evening Discourse on that occasion was attended by a whole lot of people from the telegraph companies. They swarmed around my table. Given a chance they would have whisked away my whole apparatus from right under my nose. There was a hand-written notebook, containing instructions for my assistant lying on the table—that vanished without a trace.

However, my paper will not be published right now, because I have been invited by the Royal Society to speak before them (about the same topic, more or less). They have made a special case, for they never accept anything read before any other society. During that presentation, experts in physiology would also be present. Sir Michael Foster[30] himself will communicate my paper. I shall have to perform many experiments in front of the audience....

Dr Waller, who is credited with finding the ultimate symptoms of life, has been extremely upset by my lecture....

I am in a terrible dilemma. I shall have to return in September. In India my work will come to a stop.... I do not expect [the authorities] to extend my leave any further....

Let me now send you a letter that gives an example of the kind of facility and support I get in my own country. The unfortunate student in the letter got a research scholarship at my recommendation. He is now being persecuted. Please treat the matter as confidential; otherwise the poor boy may be harmed further. Besides, if an issue turns into a 'race question', then you well know what results in the end....

Sir Robert Austen, the greatest authority on metals, was absolutely jubilant and said, 'I have all my life studied the properties of metals—I am happy to think that they have life!'....

Let me end here today. Yours, Jagadish.

---

[30]Secretary of the Royal Society at that time.

This long and important letter gives us many leads. We shall take up some of them now and others later.

First, he talked about a 'millionaire proprietor of a very famous telegraph company' who had come to him 'like a beggar to earn a few more pounds'. It is believed the man must have been connected to the only rival company of Dr Muirhead's and, therefore, was most probably Major Stephen Flood Page, the managing director of Marconi's Wireless and Telegraph Company.

Secondly, he points to the predatory attitude of the people from the telegraph industry who would 'given a chance, whisk away' his whole apparatus. As mentioned, a notebook of his was stolen from right under his nose.

Thirdly, he mentioned that the publication of his paper, just presented in the Friday Evening Discourse of the Royal Institution, would be delayed; this owing to an invitation from the Royal Society, 'for they never accept anything read before any other society', the Royal Institution being the 'other'. This delay in publication, through no fault of his own, proved very costly for Bose.

Finally, Dr Waller, who had been 'credited with finding the ultimate symptoms of life' became 'extremely upset' by his lecture. There must have been some visible, hostile reactions from Dr Waller during the lecture to draw this comment from Bose. We shall see that all the four factors just listed had the potential for unfortunate repercussions.

At this time overwork started affecting Bose's stout constitution and he began suffering from hypertension. His insomnia returned as well. Nivedita, in one of her letters, has given a vivid description of his state of mind at this time,

> He was tyrannical and when a day of work passed without result, he was apt to fall into a mood of irritation. He was depressed and harassed by a sense of constant struggle dictated by race prejudice. Every lecture he gave represented a cruel effort and hours would be spent in drawing and redrawing scientific diagrams and verifying calculations.

Bose's letter quoted earlier shows that he was bothered by the persecution of his student and the 'race question' in Presidency College, back in India.

Perhaps, Nivedita had this in mind while referring to 'race prejudice'.

At this time, Tagore wrote a science article in a popular Bengali journal named *Banga Darshan* on Bose's research on the responses of the living and the non-living. The title of the article poses the question 'Does inert matter have life?' It is easy to guess that the article answers it in the affirmative, particularly so in the light of metallurgist Sir Austen's remark, quoted in Bose's letter dated 17 May. It is worth mentioning that Bose never asserted that inert matter has life in all his formal presentations and writings, but it was heavily implied that he believed this to be the case. He might not have been so circumspect in private conversations, or even in off-the-record discussions that often took place after his lectures.

Returning to the theft of his notebook, as mentioned in Bose's letter, it contained detailed instructions and diagrams for his assistant as was his usual practice. He was quite adept at making diagrams, like most inventors, and made sketches even in his letters to Tagore. The paper that had been published in the *Proceedings of the Royal Society* in 1899, revealing his invention of self-recovering coherers or receivers for the first time, had no diagram whatsoever. Hence, the stolen notebook would have been of great help in reverse engineering the receivers demonstrated during the Friday Evening Discourse, and which the telegraph companies were so keen to take out their own patents for. There is no doubt that there was a commercial motive behind the theft. So far, this act of wrongdoing has not received the attention it deserves.

He also demonstrated his artificial eye (the galena crystal receiver) in his lecture at the Royal Institution. This lecture, and the events that occurred, more or less mark the end of Bose's time in the field of physics. As the letter to Tagore indicates, Bose was invited to speak before the Royal Society and there he presented the same electric wave experiments. However, this time his physiological experiments were cast in a format more familiar to the physiologists in attendance. All his work on electric waves up to this point had already been published in many reputed journals. Hereafter, his interest swiftly shifted to his second love, physiology.

The Nobel Prize

At this juncture occurred a momentous event—the inauguration of the Nobel prizes in 1901. It's inauguration was timed to coincide with the dawn of the new century. Experimental works, particularly with the potential for human benefit, were to be given preference over theoretical works.

In the year of its inception, the Nobel Prize for Physics was won by a German physicist, Wilhelm Konrad Röntgen, for the discovery of a certain class of radiation.

On the afternoon of 8 November 1895, Röntgen covered a Crookes–Hittorf[31] tube with a black cardboard box in order to prevent any light from escaping. He arranged to pass a sudden electric charge through the tube and intended to study its effect in a dark room. To prepare the next step of his experiment, he turned away from the tube but stopped short when he noticed a faint glow coming from an object a short distance away. He lit a match in the dark and discovered that the object was a barium platinocyanide screen, which was glowing due to the impact of some type of radiation. He repeated the sequence of events several times before becoming convinced that he had chanced upon a new kind of ray. After the publication of his first paper on the subject, it was initially called the Röntgen ray.

Conscious of the fact that he had accidentally discovered something entirely unknown, Röntgen always preferred the name X-rays for the new rays—from the mathematical practice of designating an unknown quantity—as no one understood what these remarkable rays actually were in those early days. Röntgen showed that these rays could penetrate materials such as aluminium and wood, but not denser materials like lead and human bone. He employed the X-rays to photograph the bones of his wife's hand and opened up the immense possibilities for its medical use.

That the X-ray is an electromagnetic wave was gradually unravelled years after the first Nobel Prize for Physics had been awarded, in the 1910s. Max von Laue took the first step in that direction in 1912 when he showed that an X-ray is capable of diffraction, thus proving that they

---

[31]Crookes–Hittorf tube is an early experimental electrical discharge tube in which streams of electrons or cathode rays were discovered.

could be described as waves. However, Röntgen did not suspect at all that the X-rays might belong to the same class. Between 1895 and 1897, he published three papers on the subject, before closing this chapter of his research.

Röntgen had something in common with Bose, an aversion for patents. He refused to patent his device, convinced that his 'inventions and discoveries belong to the world at large.' However, absence of patents did not deter the scientific community and the Nobel committee from highly valuing Röntgen's work. It should be recalled that Bose was the first to build an X-ray machine, which he called the Röntgen machine, and pioneered its medical use in India.

Bose had continued to extend his series of inventions and findings from 1895 until early 1901. In this period, he contributed much to the science of electric waves. Its practical applications in communication also received his attention, as he continued bettering his early receivers. He demonstrated his artificial eye before a large learned audience of many scientific disciplines at the Royal Institution in London. Most of his papers were carried by the most prestigious publication of his time, the *Proceedings of the Royal Society*. The reading of his research alone conveys much to someone with a background in physics about the direction of research that Bose was following. Apart from correctly estimating the wave speed and quantifying the laws of optics, he was responsible for resolving a theoretical difficulty that arose in Maxwell's theory of EM waves, as discussed earlier. His paper 'The Rotation of Plane of Polarization of Electric Waves by a Twisted Structure', published in 1898, should be considered as the first work on microwave analogue physics. But no one else followed his lead then, and Bose soon left the field to work on plant physiology. He was far ahead of his times; this subject developed as a new branch of physics after World War II.

It has been mentioned that Pyotr N. Lebedev was working on millimetre waves around the same time as Bose. Lebedev was unable to accurately measure wavelength but did manage to publish his first paper on the topic in a German journal in 1901. Though this paper was published much too late to be considered for the first Nobel Prize for Physics, his later papers on the pressure of light on gases did put him on the shortlist for the 1912 prize. It should be noted that no one foresaw any application for the benefit of humanity ensuing from these findings at the time, which was part of the criteria for nominees for the prize.

Like Lebedev, the whole gamut of Bose's publications, in particular his paper of 'special excellence' on measurement of wavelength and thereby wave speed, was for testing the correctness of Maxwell's theory. His paper on rotation of plane of polarization, published in 1898, was ingenious in conception and carried the mark of true originality. The potential for great benefit to humankind through his many inventions was apparent.

Were Bose's achievements worth a Nobel Prize? Judging by the comment made by Jacob Kunz earlier (see p. 100), they certainly were very substantial and ingenious. Above all, his findings were purposive and directed, and not accidental like Röntgen's. Recalling the earlier-quoted comments published in *The Electrician* (see p. 57), Bose was the first to invent reliable and robust receivers. His work in the field of wireless communication was revolutionary.

D. T. Emerson, while discussing the efforts of Marconi and Popov in sending man-made signals at a distance, unambiguously gives clear priority to Bose (see p. 66). Was Bose's work as creditable as Röntgen's, if not more? Had Bose been European, would he have shared the Nobel with Röntgen? These are the questions that should trouble the western scientific community and science historians. They should also be of concern to historians charting the course of the British colonial establishment in India.

The Physiological Phase

This is where the physiological phase of Bose's research begins. In modern parlance, it would be referred to as his biophysical phase, for he applied the methods of physics to physiology. As discussed earlier, his 'intrusion' into physiology was agitating a section of British physiologists. At the same time, the physiological content of his presentation in Bradford had made another section of this group demand to hear the same paper at the Royal Institution. Thereafter, there was an invitation for it to be substantially repeated before the Royal Society. The matter which aroused so great a curiosity was essentially a comparison of the responses of the living and non-living to various stimuli.

The non-living substances included receivers and metallic foils, and the living substance was muscle tissue. What was so surprising for the great body of scientists present was that the responses of the living and non-living were provably similar. It is suitable for us to take a closer look at Bose's experiments in this new arena of research. At the same time, in order to understand the reactions of his fellow scientists, we need to be acquainted with the mindset of various groups engaged in different disciplines. We begin at the beginning, at his lecture before the British Association.

The Association had a policy that scientists of different subjects were invited if a certain paper had interdisciplinary content. Bose's paper had obvious relevance for physicists as well as physiologists; it even held relevance for those in the field of chemistry. So, people from all these disciplines had been invited to his Bradford lecture; the title was 'On the Similarity of Effect of Electrical Stimulus on Inorganic and Living Substances'. Within a month of this presentation, he wrote to Tagore (letter dated 5 October 1900),

> The scientists of England are a divided lot. There is much conflict between the chemists and the physicists; the physiologists too are not far behind. On that day in our physical section, the chemists were welcomed with great fanfare. At the outset, our president said a few sweet words to attract and put them at ease. In reply, a chemist stood up and said, 'We have no wish to get into unpleasant exchanges, but your J. J. Thompson has said that atom is not indivisible. There are particles smaller than atom. With anyone who meddles with our atom, we shall be at war. There will be trouble if you lay your hands on our indivisible and inviolate atoms!'
>
> Later, I met a physiologist who praised my work but added, 'Hope you do not belittle our great physiology as a branch of your physics. What is this business of explaining everything with a mathematical formula but clever nonsense?'
>
> One or two physicist friends have told me, 'Psychology is not

science. So please stay away from it.' You can well imagine how carefully I have to tread....

Yours, Jagadish.

This attitude of staying confined within watertight compartments that prevailed among the British scientists of that era made Bose extremely uncomfortable; he referred to this as a 'caste system'.

Incidentally, his presentation earlier before the Paris Congress had been more or less on the same topic and titled, 'On the Similarity of Effect of Electric Stimulus on Inorganic and Living Substances'. There, he had begun by saying,

> While working with the receivers of electric waves, I found that repeated exposures to flashes of radiation resulted in gradual reduction in their sensitivity. However, if a receiver is rested for a while, it recovers the ability to respond properly. While obtaining a quantitative record of a series of responses, I was astonished to observe that they were similar to the fatigued response of a living muscle tissue. The receiver, which is an inert matter, when left undisturbed for some time recovers its power to respond, just like a tired muscle tissue recovers when rested for a while.

After Paris, his next lecture was given at Bradford and then at the Royal Institution on 10 May 1901. The reader may recall Bose's letter to Tagore on 17 May; he had written that he had been despondent and flung himself down in a pensive mood on the eve of his lecture at the Royal Institution. He had then had a strange vision: the shadowy figure of a Hindu widow appeared and spoke to him before disappearing. The vision reinvigorated and inspired him. Had he been daydreaming? Bose never mentioned her again but, given his traditional Hindu upbringing and intense love for his country, we may imagine that to Bose the woman was the impoverished Mother India. Nivedita was present at the lecture the next day and was surprised to see that the previously dejected Bose had become lucidly eloquent and almost poetic. In the peroration, he said,

I have shown you this evening autographic record of responses of the living and non-living. How similar are the writings! So similar indeed that you cannot tell one from the other apart. We have watched the responsive pulses wax and wane in the one as in the other. We have seen response sinking under fatigue, becoming exalted under stimulants, and being 'Killed' by poisons, in the non-living as in the living.

Amongst such phenomena, how can we draw a line of demarcation, and say, 'here the physical process ends, and there the physiological begins'? No such barriers exist.

Do not the two sets of records tell us of some property of matter common and persistent? Do they not show us that the responsive processes, seen in life, have been foreshadowed in non-life?—that the physiological is, after all, but an expression of the physico-chemical, and that there is no abrupt break, but a uniform and continuous march of law?

...It was when I came upon the mute witness of these self-made records, and perceived in them one phase of a pervading unity that bears within it all things—the mote that quivers in ripples of light, the teeming life upon earth, and the radiant suns that shine above us—it was then that I understood for the first time a little of that message proclaimed by my ancestors on the banks of the Ganges thirty centuries ago—

'They who see but one, in all the changing manifoldness of the universe, unto them belongs eternal truth—unto none else, unto none else!'

The last two paragraphs clearly allude to the Vedanta philosophy. In reply to Bose's letter of 17 May, Tagore wrote on 4 June 1901, 'Since I have received your letter, I am transported to a new joyous world. I bow to the God who used you as an instrument to uphold the honour of our motherland. I seem to visualize the sunlit course by which He would bring glory to our beloved country....'

We shall now turn to the experiments that he showed during this lecture. For muscle tissues, physiologists had developed a standard procedure for recording its response, well before Bose started working with living tissues. Fig. 5.2 shows a muscle tissue whose right-hand end is connected to a writing lever, while the other end remains joined to a bone which is clamped firmly. The writing lever is allowed to rotate on an immovable pivot. The upper end of the lever has a sharp point that presses down and writes on a rectangular glass plate covered with black soot. The glass plate is given a steady vertical motion by a standard clockwork device. If the tissue is excited or stimulated by application of heat, electricity, or any other means, it goes through a period of contractions and expansions dragging the lower end of the writing lever back and forth. The upper end of the lever generates a written record on the moving glass plate. This record is produced by the movements of the muscle and, therefore, called mechanical response.

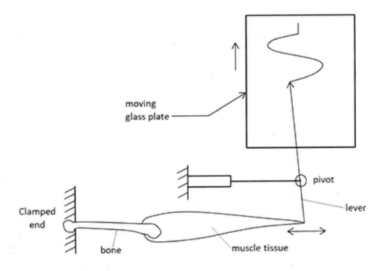

Fig. 5.2: Device for recording response of a muscle tissue.

While working with the receivers of electric waves, Bose had developed a similar but more sensitive recording device. The movement of a galvanometer needle was used to move a magnetic lever in this instrument to record the response of a receiver. Bose now employed the same technique, with slight adaptations, to record the response of a muscle tissue and a piece of tin foil. Fig 5.3 explains operation of this appliance, named the magnetic lever recorder.

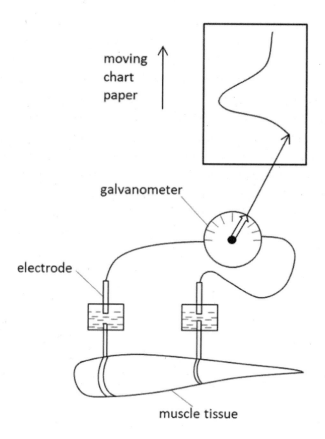

Fig. 5.3: Bose's magnetic lever recorder[32].

Two electrodes are connected to a muscle tissue and the circuit has a galvanometer in series, as shown. If any one end of the tissue is excited, a voltage difference is created between the two ends and an electric current flows through the galvanometer, deflecting its needle, and the response is recorded. This type of response is called electromotive response.

Here, it is necessary to provide context for these experiments. Dr Augustus Desiré Waller was a renowned physiologist during the Victorian era. It was the same Dr Waller who had invited Bose to visit his

[32]The schematics of Fig. 5.2 and 5.3 are similar to figures given in *Acharya Jagadis Chandra Bose*. However, they have been redrawn for greater clarity.

laboratory. He had produced the first human electrocardiogram in 1887 and devised the first practical ECG machine with surface electrodes. This revolutionized the diagnosis of heart diseases. A man of much fame, he had developed a set of criteria for distinguishing the living from the non-living. Waller's criteria had been widely accepted by contemporary physiologists, and can be summarized as follows:

The capacity of responding electrically, when stimulated, is the most extensive and reliable symptom of a living tissue. However, if it is killed by heating, burning, or poisoning, it loses its power to respond. On the other hand, a non-living substance does not respond electrically even when stimulated. This is the main difference between the living and the non-living.

Effectively, Waller's criteria provided a definition of life, though in an indirect sense. Bose thought that these hypothetical criteria, for discerning the living from the non-living, should be put to the test. To this end, he proceeded to devise a series of novel experiments.

It has been said before that his attention was attracted to this new subject when he noticed that the receivers he was working on gave a diminished response after repeated usage, only to start working as before after they had been 'rested'. This behaviour showed a surprising resemblance to living muscle tissue. While working in the Davy-Faraday laboratory between January and May 1901, Bose refashioned these experiments in a manner more in line with physiology.

A piece of tin foil was held in his newly devised magnetic lever recorder (Fig. 5.3), in place of a living muscle tissue, and various experiments were performed. A few significant samples of the recorded curves are shown in Fig. 5.4, in which time increases from left to right as indicated in the figure. These records were presented by Bose in his lecture at the Royal Institution in 1901.

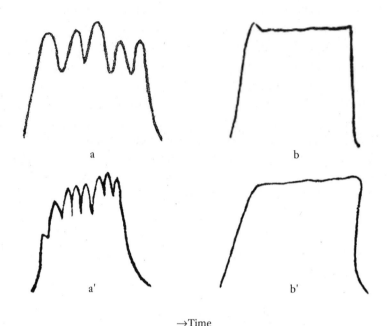

→Time

Fig. 5.4: Response of tin foil (a, a') and muscle tissue (b, b').

Fig. 5.4 (a) shows the response of a fresh piece of tin foil; (b) is the muted response of the same specimen after repeated application of mechanical stimulus (a strike or twist). Fig 5.4 (a') and (b') are for a muscle tissue, treated likewise. The similarity of the response of the non-living and the living is striking indeed.

As per the criteria offered by Waller, the piece of tin foil has life. Though Bose did not vocally affirm this, it was strongly implied that he though this to be true.

The value of a fresh mind such as Bose's, unfettered by the pre-conceived notions of a physiologist, becomes apparent. Driven by the relentless logic that something that is capable of death must have life and guided by out-of-the box ideas, he now thought of poisoning the foil and applying a chemical stimulant to it that could also stimulate muscles. The results were startling and are shown in Fig. 5.5. These records were also presented by Bose at the Royal Institution.

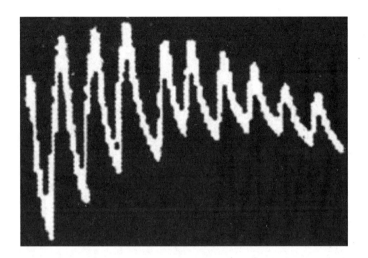

→Time

Fig 5.5(a): Diminishing response of the tin foil due to fatigue.

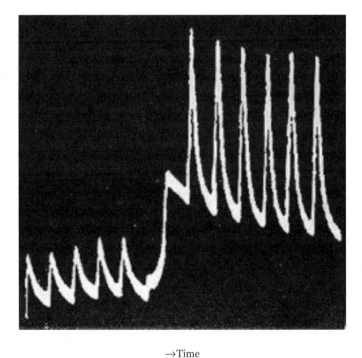

→Time

Fig 5.5(b): Effect of a stimulating agent on the tin foil.

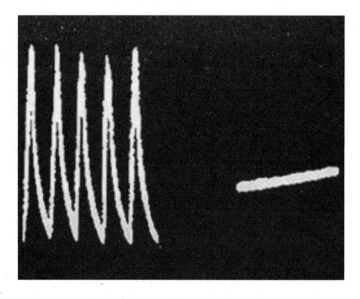

→Time

Fig. 5.5(c): Effect of a poison on the tin foil.

Fig. 5.5(a) shows how the foil's response decreases over time when the stimulus is applied repeatedly, as if fatigued. In Fig. 5.5(b), the chemical stimulant, sodium carbonate, takes effect in the middle of the curve whence the response of the tin foil jumps to a much larger value. Fig. 5.5(c) shows the effect of poisoning by oxalic acid—the foil stops responding abruptly as if death has occurred. All the curves presented here were quite similar to the well-known responses of muscle tissue, recorded by many physiologists earlier.

Bose was constantly assessing and reassessing his ideas in the light of Vedantic intuition. It occurred to him that plant life is another branch of existence that lies midway between inert matter and animal life and, therefore, was likely to show the same kind of response as the tin foil and muscle tissue.

There was a nice garden around his house in London through which he loved to take occasional walks. One day, he plucked the first leaves of a horse chestnut tree and tested them. The response was vigorous and compatible with that of the piece of foil. Then, he picked a few carrots and turnips from the grocery of his kitchen; their response was again likewise. Enthused beyond measure, he repeated the experiments with other types of metals, plants, and muscle tissues. Thus, the similarity of response in muscle, plant, and metal was established beyond doubt.

Bose now decided to poison the plant and record its death throes. Fig. 5.6 shows the occurrence of death in plant and muscle tissue due to poisoning. We have already seen the death curve (due to poisoning) of metal in Fig. 5.5 (c). They are so astonishingly alike!

(a) Action of poison in abolishing response of plant.

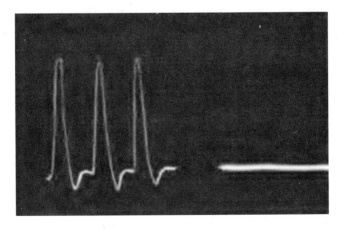

(b) Action of poison in abolishing response of muscle.

Fig. 5.6: Death occurs similarly in plant and muscle due to poisoning.

To summarize the essence of these physiological findings:

1. The fatigue curves of a muscle tissue (living) and tin foil (non-living) are almost identical.
2. The excitement curves, on application of a chemical stimulant, of a muscle tissue and a tin foil are again extremely similar.
3. The death curves, on application of a chemical poison, of a muscle tissue, plant (considered to exist in between the living and non-living at that time), and tin foil are again almost identical.

From this the following argument can be made: the various responses of all three kinds of existence in this world—animal life, plant life, and inert matter—were extremely alike. To our scientist, this was a significant step towards the scientific verification of the Vedanta philosophy, which as per his understanding was a 'life-in-everything' philosophy. The resultant joy in the mind of this scientist knew no bounds. His letter dated 22 March 1901 to Tagore bears testimony to his elation; he wrote,

> Friend,
>
> ...I cannot tell you how busy I truly am! I have made new discoveries, but no one will believe them.... I am myself astounded. I have to demonstrate one by one with infinite care, otherwise they would find them incredible...that is why I am hesitant to write a new paper. They have not come to terms with what I said last time. If I now talk about my newer findings, they would question my sanity....
>
> Yours, Jagadish.

Nivedita too commented in a letter to Josephine MacLeod,

> It is extraordinary to see Dr Bose; how the old idea of Advaita behind him saves him from the errors that other men of science walk into blind-folded. He is now like one who walks on air. Discovery after discovery, one instrument follows another and the brilliant intuition becomes the measured fact. It is with breathless awe that one watches.

At this time Sir Michael Foster, a veteran physiologist from Cambridge, was visiting Bose's lab. The latter had just started to present his findings when the former picked up a chart and said,

> 'Come now, Bose, what is the novelty in this curve? We have known it for at least the last half century.'
> 'What do you think it is?' asked Bose.
> Foster: 'Why, a curve of muscle response, of course.'
> 'Pardon me, it is the response of metallic tin.'
> Foster (jumping up): 'What! Tin! Did you say tin?'

On hearing Bose's explanation, he became truly awestruck. He asked Bose to make a submission to the Royal Society, of which he was the secretary then, and offered to communicate the paper himself. But Bose had already been invited to give an account of these experiments at the Royal Institution, immediately after Easter. Foster was not to be out done. He said, 'Well, make us a preliminary communication immediately, and thus secure your priority and that of the Society, and then you can give us a demonstration later on at the meeting next month.'

Bose complied by submitting a paper to the Royal Society on 7 May, three days before his Royal Institution lecture. The relevant Royal Society meeting was scheduled almost a month after the Friday Evening Discourse at the Royal Institution. In the meantime, on 22 May, he wrote to Tagore that he had been seriously ill twice in the recent past and had to take time off to rest for a few weeks, on medical advice. In his own words,

> Friend, I have not had a holiday, even on Sundays, for the last five months since that surgery. Twice I was taken quite ill due to a rush of blood to the head....
> My lecture at the Royal Society has been scheduled for 6th June. ...Many have encouraged me (on my work) but cautioned, 'It is so sudden—we do not know whether we are starting on our heads'. The newspapers have indulged in a bit of banter. The Globe writes that, while tormenting a piece of metal during his last lecture-demonstration, 'The Professor's eyes were full of tears. This

does him credit, but it will be long before he induces the British householder to pet the fire-iron when it falls on the fender because the fall hurts the fire-iron.'

...After my lecture I heard a famous electrician, Mr Swinton remark to his friends, 'This is something beyond science, this is esoteric Buddhism'.

...Yours, Jagadish.

Within a few months after this jovial letter, Bose's application for a further extension of the deputation was turned down by the India Office. However, he was granted a furlough, with a reduced salary, for two more years, as mentioned earlier. The news made him utterly despondent. Bose appealed to his large-hearted loyal friend for help, and Tagore immediately proceeded to Tripura. He later wrote from there,

> I am now a guest of the Maharaja for a few days. You well know how great a regard he holds you in, and hence, I have had absolutely no hesitation to ask for help. He would utilize my services to send you ten thousand rupees in the next one or two mails. Another ten thousand rupees he has promised before the year's end. In the meantime, you must save yourself from depression. I assure you the Maharaja does not consider himself a creditor. He thinks he owes it to you as a great son of the motherland.

Buoyed by the financial support arranged by his friend, Bose returned to work with renewed vigour. The Royal Society meeting took place on 6 June 1901. Bose kept up the correspondence but wrote nothing about what transpired during his Royal Society lecture because he thought it might unduly worry Tagore. He finally broke his silence in a letter to him dated 21 March 1902.

His presentation at the Royal Society was, of course, as meticulous and orderly as his purely physical papers and seemed to be received well by most. Sir John Burdon-Sanderson, the tallest figure in physiology in the country, was also in attendance. Even in his advanced age, he had taken the trouble of travelling from Oxford to London for Bose's presentation.

The Fall and Struggle for Redemption

Sir John Burdon-Sanderson specialized in the study of muscles and nerves, particularly the movements of the Venus flytrap. It was Charles Darwin, famous for the theory of evolution, who had drawn Sanderson's attention to the electrical physiology of the Venus flytrap, a plant that traps a fly or an insect using slow, deceptive movements. So, Sanderson was the acknowledged authority on electrical physiology and all looked to him to open the discussion after the paper. He began by paying compliments to Bose's physical work, then continued,

> It is a great pity that Professor Bose should leave his own subject for other fields that properly belong to the physiologists; Professor Bose's paper is still under consideration for publication and he may consider altering the title from 'The Electric Response' to 'Certain Physical Reactions'; the term 'Response' belonged to the physiologists and not physicists. Further, regarding the electrical response of ordinary plants, demonstrated by Bose, I am of the firm opinion that it is absolutely impossible, since I myself have tried to detect it for many years and never found any. It simply cannot be!

Dr Waller, who has been referred to before, spoke after Sanderson and essentially supported him.

Bose had presented his findings earlier in the Friday Evening Discourse. The physicists had applauded and the physiologists had maintained an uneasy silence, but there had been no direct challenge. Now, this strange confrontation had taken place, completely unexpectedly. He was simply flabbergasted by Sanderson's exclamation, 'It simply cannot be!' There had been no criticism of his experiments, no flaw detected in his arguments, just an absolute denial. He had always been inflexible in matters of principle and that trait came to the fore now. In his own words, excerpted from the letter he wrote to Tagore in March 1902, 'In reply I said, "scientific terms are not a monopoly of anyone. Besides, all these phenomena have an underlying unity, and I am against creating diversity in phenomena that have an obvious and apparent unity".'

After Bose's reply a stony silence fell over the audience and no one spoke. The meeting ended with formal thanks to the lecturer.

Sanderson was a man of authority, not accustomed to such defiance. He felt deeply wounded to be challenged by so young a person, and in so direct and outspoken a manner. On the other hand, Bose felt that he had been labelled an intruder because he was a physicist. As a Brahmo, he had always been steadfastly opposed to the caste system in India. Now, he had to face a new system of hierarchy. The rebel in him was not prepared to compromise.

Thanks to the efforts of Sanderson, Waller, and their supporters, the publication of Bose's paper on the subject in the *Proceedings of the Royal Society* was put on hold; the paper was placed in the Society's archives.

Until this point, Bose's career had been very successful, notwithstanding the constant obstructions placed in his way by Presidency College. Success after overcoming hurdles also brings a sense of exhilaration and so far, he had been thriving. But now, failure stared him in the face. The news of Sanderson's reservations about his research had reached India and was ruining his reputation in his homeland. He knew that unless he figured a way out of his current predicament, his future as a scientist was bleak—his superiors in the Presidency College would be quick to block all avenues for advancement.

In the same letter to Tagore, he continued,

As a consequence, the publication of my paper was stopped. There happened a conspiracy of silence due to strenuous efforts of certain leading physiologists. If my theory is accepted, their theory will be overthrown. They think my stay in this country is short, and once I cross the oceans, the danger would be over.

However, encouraged by you, I decided to stay on. But I was not finding any way out of my situation and becoming truly desperate. Most people were saying, 'Whom are we to believe— physiologists who have grown grey in working out their special subjects or a young physicist who comes all of a sudden to upset all our convictions?'

Then I had a chance meeting with Professor Vines[33], the President of the Linnean Society. He is the leading figure among

---

[33]Professor Vines had been one of Bose's favourite teachers during his time in Cambridge.

vegetable physiologists; besides, the Linnean Society is also the main society in the field of biology. Prof. Vines, accompanied by Prof. Howes[34] and another researcher came to see my experiments and they were not only surprised but joyously excited.[35]

Then Prof. Vines, as President of the Linnean Society, invited me to speak in their meeting.

There was a sizeable gathering of leading physiologists and biologists, including my opponents, and your friend stood there alone in defiant confrontation with them. Within 15 minutes I realized that I have won the day. Bravo! Bravo! etc., many cheering words, I could hear. After the lecture, the President asked three times if anyone had anything to say. There was silence. In the end, Professor Harlog rose to say, 'We have nothing but admiration for this wonderful piece of work.' The President too said a few words of praise.

Victory! I have tasted victory at last after a long hard struggle. There is still much to do. But I am exhausted and thirsting for a few days of solitude. However, I shall have to keep feeding the fire I have lit for a long time yet.

Please convey this news to the Maharaja. If you people had not arranged for my extended stay, I would have had to return defeated and crestfallen. Accept my heartiest thanks and affection.

Yours...Jagadish.

P. S.: I am sending you *John Chinaman*.[36] On reading the book, you would realize that we are accepting European values without discrimination, while ignoring [our own] gold.

---

[34]Successor of Thomas H. Huxley at the Royal College of Science, London.
[35]Bose later described the scene to Patrick Geddes as follows: 'I have never seen three sober Englishmen so thrilled—they were just as mad as boys. Howes said, "Huxley would have given years of his life to see that experiment". Said another, "What did you do to let off steam when you discovered this?"'
[36]The book, *Letters of John Chinaman,* was written by Lowes Dickinson, when he travelled in China as a Rhodes Scholar. Posing as an English-educated Chinese man, he composed these letter-essays in the name of John Chinaman. I find it remarkable that Bose had time to read *Letters of John Chinaman,* when he was embroiled in a struggle to redeem his honour.

It should be mentioned that Dr Waller had been invited but chose to remain absent, although his supporters were present in this Linnean Society meeting. Lord Rayleigh told Bose later that he himself had suffered continuous attacks by chemists, because he, a physicist, had dared to predict that a new element would be found as a constituent of air. The attacks continued until his prediction came true with the discovery of Argon. A fellow physicist had consoled Bose soon after the Royal Society lecture, saying, 'You cannot poach on other people's preserves without some resentment; and you have done worse—you have upset their apple-cart.'

President Vines wrote after the Linnean Society lecture,

> It seems to me that your experiments make it clear beyond doubt that all parts of plants—not merely those which are known to be— are irritable, and manifest their irritability by an electrical response to stimulation. This is an important step in advance, and will, I hope, be the starting point for further researches. ...This would doubtless lead to some important generalization as to the properties of matter; not only living matter, but non-living matter as well.

This seemed to reverse the disaster of the previous two quarters, and the paper, with full illustrations of apparatus, was accepted for publication. But Bose's rising fortune took a steep downturn once again. Rumours suggesting that these results were not new began to circulate. Remarkably similar findings had been communicated to a London society by Dr Waller in November 1901, whereas Bose's presentation before the Linnean Society was in March 1902. His previous paper containing an account of the lecture demonstration at the Royal Society (June 1901) had not been published and therefore was not in the public domain.

Professor Howes, as the secretary of the Linnean Society, informed Bose via a letter of the new developments. A new period of depression followed, far deeper than the previous one. However, summoning all his will, he decided to fight for priority. He formally asked for an inquiry into the matter at hand, permission for which was readily granted.

First, Waller had been present at the Royal Society meeting and taken part in the discussion. Secondly, Vines and Howes, both as Fellows of the Royal Society, had fortunately read the galley proof of Bose's paper before its publication was stopped in its tracks. Thirdly, Bose's Friday Evening Discourse at the Royal Institution, about a month before the Royal Society lecture, was in print and in evidence.

The committee of inquiry felt no hesitation in awarding absolute priority to Bose, and the paper was published accordingly. But there was no doubt in Bose's mind that a fairly large section of the English physiologists, led by a few professors of high prestige, were involved in these machinations. The whole affair left a bitter taste in his mouth. He knew that there were enemies at home, but now he came to know that there were some abroad as well. He reminded himself that there were friends, too, in both places.

Howes wrote to him, in an unofficial capacity, 'I am fully sympathetic and the facts you cite but confirm my original conviction. You have been mercilessly done by. But my advice to you would be that you should head your paper with a plain statement of facts, and beyond this you should leave fools alone.'

Bose, however, did not take this sage advice. Mindful of the teachings of the Mahabharata—'never strike a fallen adversary'—he did not stick to plain facts, but toned them down in his opening statement, giving Waller an easy way out. He chose to state facts as they were, without making any adverse comments against Waller. Howes was livid with anger and wrote to Bose, 'I have no patience with you. Eastern courtesy is misplaced here! You are trying to save his face. Mark my words!— People will forget this, and he will soon be your enemy again.'

These words proved to be prophetic, as Bose discovered at great personal cost. His antagonists soon conspired again to spread rumours and worse about the accuracy of his experimental methods. We shall return to this story in due course.

After being overly generous to Waller, Bose concentrated all his energy in devising newer experiments on the same topic. In this he was most ably assisted by his assistant, Mr Bull. Before he returned to India at the end of his furlough, Bose found a placement for Mr Bull in London Polytechnic, where he later rose to become the head of the department of photography. Bose was very gracious in providing due acknowledgement to his assistant and it is from Bose himself that Patrick Geddes came to know about Mr Bull.

Bose wrote a letter of gratitude to Vines in April 1902, stating that he hadn't understood the underlying cause of the opposition he faced this time around in England. He had expected to remove all misgivings about his new experiments and their implications within a year but now he suspected that there was a dreadful conspiracy to sully his reputation and he felt deeply hurt. Even then, he would cherish the memory of all those who rallied behind him for the sake of truth, justice, and fairness.

In May 1902, Sara and Joe, on their way from India to America, had a stopover in England, during which they stayed with the Boses. At this time, owing to his experiences with Dr Waller and his ilk, Bose had realized the limitations of the usual practice of paper publication and decided to write a book containing all his recent research. Sara helped him in this task for a month and a half. On 24 June, she wrote to her friend Mrs Briggs, who was also an admirer of Swami Vivekananda, 'Dr Bose has had any amount of proof reading etc., as he is publishing a book and various papers. We have been pleasantly busy in that way. I am not going to venture out to see the Coronation, but remain quietly in the house.'[37]

Within a few days, Sara and Joe left for America. Swami Vivekananda passed away on 4 July 1902. On 7 July, Bose wrote to Josephine,[38]

My dear friend,

I cannot tell you how grieved I am to send you the enclosed copy of a telegram which came for Mrs Bull.

India has lost her great son. But his has been a heroic life, and he carried the banner of glory.

Yours, J. C. Bose.

---

[37]At the time in question, pre-coronation festivities had begun; Sara states that she is not interested in them. The actual coronation of King Edward and Queen Alexandra took place much later, on 9 August 1902.

[38]It was so far understood that all letters received by Josephine MacLeod had been destroyed by white ants due to the carelessness of the custodian. Fortunately, a few of the Bose letters have survived. They are preserved in the archive of the Ramakrishna-Vivekananda Center, New York, USA. This author has received copies of these letters, courtesy of the Center, which can be seen in the appendix.

Bose knew Joe well, and how much she loved the Swami. Hence, he wrote this most sympathetic letter. Both Joe and Sara must have heard of the Swami's death directly from India and must have mourned his passing while keeping in touch with each other. The Boses knew the Swami personally and were grief-stricken for a while, but Jagadish had little choice but to get back to work.

Bose wrote to Tagore on 18 July 1902, in a poetic letter (in Bengali):

Sunshine and the shadow clouds are constantly following one another in my mind. Reading the proof of my book keeps me busy. It will see the light of the day in three or four weeks. The proof reminds me of the gruesome struggle of the last two years and brings back the gnawing agony afresh. Hope that my long, painful, and arduous efforts will bring solace and satisfaction to all of you.

Bose does not mention that Sara and Josephine MacLeod had been staying with him and helping him with the book. In fact, other than in the letters written to Sara, Joe, and Nivedita, there is no mention in any of his letters of the three women associating with him in any capacity.[39] The book, *Response in the Living and Non-living* was published by Longmans, Green, and Co., London, in October 1902. In addition to her proofreading, Sara also bore the cost of publication. In the dedication to the book, Bose wrote, in an expression of his love for India, 'To my countrymen.'

In England, Sara had learnt about Bose and Nivedita's dream of establishing a research laboratory in Calcutta, run by Indians, for Indians, independent of the British Raj. In the same year, Sara drew up a will which read,

That I, Sara C. Bull, widow, now of Cambridge in the County of Middlesex and Commonwealth of Massachusetts, being of full age and of sound mind, do make this my last will and Testament, hereby revoking all wills heretofore made.... I have promised my friend, Dr Jagadis Chunder Bose of the University of Calcutta, India,

---

[39]Bose might have written a few letters to Josephine, most of which are now unfortunately lost due to the negligence of their custodian.

to furnish him for his scientific work the sum of Five Thousand dollars in each of the years 1906, 1907, and 1908.

The money was transferred in tranches through banks; Bose kept the matter secret. Sara adopted many causes in her life which she considered worthy and donated liberally to people who were pursuing those causes. She neither kept records, nor cared for fame or recognition.[40]

In America, Sara found her estranged daughter Olea suffering from minor complications after an appendix operation. Sara took Olea to Norway for a change of climate, bringing along a nurse. From there an invitation was extended to the Boses and they came for a brief stay with Sara in her coast-side villa near Bergen. By that time, Olea had recovered and Sara had taken ill. Joe wrote to Sara at the end of August 1901[41], stating 'I have your note of August 9 that the Boses were with you, that you had been confined to your bed and that Olea was going with the Lunds....'

Bose returned to London. His new experiments and findings, performed while writing the book, were written up in a paper that was published by the Royal Society.

A French translation of an important paper of his was read at the Société Française de Physique in Paris, on his behalf. It was titled, 'Sur la Réponse Électrique de la Matière Vivante'. The French society also nominated him as a member and invited him to speak. In early April 1902, the Boses and Mr Bull went to Paris. Bose gave a humorous description of his journey in a letter to Tagore:

> Had you seen our condition, you would be in splits. We were carrying various delicate instruments, some on lap, some on

---

[40]A US-based science historian, Probir Bandyopadhyay, has salvaged from obscurity two wills of the American philanthropist Sara Chapman Bull. By means of these wills, she donated nearly $40,000 to Jagadis Chandra Bose to establish a science research laboratory, which came to be called Basu Vigyan Mandir or the Bose Institute. The second will of $20,000 was drawn up in 1906. In April 2021, Bandyopadhyay handed over authenticated copies of the two wills to the trust that looks after Bose's home, Acharya Bhavan, which is now a museum in Calcutta.
[41]The Bose couple's trip to Norway as Sara's guests is a new discovery by Prabuddhaprana in *Saint Sara* (2014).

shoulder, some as head load, sitting still as far as possible all the way for nine long hours. We had to bear with the hostile reaction and comments from the inconvenienced fellow-passengers.

I have been invited to speak at four places. Last night I was the Principal Guest at a dinner of eminent scientists....

On 2 May, Dr Busheri of Bonn University in Germany cordially invited Bose to visit. However, it was not possible for him to visit Germany due to lack of time, as his furlough was coming to a close. Around this time, the Royal Society decided to publish all his controversial papers, which had been archived earlier. The Boses returned to London on 8 April. On the same day in a letter to Tagore, he wrote,

So far, they have been saying that science and India are not compatible. Now they are saying an isolated instance, entirely by chance, should not be counted. Even Professor Ramsay[42] said to me the other day, 'Your case is an exception. One swallow does not make summer.' If one wishes one can forget all this. Life after all is short. Perhaps love and attachment for a particular country is nothing but *Maya*.

Bose was then invited to speak before the conference of the British Association in Belfast. He spoke there on 12 May 1902 on 'Electric Response in Animal, Vegetable, and Metal'. He also spoke at the Royal Photographic Society's meeting, which we have mentioned earlier. With his furlough coming to a close, Bose began planning to set sail for India in September. But Abala fell ill all of a sudden and the voyage had to be postponed. She too convalesced in the Wimbledon home of Nivedita's mother. They returned home in mid-October.

Bose had apprehensions, for obvious reasons, about how his new book, *Response in the Living and Non-living*, would be received by the scientific community. However, he need not have worried for it was received very well by all. It was praised by the famous philosopher and botanist Herbert Spencer, Carveth Reed, *Science Abstract Review of Reviews* (October 1902), *Daily Chronicle* (22 November 1902), and

---

[42]William Ramsay, a famous Chemist who later won the Nobel Prize.

The Electrician (26 December 1902), not only for its scientific content but also for its literary quality. The book attracted much interest in Germany and France as well. A publishing house in Leipzig proposed to translate it into German immediately. Dr Bushli of Heidelburg University and Dr Busheri of Bonn University wrote to Bose expressing their appreciation. There were requests from France and Germany for another visit, but Bose could not comply due to lack of time.

Herbert Spencer, then the president of the Botanical Section of the British Association, wrote to Bose, 'What I have written on plant physiology in my book *Principles of Biology* seems incomplete. I shall complete it in the second edition by including a detailed description of your discoveries.'

On returning to India, Bose was hoping to rest, away from the hustle and bustle of the maddening controversies. Soon enough, the Boses went to Shantiniketan, Tagore's residential school to spend a few weeks in peace and tranquillity in the hospitality of his friend's family. Both refreshed, the Boses returned to Calcutta, and Jagadish plunged into research with renewed vigour. Now his main aim was to study the physiology of plant life.

Lord Curzon, then viceroy of India, called a durbar in Delhi on the 1 January 1903 to announce the coronation of Edward VII and felicitate the new monarch. On this occasion, the Government of India conferred the title of CIE (Companion of the Order of the Indian Empire) on Jagadish Bose for his path breaking research and contribution to science. Bose, in an allusion to the title added to his name, humorously wrote to Tagore on the same day, 'I was astonished to see a news item in today's paper. A "tail" has been attached to me.' Bose was, however, least distracted by such an honour, and kept on with his research work as usual.

Waller Exacts Revenge

In the two years Bose had been away from India, Sir John Woodburn had been replaced by Lord James Bourdillon as the lieutenant governor of Bengal. No sooner had this happened, that the authorities of the Presidency College resumed their hostile behaviour. Bose again stood his ground, and continued to resist and work at the same time.

During the course of the year Bose succeeded in recording various responses in plants with the help of newly invented apparatuses. He wrote up a number of papers with these results and sent them to the Royal Society in December 1903. At that time, the society had two regular publications—the *Proceedings* and the *Philosophical Transactions.* The papers that had the potential of opening up new horizons were published in the latter. Bose's papers were initially accepted for the *Philosophical Transactions.* But due to stiff resistance from established British physiologists, the publication was interrupted at the last moment, and then unceremoniously archived. This was the second time this was happening to Bose.

The journal's administration wrote to Bose that his papers were valuable and their appreciation was obvious in their initial acceptance. But his results were totally unexpected and contrary to the current established opinion and therefore, 'Nothing short of the plant's automatic response would carry conviction'. Hence, the publication would be withheld until plants were shown to give unambiguous and automatic response. It seemed to be an impossible condition to meet, and many in India again touted their opinion about the dubiousness of all of Bose's discoveries, whether in the field of electromagnetic waves or physiology.

Bose had thought that the ugly controversy had been put to rest, once and for all. But he had been horribly wrong—Howes's prediction had come true. Bose had ignored his advice and the magnanimity he had shown to the plagiarist Dr Waller had been lost on the latter. Waller, stung by jealousy, now made good use of the face-saver gifted by Bose to create fresh trouble. But he was not alone in this; many sided with Waller. Sir John Burdon-Sanderson was also part of the opposition.

It is relevant here to point out another strange fact—Bose had earlier detected that the physiologists in general were confused about the sign of electric charge and always wrote positive in place of negative and vice versa. This fundamental error in sign convention had been pointed out in Bose's book. As part of his attack on Bose, Dr Waller published a new book, from which Bose quoted the following verbatim, in English, in a letter to Tagore, dated 29 June 1904. Waller wrote, without any reference to Bose's work, 'Previously people thought that only sensitive plants give electric response. But these notions are to be extended and we are to recognize that any vegetable protoplasm gives electric response.' Alluding to Bose's criticism on the incorrect usage of electric charge sign conventions, he continued,

> ...in the present state of our physiological literature, is it wise to use the proper expression? No doubt the confusion is very great, no doubt the main bulk of our electro-physiological literature is totally unintelligible to physicists. Shall we not, however, lay the foundation of a further mess of worse-confounded confusion by any sudden and unauthorized endeavour to call white white and black black, when for the last 20 or 30 years our leaders have been content to call white black and black white?

On reading the last paragraph any scientist would be in a fix whether to laugh or cry. It took Bose, a physicist from India, to arrive in England and point out this all-pervasive blunder to Britain's physiologists—so great was the divide between physicists and physiologists during that era. This episode also speaks to Bose's versatility as a researcher, for he seemed to have acquired a good command of the vast electro-physiological literature, in spite of being a physicist.

Bose wrote to Tagore on 29 June 1904, 'I have been feeling rather low lately. I have written nineteen papers, but they are all being denied publication. I am thinking of writing a book, but do not feel like revisiting the old matter.' Drawing on the reserve of his tremendous will, he wrote his next book *Plant Response*, which initially got a cold reception from British physiologists but won much appreciation in America.

Much later in life, when asked by his friend Patrick Geddes if his generous concession to Waller had been a mistake, Bose said he had no regrets. Given the same circumstances, he would do the same thing again, sticking to the ancient principles given in the Indian epics.

In writing all his books, Bose received invaluable motivational support and secretarial help from Nivedita; this continued as long as she lived. In fact, with her adaptability, brilliance, and grasp of science, her assistance, one dare say, was likely to have been more at the level of a research student with a great command over the English language, not easily found in an Indian student at the time. Perhaps she treasured Bose because he was not only brilliant but also indomitable in his effort to bring scientific glory to India, her beloved adopted land and the land of her prophet. Whatever her motivations, Bose gained immensely from her services.

Some Significant Letters (1899–1904)

Certain selected letters, written by some of the most important people in Bose's life, will be presented here. The aim is to bring out what inspired them, how they interacted with one another, and the attitudes and emotions they displayed.

Sister Nivedita

It has been mentioned that Sara Bull was estranged from her only daughter, though the reason for this is unknown. Having lost her husband at a young age, Sara could have married again. Yet she chose a life of chastity. In spite of being wealthy, she chose a life of simplicity and contemplation. Sara gave all her undivided affection to her only daughter. Yet when Olea grew up, she became estranged from her mother. Sara, as long as she lived, was unhappy and troubled on Olea's account, and always lonely at the bottom of her heart.

In the winter of 1899, Nivedita, Sara, Joe and their beloved Swamiji, were all in America. It had been agreed that the Swami would spend Christmas in Cambridge with his American mother, Mrs Sara Bull. However, his health deteriorated to such an extent that he decided to avoid the severe winter of the east coast, and to go to California instead. Sara reached New York on 20 November to see him before he left, and returned to Cambridge. She found him very ill and was extremely worried.

Scorned by her biological daughter, Sara was afraid of losing her spiritual son, and became utterly disconsolate. It seemed to her that everyone had left and she was all alone, and had an urge to give up all work. Nivedita sensed this and wrote immediately to Sara to cheer her up and to enthuse her about the work in India.

> Darling Saint Sara! I suddenly realized how we had all been caring for everyone but you! There is so much to do and life just opened on a whole new world of blessing-giving for you; don't be tired!

I hope you saw your son before he left New York....

Dear, dear, dear Mrs Bull, do remember that you are not unappreciated, though you are so dreadfully unselfish that we rarely tell you how we love you! And we are more apt to bring you our own troubles than to try to help to bear yours! Numbers of people will be inconsolable without you. Doesn't this give you strength?

...You are so necessary! I am dismayed at the thought of the long battle without a head. Oh, won't you be willing to stay till you have mothered India and the work for the women, that is only an infant now?

...You would not take all your life and strength and wisdom out of it? No, we can't and India can't, can't, can't, can't, do without you. Grannie dear, the Queen-Mother of us all.

...I am your ever-loving grandchild and representative in battle,

Margot.

The letter helped Sara regain her usual serenity and cheer, and she began to help Nivedita in her fundraising campaign in America. Fortunately, the Swami's health improved and they met later in France. It should be recalled that, at this point in time, she had met Bose but only once, in his laboratory briefly. This letter of Nivedita is important because it served to rekindle Sara's interest in India. Later when Sara became more acquainted with Bose, she looked upon him also as a son. She justified her chosen role as a mother to the Swami, Nivedita, and Bose, in every possible way, with money and other resources, as long as she lived, and also in death by leaving a substantial will on how her wealth was to be distributed.

There exists a letter from Nivedita to Tagore which is informative in many respects. That Tagore's understanding of Bose's work was much more than a layperson's becomes apparent from his many writings in *Banga Darshan*. In Tagore's estimation, Nivedita's appreciation of science was greater than his own. Hence, he requested Nivedita to write a short appraisal of Bose's achievements and the hindrances that he had faced in the process. Nivedita wrote to Tagore on 18 April 1903, about six months after Bose's return from Europe to Calcutta. She briefly described the difficulties he faced in the college, that 'the college routine was made as arduous as possible for him', so that he did not have time for research. Then she went on to write,

> Dr Bose not only demonstrated the existence of these particular etheric waves, he also proved himself as great in constructive ability as in research itself, and his instrument, popularly known as the Artificial Eye, was considered a marvel of compactness and simplicity. Prince Kropotkin was talking of Prof. [J. J.] Thompson, who the week before had exhibited an apparatus some yards long to act as a polarizer—and Prof. Bose the following week, to do the same thing, simply took up a book.... 'I said to myself', said Prince Kropotkin, 'that this was the simplicity of the highest genius'....
>
> [Bose] was like a man haunted by the fear that if he failed at any point, his people will be held to have no right to [higher] education. ...Lord Rayleigh and Sir William Crookes, both told him that while the perfection of his methods was unquestioned, no one had yet been able, in 1901, to repeat his experiments in 1895–96. His manipulations were beyond rivalry.

The term 'etheric waves' refers to waves that travelled in the medium of ether, light, heat, electric (Hertzian) waves. She, therefore, added a qualifier 'particular' in order to indicate only the 'electric waves', the kind dealt with by Bose. The letter is very long and deals with Bose's physiological work and the great generalization of responses with philosophic ramifications, which we have already touched upon. Then she went on to write in the closing paragraph,

> Ah India! India! Can you not give enough freedom to one of the greatest of your sons to enable him—not to sit at ease, but to go out and fight your battles where the fire is hottest and the labour most intense, and the contest raging thickest? And if you cannot do this, if you cannot even bless your own child and send him out equipped, then—is it worthwhile that the doom should be averted and the hand of ruin stayed, from this unhappy and so beloved land?
>
> This is all very inadequate, dear Mr Tagore....

Yours Faithfully
Nivedita of Ramakrishna-Vivekananda.

The letter gives an expert summary of Bose's work, and shows the kind of grasp Nivedita had on physics. Bose himself never reported the aforementioned comments of Lord Rayleigh and Sir William Crookes. Nivedita must have heard them herself, as she was present in many of Bose's lecture–demonstrations. Towards the end of the letter, she became emotional and lamented India's weaknesses.

Jagadish Chandra Bose

Bose's letter dated 2 November 1900 to Rabindranath Tagore, has been quoted earlier but partially. The remaining part was omitted then because it would have been a digression from the main scientific narrative; Bose addresses Tagore directly to say,

> Now a few words about you...I will not let you remain hidden in a remote village. Why do you write poetry in such a language that they are untranslatable into another tongue? However, your short stories are a different matter. I shall publish them in this country.... I have persuaded someone, who will leave [this place] soon. If you send me a few stories in the meantime, then I would publish them here.... If the aforementioned friend does the translation, it is sure to be an excellent one.
>
> Yours, Jagadish.

In the midst of dealing with ill health and the anxiety of his deputation coming to an end well before the day of his prestigious Friday Evening Discourse, Bose was still planning to present his literary friend before the world.

Tagore sent over a book of short stories that had just been published. Three stories, 'Kabuliwallah', 'Chhutti', and 'Daan Pratidaan' were selected for translation. There is no doubt that Nivedita, who was in London with the Boses, translated them, probably with much help from the Bose couple. However, Bose avoids taking her name in the letter and refers to her as 'someone who will leave soon' and 'the aforementioned friend'. As has been mentioned before, she was to leave for Scotland soon on a lecture tour.[43]

---

[43]Tagore, however, was not so reticent; he guessed that the translator of his stories was

In a letter dated 16 January, about five weeks after his surgery, Bose writes to Tagore,

Three stories have been translated. These days short stories from Norway, Sweden, Italy, etc. are read here with eagerness. I wish to bring out your stories so that the reader has chance to compare. However, of late people here have taken to blood and gore and Kipling is their most admired author. Therefore, I don't know if your stories will be popular or not. I have had one of these read by three of my friends.

The first was an American lady of high social standing and great literary appreciation. On reading Chhutti, she was so touched that could not help shedding profuse tears.

The second was a typical John Bull. He said, 'I find no local colour—Phatik is like an English boy of his age, I personally know one or two such, true to life.'

The third is a friend of extraordinary background. He is a true aristocrat and master of many European languages. He has not seen such a fine touch in any European literature....

It is obvious who the American lady is. It is none other than Mrs Sara Bull, the ever-ready benefactress of the Boses, who was in London then. We do not know who the 'typical John Bull' was. We know from other sources that the third was Prince Kropotkin, a Russian noble, who was then a fugitive from the Tsar's empire, and the famous author of *Memoirs of a Revolutionist*. He was a polymath, having mastery over several languages and a good understanding of the sciences. Sara knew him well and had introduced Bose to him.

Mrs Bull was known to Rabindranath Tagore and yet Bose chooses to keep her anonymous in the letter, just as he does with Nivedita. He seems to have decided, as a matter of policy, not to leave any trace of his personal connection with these ladies in writing. Yet he wrote letters to Sara and Nivedita, and a few of these have survived.

But why set such a strange policy? We shall look for clues while

Nivedita and passed on this information to his biographer Prasanta Kumar Pal, and it got reflected in his biography *Rabi-Jivani*, p. 297, Vol. 4.

studying the rest of Bose's life.

Tagore may perhaps have guessed who the 'American lady of high social standing' was, as he had done for the identity of the translator. He must have been aware of Bose's policy and never wrote anything connecting Bose and Nivedita, until after Bose's death. The letters, however, bring out Bose's love for his friend and Bengali literature. In spite of his busy schedule, illness, and a life full of uncertainties, he finds time for his friend and his short stories.

Bose wrote the following letter[44] to Sara, in an expression of gratitude for all that Sara and Nivedita did for him in England. It was written after Sara left England in January 1902:

> You will never know what your affectionate sympathy has been to me. I cannot remember any other time when I was so peaceful and contented, when thoughts came so spontaneously, when work was done with such strength and stores laid up for the future. It has been the fullest and happiest time of my life.
>
> It is for the word of loving sympathy that the soul hungers. This you gave me beyond measure....
>
> You and our dear sister Nivedita were but strangers not long ago. Yet your love for our people and service make me ashamed: What have I done? What can I do? What offering can I lay to express my gratitude?

Sara was an inspired and saintly person, and loved to embrace certain causes, compatible with her spiritual aspirations. In India, she fell in love with Swami Vivekananda's mission, Nivedita's women's education project, and Bose's scientific pursuit. Her mission in life was to offer help, without any strings attached.

Bose wrote a letter of appreciation to Nivedita for her exposé of Lord Curzon's empty pomposity. It would now be appropriate to introduce the context in which the letter was written. Lord Curzon had taken over from Lord Elgin as viceroy of India in 1899. He was arrogant and convinced that Europeans were culturally superior to the Indians. Towards the

---

[44]The primary source of this letter is the Sara Chapman Bull Collection of the Vedanta Society of Northern California; also *Letters of Sister Nivedita*, p. 451.

end of his tenure in February 1905, Lord Curzon, as the chancellor of the Calcutta University, was addressing a gathering of the students and teachers in a convocation ceremony. His lecture contained a statement that the ideal of truth was largely a Western concept, and had been an honoured value there, long before it was likewise honoured in the East.

This was a direct insult to the Indians, yet no one, not even the students present in the gathering, protested. The next day Nivedita wrote in a newspaper about Curzon's own confession in a book, *Problems of the East*, about how he had fooled a Korean noble by telling a lie. Though she remained incognito by writing under a common Bengali name, Bose was not one to be deceived. From the style of the article, he knew it was Nivedita, and wrote to her immediately,

> Personally, I feel much strengthened by the thought that many illusions which blind our men will now end. I do not wish that they should find out who wrote the article. The thunderbolt[45] should always be behind dark clouds and they should not know from what part of the heavens the weapon is hurled.

The letter has humour couched in mystery. It also contains a veiled comparison of Nivedita's writing prowess with the thunderbolt of Indra, the King of the Gods in Hindu mythology. Indra is said to have hurled the thunderbolt from behind the clouds to slay the demon Virittasura.

Rabindranath Tagore

In one of his letters to his friend, Bose wrote that he missed Tagore very much and hankered for his company whenever he felt depressed. In May 1902, Rabindranath replied in Bengali, in his usual language full of metaphors and Indian imagery; here is a translation:

> God impressed a mark of victory on your forehead before he sent you down to the earth. Why should you care for words of encouragement from ordinary mortals like me? Wherever you are, in joy or sorrow, in despair or difficulty, you must succeed! Fight depression and do not allow yourself to be defeated. The one who

---

[45]An allusion to Nivedita's bringing back the vajra from Bodh Gaya, mentioned earlier.

is inside you[46], yet of whom you are unaware, and who has been
guiding you for all these years toward success—how can He allow
any interruption of your progress to the goal halfway through?
Caesar's boat never sinks. ...On returning to India, you will become
a sage and in a quiet retreat, reveal to your disciples the secret
and arduous path to the fortress of knowledge—that is what we
wait and hope for.

Tagore's letters to Bose were numerous, always encouraging and morale-
boosting, for he knew how fierce was the battle his friend was in and
how besieged he felt.

Mrs Sara Bull

Nivedita wanted that the essential spirit of ancient Indian literature and
art be revived and expressed in modern idiom. On 12 April 1903, Sara
wrote about Nivedita and her revivalist ideals to her friend Mrs Briggs
(alias Santi, an Indian name given to her by the Swami),

> She hopes to make it the ruling impulse in the new current of
> national consciousness [of India]. ...It must always be brought
> about by a return to the ancient literature for inspiration and
> renewal of thoughts, in facing the new problems. To familiarize
> the women that it is 'Arise, awake and stop not till the goal is
> reached' with which they have so much to do to contribute....
> This feeling which is so intense with her...dawned, I believe, on
> her especially in Norway, where she found the Norse renaissance
> was brought about by the revival of the Saga literature. Think
> what the Mahabharata, with the teaching concerning action of
> the Gita can do for any people.

Sara knew well that Nivedita's revivalism was not only about literature
and art, it was about science too, in which they both pinned their hopes
on Dr Bose; he too was fired by the same revivalist idea.

---

[46]Hindus believe that the divine resides inside every being.

Josephine MacLeod

Joe realized that Bose needed Sara's support and continued presence. With this in mind, she wrote to Sara on 21 February 1901,[47]

> [Y]ou, Margot, and I are sufficiently one to make our worlds one— we are the only link required. I see quite different careers opening up for us. If the Boses return to India and want you, I certainly think you have a role to play here—none else can fill....
>
> The Brahmos need your quality of drawing room grace, your music, the refinement and simplicity of touch you always give to your surroundings, coupled with the reverence you have for such a nature and life as Sarada Devi's.

Joe shrewdly observed that the Indian society of Calcutta was sharply divided in two cultures, the Brahmo and the new form of traditional Hinduism of the Ramakrishna order, and believed it was only Sara who could straddle the two cultures.

A Philosophical Appraisal

As discussed, because the results of Bose's physiological experiments thus far were contrary to prevailing theories, the publication of his papers was being impeded again and again. It has also been said that a few of established physiologists attempted to discredit Bose, and not always by fair means. It is unfortunate that in Bose's time the philosophy of science was not a developed subject. Since then, this subject has come a long way.

One of the leading philosophers of science, Karl Popper, stipulated that scientific practice is characterized by its continual effort to test theories against newer experiments; that science advances by disproving a well-accepted tenet or theory; alternatively, by including it in a higher and more unifying theory. Had this Popperian formalism been as well accepted and known as it is now, Bose might have received a fairer

---

[47]Primary source of this letter and the one before is the Sara Chapman Bull Collection of the Vedanta Society of Northern California.

deal. As things stood, Bose struggled for about three years to prove that there is life in inert matter, but ended up only disproving the existing theory and definition of life.

He was carried away by an interpretation of the Vedanta philosophy, aided by his friends, Nivedita and Tagore. That he was getting carried away was noticed by some of his well-wishers; within a month after his Bradford lecture at the British Association, Oliver Lodge wrote, 'Many congratulations on your very important and suggestive experiments; but go slowly, establish point by point and restrain inspiration.' Lord Rayleigh wrote, 'You are going too fast. Proceed slowly.'

We shall now look into what exactly carried Bose away. There are various terms in Sanskrit scriptures to describe the attributes of an omnipresent God. One of them is 'Chaitanya'. This word is used often in the Vedanta texts, the Upanishads. Unfortunately, this word is usually translated into either 'consciousness' or 'spirit', and they mean two different things. Under the action of anaesthesia, a man loses his consciousness, but the spirit does not leave him. The spirit is not lost even in death, as per the Vedanta, and permeates all living and inert matter alike. Thus, spirit is not life—it is a supra-existence that permeates all existence, living and non-living. Therefore, the Vedanta is often called a 'spirit-in-everything' philosophy; alternatively, 'God-in-everything' philosophy.

Bose seems to have taken Chaitanya for 'consciousness', whose pre-requisite is life, and which is unthinkable without life. Had he not been carried away by a particular interpretation of the Vedanta, he would have realized that (a) the prevailing definition of life at that time, based on electric response, was at fault, and (b) even though inert matter and living tissue gave similar electric responses, the former was devoid of life.

Tagore seems to have realized, although much later at an advanced age, that both he and his scientist friend had been unduly swayed by the Vedanta philosophy. After Bose's death, in a memorial message, he wrote,

I was made familiar from my boyhood with the Upanishad which, in its primitive intuition, proclaims that whatever there is in this world vibrates with life, the life that is one in the infinite.

This might have been the reason of the eager enthusiasm with which I expected that the idea of the boundless community of life in the world was on the verge of a final sanction from the logic of scientific verification....

The significant expression in Tagore's statement is 'eager enthusiasm'. He seems to mean excessive enthusiasm, and it implies the sense of being carried away. Physiologists in general however were not swayed. They intuitively sensed that there was something wrong with the position that inert matter has life, which Bose had wished to suggest. They also realized that Bose had shattered Waller's old theory and definition of life; so, they evolved a new one over time which says that life must show the following characteristic symptoms:

It assimilates material from the surroundings; it grows; it reproduces; it responds to stimulus; it has the ability to adapt to its surroundings.

Bose succeeded in proving, beyond any doubt, the uniformity of electric response in animal life, plant life, and inert matter. Had he not been carried away by the Vedanta, he might have been at the forefront of redefining the symptoms of life.

However, it must be said, to Bose's credit that he was responsible for singlehandedly demolishing the prevailing definition of life. Thus, it was because of him, although indirectly, that the science of physiology took an enormous leap forward.

Politics of Science in Colonial India

In the meanwhile, there were other developments in India that had a bearing on Bose's wish to start a research laboratory for Indians in the country. One person who was familiar with the workings of the University of Bombay and had the wisdom to think originally and act innovatively was Sir Jamshetji Nusserwanji Tata. In 1893, when he was travelling via ship from Yokohama, Japan to Vancouver, Canada, Jamshetji met an unknown Hindu monk as a fellow traveller. Named Swami Vivekananda, he was going abroad for the first time in his life to attend the Parliament of Religions in Chicago. In the course of a discussion, the Swami said that the ascetic spirit of India should be rekindled and harnessed for all nation-building activities and his priority, of course, was education. These words remained etched in the mind of Jamshetji, and in due course of time led to the idea that it was his duty to promote indigenous development of science in India.

Tata must have been observing with interest the rising worldwide fame of the venerable Swami, while formulating his own scheme for higher education. In 1898, Jamshetji pledged half of his personal wealth (amounting to £200,000 then) for an independent university for postgraduate education and research in 'natural and humanistic' sciences. The university was to be run entirely by Indians.

Simultaneously he wrote a letter to the Swami recalling their conversation and offered to place the Swami at the helm of the institution. The letter is an interesting historic document and is given below:

Esplanade House, Bombay.
23rd Nov. 1898

Dear Swami Vivekananda,

I trust, you remember me as a fellow traveller on your voyage from Japan to Chicago. I very much recall at this moment your views on the growth of the ascetic spirit in India, and the duty, not of destroying, but of diverting it into useful channels.

I recall these ideas in connection with my scheme of Research Institute of Science for India, of which you have doubtless heard or read. It seems to me that no better use can be made of the ascetic spirit than the establishment of monasteries or residential halls for men dominated by this spirit, where they should live with ordinary decency and devote their lives to the cultivation of sciences—natural and humanistic.

I am of the opinion that if such a crusade in favour of an asceticism of this kind were undertaken by a competent leader, it would greatly help asceticism, science, and the good name of our common country; and I know not who would make a more fitting general of such a campaign than Vivekananda.

Do you think you would care to apply yourself to the mission of galvanizing into life our ancient traditions in this respect? Perhaps, you had better begin with a fiery pamphlet rousing our people in this matter. I would cheerfully defray all the expenses of publication.

With kind regards,
I am, dear Swami,
Yours faithfully,
Jamsetji Tata

The Swami declined the offer since he was too busy building a monastery at Belur near Calcutta, and also in indifferent health. Jamshetji and his assistant Burjorji Jamaspji Padshah met Lord Curzon, the viceroy of India, in 1998. The latter summarily shot down the project on the specious ground that Indians were incapable of achieving real mastery in science; there would not be enough students, and even if there were some, they would not find employment afterwards. This was a good three years after Bose's recognition in Europe as an eminent scientist and two years after his first scientific tour covering three countries in Europe.

Jamshetji's dreams were shattered. In April 1899, he sent Padshah and his sister to meet Swami Vivekananda in Calcutta and discuss the matter. They sought help from the Swami and it was given in full measure. Soon after this, *Prabuddha Bharata*, the English newsletter of the Ramakrishna Mission, published from Madras carried the following appeal by Swami Vivekananda, fully supporting Jamshetji's decision to defy Lord Curzon's will:

> We are not aware if any project at once so opportune and so far-reaching in its beneficent effects was ever mooted in India, as that of the Post Graduate Research University of the Tata. The scheme grasps the vital point of weakness in our national well-being with a clearness of vision and tightness of grip, the masterliness of which is only equal by the munificence of the gift with which it is ushered to the public. ...If India is to live and prosper and if there is to be an Indian nation which will have its place in the ranks of the great nations of the world, the food question must be solved first of all. And in these days of keen competition it can only be solved by letting the light of modern science penetrate every pore of the two giant feeders of mankind—agriculture and commerce.... We repeat:

no idea more potent for the good of the whole nation has seen the light of the day in modern India. Let the whole nation therefore, forgetful of class or sect or interests join in making it a success.

Sister Nivedita wrote several articles in *The Statesman* supporting the Tata project and wrote to many British educationists. There were also others who bolstered the campaign. As a result, Sir William Ramsay was appointed by the government to examine the project in 1900. This was the same Ramsay who had told Bose, 'You are an exception. One swallow does not make summer.' Although brilliant as a scientist and destined to win the Nobel Prize four years later, Ramsay had the usual race prejudice regarding Indians. He too echoed Curzon and added further that an institute that combines science and humanities was infeasible. The viceroy suggested that Tata make the gift to the government and leave the rest in its hands.

It has been broached earlier that, in late 1900, there was a confluence of personalities in London. Nivedita and the Boses had already arrived. Jamshetji Tata came from Bombay to press for an independent university and find out why his project was being blocked. Sir George Birdwood was the chief of educational affairs in the India Office and Tata was keen to meet him. Mrs Bull, who had arrived in London from Europe, threw a luncheon party at her house, in order to facilitate this meeting, in which Nivedita too was a guest. However, the Boses were not present. At the table, Sara sat next to Birdwood and started a conversation exchanging pleasantries to allay his suspicions that she had an ulterior motive in inviting him. Then Tata and Nivedita joined the conversation.

In the course of conversation, Nivedita asked Sir George whether there was any hope that account would be taken solely of the applicants' scientific qualifications when state appointments were made in the future. He replied that this was impossible.

'And do you think that such state of thing involves the greatest dangers?' she asked.

'It ought to do so,' the government official admitted, 'but I do not for one moment believe that it does. The people of India will never rise against us. They are all vegetarians!'

'I was thinking of dangers to India, not to ourselves,' Nivedita said.

'Oh, I hadn't thought of that,' Sir George responded. 'True, that point of view would be very interesting'.

The dessert arrived before Mr Tata had had an opportunity of broaching the subject which so occupied his mind. And then it was Nivedita who asked,

'What form of regulation would you propose, Sir George, in order to ensure, under the Post Graduate University Scheme proposed by Mr Tata, that the appointments are reserved strictly for Indians?'

He replied, 'The Indian universities are already deteriorating, and Calcutta is the worst.'

Nivedita protested, 'But they are completely under government control'.

Birdwood realized that he had put his foot in his mouth and tried to change tack, 'Yes, but they are deteriorating. The advisers should be from Europe and America exclusively. Indians would not be reliable advisers. The money should be given to the government'.

Turning aside, Nivedita said, 'Mr Tata, Sir George makes out a strong case that you should throw your money into the hands of the authorities who have already proved themselves so incompetent!'

This remark led to some fireworks, as expected. Birdwood said animatedly, 'Indians have not turned out one man of pre-eminence in literature, science or art these fifty years!' Nivedita retorted, 'But they didn't get a chance. When do you propose to give them one?'

Now Sir George stared at Nivedita and said with finality,

'I would propose nothing!' he said. 'It would be suicidal to the interest of science to do anything of the sort. That is a world question, not an Indian problem at all.'

No further discussion was possible. At the end of the luncheon, Sir George labelled something that Tata had said as 'disloyal'. 'Write me an open letter in the *Times*', Sir George said to Mr Tata, 'I shall reply officially, I assure you; your point of view is very interesting.'[48]

That same evening the Boses received a note from Nivedita,

---

[48]Slightly differing versions of this conversation have been handed down to us by Prabuddhaprana (2014) and Reymond (2017). What is presented here is the author's understanding of it, after reading both.

describing verbatim what had transpired. The Boses were keenly interested in the outcome of the luncheon meeting for very obvious reasons. Well aware of the developments in India regarding the Tata proposal, they knew that the fate of the Tata proposal would serve as a precedent for the institute they wanted to build, one for which they were assiduously saving money.

Sensing a dead end with Birdwood and the government, Nivedita started contacting the eminent people she knew, and mounted a campaign in England. A circular letter was printed as follows:

> A Parsi gentleman, Mr Tata, who is anxious to promote higher education among the Natives of India, and especially to encourage scholarship and scientific research, has offered to fund a sum of £200,000 for the purpose.... His generosity should be devoted purely to the achievement of Native learning on National lines.

It is obvious that the cost of the campaign was covered by Sara, since Nivedita had no money of her own. The success of Jagadish Chandra Bose and his fortuitous presence in England around that time helped her campaign. Sir William James, the famous psychologist, supported Tata's ideas in an essay. Patrick Geddes wrote to Nivedita, praising Tata, 'Utilize all that is best in Europe, but do so by the help of all the best in India, not by abandoning it. Your new school of science would thus acquire an individuality and an interest of its own.'

Meanwhile public opinion in India was gathering momentum in support of the Tata project. *Prabuddha Bharat* carried another editorial in March 1901. However, Lord Curzon was relentless in his effort to suppress nationalism in education. The nationalist sentiment had been on the rise in British India for quite some time. There were several schools and colleges that had sprung up, purely due to Indian initiative, around the metropolitan cities, affiliated to the Universities of Calcutta, Bombay, and Madras. These institutions determined their own curriculum and prescribed text books written by Indians. Curzon first appointed the Indian Universities Commission in 1902 in order to 'reform' education, then he enacted the Indian Universities Act 1904, following the recommendations of the Commission. Indian educationists understood that the Act was for regulating and monitoring the Indian institutions. It would also serve to curb the 'independence' of the Tata project, the viceroy calculated. There was an uproar in India and again Nivedita used her pen to oppose the Act. She wrote in an article,

> We have had a Universities Commission lately, which has done its very best to kill all education and specially all science education. The point in India's wrongs that fires me is the right of India to be India, the right of India to think for herself, the right of India to knowledge. Were this not the great grievance, I might be fired by her right to bread, to justice, to other things, but this outweighs all.

Tagore too wrote a critical review of the University Act. However, Lord Curzon refused to give up. Now the government tried to regulate the schooling of Indian children and tried to stop their entry into English-medium schools. On 29 June 1904, Bose wrote to Tagore in this context,

> The fee for Indian students in St. Xavier's had earlier been raised to Rs 10 from Rs 5; some Indians in positions of authority were very happy about it. Now the Government has ordered that Indian students are to be denied admission altogether [in St. Xavier's]. Loreto has received a written order to throw the [Indian] boys and girls out. ...Now many gentlemen have started to look at your school as an alternative. Alas! This is the reward for their great loyalty to the British Raj!
>
> ...I have read your article about the University Bill. It is very apt and beautifully written.

In quick succession, Lord Curzon took another political measure to nip the nationalist movement in the bud; he partitioned Bengal, the most vocal province in opposition to his rule, along religious lines, separating Hindu majority districts from the Muslim majority ones. A mass movement, demanding the withdrawal of the partition, began growing and gaining followers by the day.

Feeling the pressure, the British government replaced Lord Curzon with Lord Minto, someone with a more liberal outlook. Minto greenlighted the Tata project in May 1909 by signing the Vesting order. By that time, both the Swami and Jamsetji had passed away. The Swami, however, had sent a request letter on behalf of Tata to K. Seshadri

Iyer, the dewan of the maharaja of Mysore. Tata's sons were pursuing their father's project with equal zeal. A huge piece of land in Bangalore, 372 acres in size, was donated by the Maharaja of Mysore, Krishnaraja Wadiyar, an admirer of Swami Vivekananda. He had seen the Swami as a young prince, during the reign of his father Maharaja Chamaraja Wadiyar, when the Swami was a guest in the royal palace. The senior Wadiyar had become a disciple of the Swami and had contributed to the fund for sending him to America the first time.

Just a few months before Lord Minto granted permission to the Tata project, on 14 February 1909, Josephine MacLeod wrote to Bose from America; she made a suggestion about how to generate funds for the institute:

Dear Dr Bose,

...It seems to me imperative that if we are going to have anything like a national scientific movement in India at all, a parallel with Swamiji's religious movement, it is well to begin it now, while we have you to lead it—and so, I want to start a fund for the foundation of an Indian laboratory and a fund to support the staff and pupils. So, will you draw a rough sketch—of such a building as you conceive it—and its cost of erection and maintainance (sic)—and send it to me immediately? ...If instead of fighting for political freedom—we can further a new school of Indian research and discovery.... So that in 20 years much more will have been achieved really for freedom—than a direct attack....

Yours sincerely,
J. MacLeod.

The British government and Josephine were thinking along the same terms regarding the idea that a science movement would add to the strength of the freedom movement. But Joe was naive to openly write about it. When Nivedita learnt about this letter, she reacted swiftly and wrote a letter of warning to Joe,

About Dr Bose's laboratory—one must not talk of it. One dare not call it by such a name. There is nothing that would so quickly bring down the wrath of the Government, as any whisper of such an undertaking. I am engaged in no politics. But science is politics in the eyes of the Gov.... I am sure you would not speak of 'politics' as you do, if you realized that any detective, reading your letters, would inevitably say, 'This lady knows that her correspondent is engaged in political activities—and these must be the more dangerous in that I cannot trace them!' As a matter of fact, I am not in politics, but I cannot afford to have this idea get abroad! So please never let the word appear. There is no other way.

Although Nivedita was an intrepid warrior, afraid of nothing, fear and apprehension are palpable in this passage. She was afraid not for herself, but for India. Nivedita had been experiencing surveillance, but since when it is hard to tell. Most probably, from the days of Viceroy Curzon, when she was travelling widely in India and trying to arouse nationalism in the youth. She often received letters and packets addressed to her in a completely torn state. In irritation, she wrote a sarcastic letter to the postmaster general,

> Dear Sir, it is of course easy to understand the overwhelming curiosity of some members of your staff about the confidences of my sister in regard to her babies and her cooking. I should be grateful, however, if you would instruct them to close up again the letters they have opened and read.

This letter illustrates how surveillance of certain prominent people, connected with the nationalist movement, was quite prevalent in British India.

The episode with the letters, Joe's to Bose followed by Nivedita's letter of warning, happened a good nine years after her first brush with a British colonial administrator, Sir George Birdwood, and eleven years after her arrival in India. By now, she was experienced in dealing with the government of the British Raj. One wrong step or unwise utterance, and there would be a huge repercussion and years of setback for science in India and the nationalist cause. Fortunately, this correspondence took place while Nivedita and the Boses were in England, where they were not under surveillance, and Josephine was in America.

6

MARCONI AND BOSE: THE PATHS CROSS

When we look deeper...we shall find that failure must be the antecedent power to lie dormant for the long subsequent dynamic expression in what we call success. It is then and then only we shall begin to question ourselves, which is the greater of the two, a noble failure or a vulgar success.

—Jagadish Chandra Bose

A Historic Rescue

It was a bitterly cold night covered with dense fog. SS *Republic*, the largest shipping liner in her day, was cruising through the North Atlantic Ocean on 23 January 1909. The visibility was next to nothing. The ship's passengers were suddenly woken up by the sound of a loud thud and pandemonium broke loose. Once order was restored, it became clear that the *Republic* had been rammed on the port side by another ship. Two passengers had died immediately, crushed by the collision, and there was a gaping hole through which ice-cold saline water was pouring in rapidly. The captain knew that the ship could not be saved and was going down. It was only a matter of a couple of days. The ramming ship, the *Florida*—an Italian steamer—was luckier. Its bow had entered straight and square into the side of the larger ship and was badly damaged, but was still repairable.

There were 1700 people on board, likely a mix of Europeans and Americans, whose life hung in the balance; or, rather, hung on a new tool of wireless communication, an instrument supplied by Guglielmo Marconi's company. For the first time in maritime history, the Marconi apparatus was used to summon aid over invisible radio waves. Jack Binns, an operator who had been specially trained to use this new piece of technology, worked non-stop and sent out more than 200 messages in two days. The initial message said, 'SOS. SOS. Two ships in collision. 1700 people on board. SOS. SOS.'

SOS stands for 'Save Our Souls'. A ship, the RC *Gresham*, and a destroyer, named *Seneca*, rushed to the site of the disastrous collision. It was difficult to locate the two damaged vessels in the dense fog, and Binns kept guiding them by means of the wireless set. All remaining passengers and crew were rescued. The *Gresham* towed the *Republic*, but before reaching shallow waters she sank. Jack Binns became a hero, and Guglielmo Marconi a star in the public eye. In the same year, Marconi received the Nobel Prize for Physics, for his contribution to wireless communication. It was shared with German physicist Karl F. Braun.

A photo of the Italian ship, SS *Florida*, its bow completely crushed,
after the collision with SS *Republic*.

Early Life of Marconi

Guglielmo Giovanni Maria Marconi was born in April 1874, at his father's estate in Bologna, Italy. His father Giuseppe Marconi was a wealthy Italian nobleman from Poretta Terme, and mother, Annie Jameson, was an Irishwoman, born into the famous Jameson family of whiskey distillers. Her father was one of the owners of Jameson & Sons and

Guglielmo Marconi

much of their business was based in London, the capital of the British empire and the largest trading town in the world.

Guglielmo and his elder brother Alfonso lived in Bedford, England, with their mother for four years, as Annie Jameson wanted her sons to speak fluent English. While Alfonso attended school in Bedford, five-year-old Guglielmo received elementary education from a private tutor.

Later, in Bologna, Guglielmo Marconi was never sent to a school; instead, a number of private tutors were hired who taught him general science and mathematics. In winter, the family usually left the cold climate of Bologna and moved to the warmer coastal town of Livorno, where Marconi had a remarkable teacher in Vincenzo Rosa, who taught physics in a high school and tutored him in the fundamentals of physics and the new theories of electricity. Marconi never received any formal higher education. In his own words,

> In sketching the history of my association with radiotelegraphy, I might mention that I never studied physics or electrotechnics in the regular manner, although as a boy I was deeply interested in those subjects. I did, however, attend one course of lectures on physics under the late Professor Rosa at Livorno, and I was, I think I might say, fairly well acquainted with the publications of that time dealing with scientific subjects including the works of Hertz, Branly, and Righi.

This is an excerpt from his lecture delivered on the occasion of the Nobel Prize ceremony. In this speech, Marconi did not take the name of any other teacher or mention attending lectures at any formal universities or institutes. He said that he was well acquainted with the works of Hertz whose writings were all in German. Marconi did not know any

German, but was fluent in Italian and English; therefore, he was likely to have accessed Hertz through the work of Augusto Righi, who was an Italian pioneer of electric waves.

Augusto Righi, a professor and the director of the physics department at Bologna University, was a friend of Marconi's family. Marconi became well acquainted with Righi and is known to have visited him many times in his laboratory at Bologna University. Righi permitted Marconi to use the library and the laboratory of the university as well as to attend his lectures there informally. Marconi's daughter Degna Marconi (1962) writes in her father's biography,

> Guglielmo lacking regular learning, could not enrol at the University of Bologna. He had to adapt to follow Righi's lectures as a simple hearer. ...And from a recently found letter of Guglielmo to his brother, written in 1892, '...I am studying very hard to get a Technical High School degree as professor Righi wishes...'.

There are other testimonies, not quoted here, that clearly indicate the deep influence that Righi exerted on a young Marconi. It is no wonder then that Righi is often referred to as Marconi's mentor. Hertz's death in 1894 and the obituary, written by Righi, triggered Marconi's interest in wireless signalling. Of course, he was not alone in this. In many countries around the world, the potential for using the Hertzian waves for some form of wireless communication was recognized.

Marconi was very proficient in English, which was the most dominant language in the West then, as it is now. We have already seen that Bose's papers in English were being quickly accessed by physicists and physiologists in France and Germany, and Bose visited various universities in Europe and lectured in English. Hence, Marconi must have been putting his facility in English to good use and reading scientific literature in English to keep abreast of the latest developments in the UK and USA.

In spite of his love for 'electrotechnics', Marconi's first choice was not a career in that subject, but the Italian Naval Academy, for which he took the entrance test. Unfortunately, he failed to qualify. A disappointed man, he was advised by his mother to concentrate on his engineering pursuits; Annie Jameson had noticed in him a scientific aptitude for tinkering and hands-on dexterity since his boyhood.

The attic of the ancestral home, Villa Griffone, became Marconi's first laboratory where, starting in 1895, he tried rudimentary experiments for wireless signalling. He found the Branly coherer too erratic and unreliable, and improved upon it by using nickel and silver filings in a small gap between two silver plugs in a tube. Initially, he succeeded in sending a signal only to a distance of a few metres within the confined space of the attic. He then advanced to outdoor experiments in order to improve the signalling distance. It is but natural that, all through his amateur experiments, Marconi kept in touch with Righi, for he also had a peripheral interest in wireless telegraphy, and eight years later would author a book on the subject.

Marconi gradually improved the distance of signalling to more than two kilometres. None of these, however, formed part of a public demonstration. His improved receiver was more reliable but still suffered from the same drawback as Branly's—it had to be manually shaken or tapped after every receiving event. Sir Oliver Lodge had arranged for automatic tapping by adding a relay coil in the circuit; on receiving the Hertzian wave signal, the relay would actuate a secondary circuit to ring a bell, whose hammer would vibrate against or tap the coherer to restore it. Marconi started using this kind of automatic tapping arrangement.

Villa Griffone, Marconi's ancestral home near Bologna, Italy.

Marconi effected another significant improvement. He connected one terminal of the oscillator or transmitter to a high metal plate aerial, and the other terminal to the earth. The receiver was similarly connected to another aerial at the same height. Fig. 6.1 shows the arrangement schematically, and is based on a simplification of Marconi's diagram presented during his Nobel Prize lecture. The aerial increases the power of transmission at one end and the power of reception at the other end. Thus, the range of the signal, that is the distance between transmitter and receiver, could be increased to about 2.4 kilometres.

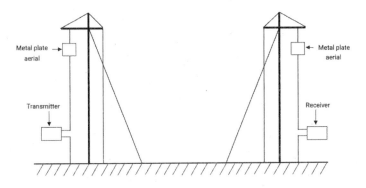

Fig. 6.1: Marconi's experiments with aerials in Bologna, Italy.

This convinced Marconi that by continually increasing the power of the transmitter, greater and greater distances could be ranged. Marconi, being a simple engineer, had no explanation of how the aerial worked and freely said in his lecture that it was for the physicists to explain his findings.

It should be recalled that Bose also had used a pair of elevated aerials in his Calcutta Townhall demonstration of 1895 (see Ch. 3). Bose was then an accomplished physicist and might have had good reasons for using a pair of aerials, but unfortunately, he did not write down any explanation. The kind of aerial Bose used is now called 'monopole antenna'. Marconi claimed that he had arrived at the idea of using elevated aerials independently of Bose. We shall closely examine this claim later.

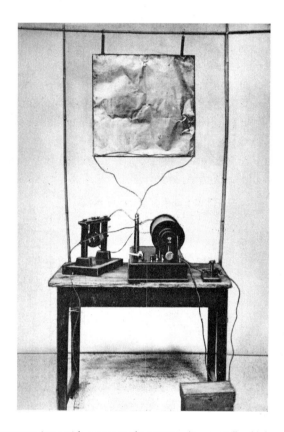

Marconi's first transmitter with a monopole antenna (i.e., aerial) which was an elevated copper sheet square (shown at the top); it is connected to a Righi spark oscillator (at the left), powered by an induction coil. The telegraph (Morse) key at the right is the on and off switch, to send Morse code signal.

Marconi's family, at this stage, decided to launch him into business, and approached the Italian Ministry of Post and Telegraph. The Italian Ministry proved indifferent, and, in February 1896, Annie Jameson took her twenty-one-year-old son to London. Henry Jameson Davis, Marconi's maternal cousin, gave them a warm welcome.

Marconi's Early Experiments in England

Henry Jameson Davis acted as a mentor for young Marconi initially. At this time, the Jameson family's business interests had diversified, with much of its activities located in London, and Henry, a professional engineer, specialized in erecting mills for grinding food grains. He was forty years old and had acquired considerable experience in business management, and knew many of the influential people in London.

Guided by Jameson Davis, on 2 June 1896, Marconi filed the application for his first patent, Morse Code[49] Wireless Transmission over Short Distances. Remarkably, in this application Marconi included a metal reflector as antenna, and not an elevated metal plate antenna, called aerial. The patent office rejected this application because it lacked clarity and had no diagram of the device. However, Marconi would be allowed to submit a revised application, if he were to so choose. Marconi did submit a revised application nine months later, on 2 March 1897.

In between the original and the revised patent applications, he met Captain Henry Jackson of the Royal Navy, who had also been interested in wireless signalling and had achieved a fair amount of success. This meeting took place in September 1896.

Jackson, who had joined the Royal Navy at age thirteen and risen through the ranks to become a captain, became the commanding officer of HMS *Defiance* in 1895. He had been technically trained by the navy and was an expert on torpedoes. The ship, under his command, was a torpedo school for training cadets, and therefore, fairly large. Later Jackson received many promotions and honours, including a knighthood, and was made admiral of the fleet. He died in December 1929 and the following excerpt from his obituary is a significant historical document in this context:

In 1891, the Navy was seeking some means by which a torpedo boat could announce her approach to a friendly ship, and the idea first came to Sir Henry Jackson of employing Hertzian waves.... [I]n 1895, when in Command of the *Defiance*, he read of some experiments of Dr Bose on coherer. Having obtained a satisfactory coherer, he managed in this year to effect communication by means

---

[49]Telegraph messages are conveyed through wires by means of Morse code, which consists only of two symbols a dot (.) and a dash (-). All letters in the English alphabet can be represented by different combinations of these two symbols. For instance, the letter S is represented by a succession of three dashes (- - -).

of electro-magnetic radiation from one end of the ship to the other. During the next two years he continued his experiments with increasing success. On September 1, 1896, he first met Marconi, and the two pioneers of radio-telegraphy kept in close touch and gave each other much mutual assistance until Sir Henry Jackson was appointed Naval Attache in Paris early in 1897.

Jackson read about Bose's experiments in 1895, as the obituary says. The question is what did he read and where? By the middle of 1895, Bose had published three papers in *The Electrician*. The journal was a typical product of its times, when the distinction between physics and electrical engineering had not fully emerged. No wonder that *The Electrician* billed itself as a weekly illustrated journal of electrical engineering, industry, and science, a three in one. On one hand, the journal used to publish articles on generators and circuitry, on the other, it carried theoretical matter such as Oliver Heaviside's paper on electromagnetism and Oliver Lodge's papers on Hertz's works. It was read by both electrical engineers and physicists.

One of Bose's papers in *The Electrician* contained a description and diagram of his spiral-spring coherer, as shown in Fig. 3.17(b); further, the same coherer was editorially reviewed in the December 1895 issue of the journal. *The Electrician,* as an illustrated weekly, also carried news items of significant events in electrical engineering. A weekly of this character would most likely be a regular read for an electrical engineer like Jackson.

The only experiment of Bose, that was widely publicized and created a sensation in 1895, was the Calcutta Townhall demonstration, and this was on wireless signalling, involving a coherer and a pair of elevated aerials. The news of this event was even carried by ordinary news dailies; *The Electrician,* too, must have reported about this experiment and from a more technical point of view. This would have definitely attracted the attention of an innovative person like Jackson, who had wished to utilize wireless communication to establish contact between a friendly ship and an approaching torpedo.

As per the obituary, Jackson managed to establish 'communication by means of electro-magnetic radiation from one end of the ship to the other', a feat that would have been impossible without a pair of aerials. This proves that he had read about Bose's Calcutta Townhall experiment. In September 1896, Jackson was a technically trained officer, forty-one years old, and had one and a half years' experience in wireless signalling. Marconi, who was then a young man of twenty-two, received 'assistance' for several months from an experienced person like Captain Jackson. From the obituary we know Marconi definitely met him at least once, but we may assume that they met more than once.

In March 1897, when Marconi submitted a revised application, he introduced a significant change. There was no mention of the reflector now, but instead, the elevated metal plate aerial was featured prominently. This patent, in due course, was granted (British Patent No. 12039).

The central theme in this patent, as the title given above suggested, was the transmission of a message via Morse code. The idea of combining Morse code with Hertzian waves was not new. It had been demonstrated earlier by Oliver Lodge at the Royal Institution, but only within the laboratory, and had not been patented.[50] In fact, Lodge's automated receiving apparatus, mentioned earlier, had a secondary circuit, actuated by a relay, in series with a Morse printer and a hammer for tapping. Sending a Morse code signal involved transmitting a wave over a long duration for a dash, and a much shorter wave for a dot, and a relatively long pause for a space between words. In Lodge's demonstration there was no obstruction whatever between the receiver and the transmitter.

The addition of an elevated aerial (also called antenna) and the improved receiver (the coherer) were the novel elements in Marconi's patent. But he claimed priority for the use of the tapper and Morse code also, since he did not acknowledge Lodge. Fig. 6.2 shows a schematic diagram that has been prepared following the description of Marconi's system. It should be noted that though antenna is the modern name of an aerial, at the turn of the nineteenth century 'aerial' was in common usage. The antenna or aerial is connected, by a vertical conducting line,

[50]Bandyopadhyay has credited Marconi with the first use of the Morse code in conjunction with the Hertzian waves, p. 265. However, evidence exists that Lodge had priority over Marconi.

to the coherer, which is then connected to one terminal of the battery. The other terminal of the battery is connected to earth via the relay.

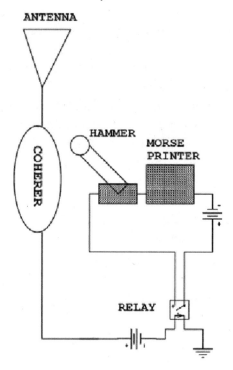

Fig. 6.2: Apparatus for receiving electric waves,
consisting of antenna, coherer, relay, Morse printer, and tapper.

The antenna captures the signal spreading out from the transmitter (not shown above) and conveys it to the coherer. Its resistance changes and a current flows momentarily in the coherer-circuit, which is called the primary circuit. This causes the relay switch to close so that a current flows momentarily through the secondary circuit also, which actuates the Morse printer and the hammer. The hammer strikes the coherer and restores it to the initial state, readying it to receive the next signal.

The set-up depicted in this figure, minus the antenna, would be substantially similar to Lodge's. Hence, the patent came under attack five years later from Silvanus P. Thompson, a professor of physics and Fellow of the Royal Society. He wrote in *Saturday Review*,

From the patent which [Marconi] took out about that time—a document in which he apparently puts himself forward as the inventor of the oscillator, coherer, tapper and all, it would appear that the only real point of novelty that he could embody in his claim is that of connecting one end of his coherer to earth while the other was connected to an elevated, insulated conductor. All else is simply details or surplusage.

Thompson was not pleased with Marconi's practice of not acknowledging his predecessors. In particular, the acknowledgement of Lodge for the use of Morse code and the tapper was certainly in order. However, acknowledgement of Bose for the elevated aerial was also warranted, something Thompson fails to notice. Thompson apparently did not give much importance to Marconi's 'improved' coherer. Marconi published a sharp rejoinder in the same journal, which was followed by an even sharper reply from Thompson. Marconi seemed to be losing ground; the correspondence continued for quite a few rounds. These exchanges took place in 1902, and in the intervening five years, between 1897 and 1902, much development had taken place, and there were other issues in these exchanges, which shall be revealed by and by.

In 1897, Jameson Davis introduced young Marconi to a leading electrical engineer in London, A. A. Campbell-Swinton, who in turn introduced Marconi to William Preece, engineer-in-chief of the general post office. Preece was a man of vision and became immediately invested in Marconi's ideas. In the same year, Marconi gave a few successful demonstrations with the active help of Preece and Jameson Davis. The latter invited engineers and businessmen to these events. Signals were sent over distances of up to 6.4 kilometres across the Salisbury plain. Then the Bristol channel, with a width of 14.5 kilometres, was spanned.

In these experiments, Marconi was using a kite or a hydrogen balloon to hoist the aerial. Preece gave public lectures to attract attention to these developments. There was considerable coverage by the print media in the UK and Europe, and the Italian government became interested. Marconi erected a land station at La Spezia and established communication with Italian battleships at distances up to 19 kilometres.

Jameson Davis Founds a Company in the Face of Scepticism

Though there still persisted much scepticism about wireless telegraphy, Jameson Davis, an accomplished engineer, was far-sighted in recognizing the real potential of these developments. Rather than tying into an agreement with the British post office or a telegraphic firm, he suggested founding a new company. Marconi hesitated for months, but finally gave in, and on 20 July 1897, the Wireless Telegraph and Signal Company was founded. Financial support, in the form of purchased shares, came from many of Jameson Davis's business associates, who were mainly grain merchants; and, of course, from the two wings of Marconi's wealthy family. Marconi was appointed the technical director and Jameson Davis, the financial director.

The company was set up on the Isle of Wight. It happened to be the ideal place, not only for transmission purposes, but also because of its proximity to the royal residence, Osborne House. During July and August 1897, Marconi arranged the exchange of messages between the royal residence on the island and the royal yacht on the sea, carrying information about Queen Victoria's son, the Prince of Wales, later to become King Edward. It is said that on Marconi's arrival, the queen first mistook him for an electric mechanic, but her impression of him soon changed. His service was much appreciated by the queen and the prince and the news of the event was a great advertisement for Marconi's company.

It is remarkable that traders in agricultural produce were interested in such a high-tech, high-risk company, and speaks volumes about the enterprising nature of British businessmen, and their penchant for supporting industrial research. It also speaks volumes about the quality of support Jameson Davis gave to his cousin. Marconi, however, wished to be in the pubic gaze and in 1900, the company's name was changed to Marconi's Wireless Telegraph Company. Hereafter, Jameson Davis stayed, more or less, behind the scenes, managing the financial aspects of the company as efficiently as ever.

During the first two or three years, the company concentrated on exploring and showing the utility of the new technology by continually widening the signalling range. At this time, some physicists spoke publicly that Hertzian waves had the same properties as light and travelled in a straight line. Therefore, given the curvature of the spherical earth, the wave would veer off the earth's surface along a tangent. Even after adding a few extra miles on account of diffraction, the longest distance it could cover would not go beyond 32 kilometres or so, the horizon being at 19 kilometres.

However, Marconi remained undeterred and pressed on. After clearing the Bristol Channel, it was time to cross the much wider English Channel. In 1899, a distance of 135 kilometres was covered from Wimereux, France to Chelmsford, England. Even greater distances were ranged in shore-to-ship experiments with the help of the Royal Navy. Next, a signal was successfully sent from the Isle of Wight, situated off the eastern part of the south coast, to the furthest point in the southwest of Cornwall, a distance of nearly 300 kilometres.

At this point, Marconi and his technical team, consisting of his scientific adviser, J. A. Fleming, originally a physicist who held the first chair of electrical engineering at the University College London, R. N. Vyvyan, an electrical engineer, and Jameson Davis were convinced that the physicists were in the wrong; there had to be some other explanation for this unexpected phenomenon. Marconi himself had the fantastic notion that the electric waves were propagating along land and sea because of the grounding of the equipment. No one had the faintest suspicion that reflection from the upper atmosphere was responsible. In any case, Marconi was very interested in understanding the physics behind this occurrence, but in the commercial exploitation of radio telegraphy—he was engrossed in what worked and not in why it worked. The Nobel Prize did not figure even in his wildest dreams.

In September 1899, an opportunity arose in the shape of the yacht race for America's Cup, and Marconi grabbed it with both hands. His company equipped two American ships to report the progress of the race live; the messaging was, of course, in Morse code. This attracted wide publicity in America.

In 1900, Marconi filed for patenting a device that allowed transmitting and receiving signals at a particular frequency. He called it 'tuned or syntonic' telegraphy that avoided interference between adjacent stations. This was, the now-famous, Patent No. 7777. Two years earlier, in January

1898, Oliver Lodge had patented a similar device in the United States on 'syntonic' tuning; so, Lodge filed a lawsuit accusing that Marconi had used much of the content of his patent.

Marconi's argument was that he had not known about Lodge's earlier patent and had developed his device independently. The case dragged on for years and finally, anticipating defeat, Marconi settled out of court in 1911. He purchased Lodge's patent and gave him an honorific position of a science adviser in his company. However, in 1943, the US Supreme Court overturned this patent, assigning priority to Lodge, Nikola Tesla, and Stone. By that time, of course, the patent had far outlived its utility and Marconi was no longer alive.

No matter what the future held in store, at that point in time, tuned telegraphy became a powerful tool in Marconi's hands when it was used in conjunction with an elevated aerial. By using a receiving aerial tuned to the transmitter aerial, Marconi was able to span longer and longer distances.

The world came to know of Bose's elevated aerial much before Marconi's aerial. However, the former did not use a tuned aerial. This piece of Marconi's invention and discovery revolutionized wireless telegraphy, and he is rightly called the father of long-distance wireless communication.

Like Jameson Davis in England, Marconi had a loyal and influential facilitator in Italy—the Marchese Luigi Solari. Solari held the rank of lieutenant in the Royal Italian Navy and the two had been intimate friends from their boyhood days. Marconi's biographer W. P. Jolly described their friendship in the following words,

> [Solari] became Marconi's lieutenant, friend, and confidant. He assisted him with his experiments all over the world, he persuaded the King of Italy to lend [Marconi] a war-ship for wireless trials, he walked by his side to the operation theatre when one of his eyes was removed, and Solari was with him in the last busy day of his crowded life.

In the summer of 1901, Solari was sent by the Italian government to London to meet with Marconi and fetch some of his latest apparatuses for use in their own naval radio experiments. Soon after this visit, on

10 September 1901, Marconi initiated the patenting process for a new device, a novel coherer, in his own name.

Across the Ocean

Now Marconi decided to go across the Atlantic with his waves. For this purpose, a very powerful transmitting station, consuming 25 kilowatts of energy, was set up at Poldhu in Cornwall. The design of the transmitter was carried out by Dr Fleming. An especially large and tall antenna, a cone antenna, was hoisted into position. A suitable land point on the American continent, at the shortest distance from Poldhu, Marconi estimated, was the city of St. John's in Newfoundland, Canada—a distance of more than 3000 kilometres.

Marconi supervising the work of his team, raising the wire-kite aerial in St. John, Newfoundland, Canada, in December 1901.

Marconi proceeded to St. John's in late November, with two assistants, to select a site and erect a temporary station. A hill near the city with old barracks was chosen; the hill would later be named Signal Hill. It was decided that the equipment would be set up in a room of the building, with a line going out of the window to the wire-kite antenna, hoisted aloft. Marconi and his team faced inclement weather conditions with a gale-force turbulent wind prevailing most of the time. Fig. 6.3 gives a line diagram of the bleak landscape and the arrangement made by Marconi's team.

Fig. 6.3: The test site at Signal Hill. The sketch is prepared by this author and inspired by an artist's rendering of the site, given by Bandyopadhyay (1998).

The tests commenced in early December 1901 and on the twelfth, Marconi and his first assistant clearly received the Morse signal from Poldhu—the pre-arranged letter 'S' and a succession of three dashes. They repeated the tests on the following day, to ascertain beyond any doubt, that the reception was actually taking place. Marconi kept the entire development at St. John's under wraps. Only a lone reporter, R. S. Baker of *McClure's Magazine*, was given an interview while Marconi was still there at the hill site, but his report would be published nearly two months later in February 1902. Immediately after the successful telegraphy, Marconi went to New York. It seems he made a cautious announcement there, for we see that within a week Lodge expressed scepticism. The *Times of London* published the following letter of his on 20 December 1901:

Atlantic Wireless Telegraphy—It is rash to express opinion either way as to the probability of the correctness of Mr Marconi's evidently genuine impression that he has obtained evidence on the other side of the Atlantic of electrical disturbances purposely made on this side, but I sincerely trust that he is not deceived. He has probably been using as detector the very simple device depicted in my little book on the subject.... I should not like to be behindhand in welcoming, even prematurely, the possibility of so immense and barely expected an increase of range as now appears to be foreshadowed. Proof, of course, is still absent....

In response to Lodge's letter, the managing director of the Marconi company, Major Stephen Flood Page wrote in reply immediately,

Prof. Oliver Lodge is altogether wrong in his suggestion that Marconi was 'using as detector the very simple device depicted in my little book on the subject'. If this 'simple device'...had been the means...it would not have made the fact of the communication less wonderful, but Mr Marconi was using something that Principal Lodge has never yet seen....

This exchange tells us that a new receiving device, a novel coherer, was being used by Marconi. This seems to have remained a well-guarded secret. Reading between the lines of the statements made and the letters written by Marconi and his associates, we shall try to ascertain the nature of this new receiving equipment.

In New York, the American Institute of Electrical Engineers (AIEE) hosted an annual dinner in Marconi's honour on 13 January 1902. Alexander Graham Bell, the famous inventor of the telephone, was present, among numerous other eminent persons. Marconi depicted the first trans-Atlantic telegraphy in his own inimitable style,

I thought that this temporary installation, the first shot at getting messages across the Atlantic, should be tried on the island of Newfoundland, at St. John's, which is about two thousand land miles from England. Instead of poles, as are generally used for permanent work, kites and balloons were employed to elevate the aerial wires, the necessity of which, I think you are pretty well acquainted with. These kites or balloons gave a great deal of trouble, as, owing to the tempestuous weather...it was found almost impossible to raise the kites and balloons to the required height. However, I am glad to say, that at certain intervals, on December 12 and 13, the kites for a short time got into satisfactory position, and my assistants and I had the great satisfaction of receiving a number of prearranged signals from Cornwall, at the right time and at the prearranged speed.

...I have built very greatly on the work of others.... They are Clerk Maxwell, Lord Kelvin, Prof. Henry, and Prof. Hertz (Applause). ...These messages were received on the telephone which was actuated by the impulses translated through it from a coherer.... And I wish to mention the name of Prof. Graham Bell in that connection (Applause). ...An ordinary recording instrument was not sufficiently sensitive to work at that distance, but by the aid of the telephone, it did work (Applause).

Marconi knew when to name names, such as Clerk Maxwell and Lord Kelvin, and when and where to praise the local hero, in order to draw applause. He was an effective public relations man, no doubt. He did not disclose anything about the coherer, even in this lecture, but informed the world that a telephone was used, because it was the most sensitive recording instrument in combination with the human ear; it responded to the faintest signal; so faint that no other instrument, neither a galvanometer nor a Morse key, could be used.

If we piece together Page's reply to Lodge with what Marconi said, we learn that a new coherer in conjunction with a telephone was the receiving apparatus. But the question arises—why was Marconi so secretive about the new coherer?

The reporter, who had interviewed Marconi in situ, published his report in February 1902, as follows,

At noon on Thursday Marconi sat waiting, a telephone receiver at his ear, in a room of the old barracks on Signal Hill. ...Arranged on the table before him, all its parts within easy reach of his hand, was the delicate receiving instrument, the supreme product of years of the inventor's life, now to be submitted to a decisive test. A wire ran through the window, thence to a pole, thence upward to the kite which could be seen swaying overhead. It was a bluff, raw day; at the base of the cliff 300 feet below thundered a cold sea; oceanward through the mist rose dimly the rude outlines of Cape Spear, the easternmost reach of the North American Continent. Beyond that rolled the unbroken ocean, nearly 2000 miles to the coast of the British Isles. Across the harbour, the city of St. John's lay on its hillside wrapped in fog; no one had taken enough interest in the experiments to come up here through the snow to the Signal Hill. The faith of the inventor in his creation, in the kite-wire, and in the instruments, which had grown under his hand was unshaken.

'I believed from the first', he told me, 'that I would be successful in getting signals across the Atlantic'.

Only two persons were present...—Mr Marconi and Mr Kemp. ...The receiving apparatus was of unusual sensitiveness, so that it would catch even the faintest evidence of the signals. A telephone receiver which is not part of the ordinary instrument had been supplied, so that the slightest clicking of the dots might be conveyed to the inventor's ear. For nearly half an hour not a sound broke the silence of the room. Then suddenly Mr Kemp heard the sharp click of the tapper as it struck against the coherer.... The inventor's face showed no evidence of excitement. Presently he said, 'See if you can hear anything, Mr Kemp'.

Mr Kemp took the receiver and a moment later, faintly and yet distinctly and unmistakably, came the three little clicks—the dots of the letter S.

The report was long and presented the palpable tension in the operations room dramatically. The Morse code for the letter S was heard on the telephone around half past twelve in the afternoon, and then again ten minutes later. Then the wind became turbulent and the wire-kite aerial gyrated too violently to make any reception possible. The next day, when the weather conditions were a little more conducive, the inventor and his assistant heard more signals.

The interview took place after the receiving events were over, and Marconi gave the reporter the impression that the same old coherer with a tapper was in use. The only difference was that the signal from the coherer went straight to the telephone. But he did tell him that the coherer was of 'unusual sensitiveness', and the telephone was 'not part of the ordinary instrument'. Due to the sluggishness and unreliability of the relay-tapper device, quite a few seconds would elapse before the coherer would be ready for the next signal. Hence, the pauses would be too long and unreliable. With such a device, Morse telegraphy could have been possible at a short distance, but at thousands of miles, the possibility was next to nil.

Marconi's statement, before the learned gathering at the AIEE's annual dinner, contains the expression, 'An ordinary recording instrument was not sufficiently sensitive to work at that distance'. So, here is the admission that the coherer used was not an ordinary one. With the reporter, Mr Baker, Marconi had used the term 'unusual sensitiveness'. So, what was this unusual or extraordinary coherer that Marconi was so secretive about? Why did he mislead the reporter by mentioning a tapped device? From where did he get the idea of combining a telephone with a coherer?

By the end of January 1902, Marconi returned to England. In spite of adverse remarks and scepticism in the press, Marconi seemed confident. He immediately embarked on his next experiment, this time in a more secured environment, aboard SS *Philadelphia*. The transmitting apparatus and the antenna at Poldhu were exactly the same. The receiving antenna on the ship was a properly secured, hoisted antenna, much better than a kite-wire being tossed about in the wind. Additionally, it was specially tuned to the transmitting antenna at Poldhu.

The test signals could be recorded on a Morse printer tape up to a distance of 2,490 kilometres, and the reception, with the help of a telephone, was possible up to 3,400 kilometres. It was proved beyond doubt that the telephone–human ear combination was the most sensitive instrument at that point in time. Further, Marconi made an important discovery—signals reached much further during the night than during the day. He proved beyond doubt that the radio waves could reach thousands of miles and were not deterred by the curvature of the earth. Though the explanation of these two discoveries came much later, Marconi returned to England triumphantly in April 1902.

However, even now, Marconi was reticent to give any information whatsoever about the coherer. Nonetheless, any technically informed person, after taking one look at the taped signals in Morse code, would have known that the coherer was recovering instantly and automatically, and needed no tapping. It indeed was a new and unusual coherer, a self-restoring coherer or autocoherer. We can presume that the same coherer, which had received the signals in the Newfoundland experiments, was used. First, it is an important principle that from one experiment to the next, only one major change, a variable, should be introduced, and this is followed by all experimentalists. Between these two experiments that change was the tuned antenna. Hence, everything else, including the coherer, was retained unchanged.

Secondly, in spite of the well-secured tuned antenna, the Morse key recording arrangement failed beyond a distance of 2,490 kilometres. However, the telephone–ear combination worked up to almost 900 kilometres more than the distance covered during the Newfoundland experiment. It worked better because of the absence of weather and a secured environment. It is a kind of confirmation that it is the same instrument as on Signal Hill of St. John's.

In these experiments, the distinction between engineering and physics disappeared. Marconi deserved credit not only for inventing the tuned antenna, but also for discovering two important physical phenomena with regard to the radio waves. Had it not been for his drive and penchant for experimenting on an enormous, almost global, scale, these discoveries might have been delayed for decades. So, he should not be considered just a tinkering engineer, but also a successful experimentalist in physics. However, by that token, Marconi's technical adviser, J. A. Fleming, who designed the world's largest and steadiest transmitter of the day, which made these audacious experiments possible, also deserves a fair share of the credit.

The 'Italian Navy Coherer' Scandal

While Marconi was busy conducting experiments aboard SS *Philadelphia*, a rumour spread in Italy that Marconi received the trans-Atlantic wireless signals using a new instrument called 'mercury coherer' with a telephone. A. Banti, editor of the *L'Elettricista*, claimed in an article that the actual inventor of the mercury coherer was a signal man in the Italian Navy named P. Castelli. Marconi defended himself by saying that the device was invented, not by Castelli, but by his childhood friend Lieutenant Solari, also of the Italian Navy, and presented to Marconi in the summer of 1901. Marconi then patented it in his own name. This was a weak defence, and raised another cause for concern—if it was invented by an employee of the Italian Navy, then it was a property of that organization. It would be illegal for Marconi to patent it in his own name. Besides, Solari repeatedly denied that he was the real inventor.

Banti's article reached England and S. P. Thompson was unsparing in his attack, which was published in *Saturday Review*. Marconi's sharp practices with respect to patenting had been noted in England for some time, but physicists had not vocalized their concerns earlier. Now, Lodge and Thompson joined forces, leaving Marconi feeling disturbed and vulnerable. He made a good reply, but the attacks continued. Even in these exchanges, Marconi refrained from disclosing anything about the coherer–telephone device in question. Instead, he bought time by saying that Thompson should wait until his presentation before the Royal Institution, scheduled for later that year.

One remarkable incident during this exchange stands out—a political intervention on behalf of Marconi. Mr Henniker Heaton, a Conservative Party member of the British parliament waded into the correspondence by writing a letter to the *Times* on 14 July 1902. Not being a man of any technical competence, he referred to the Irish origin of Marconi and said that the tenor of Thompson's letters was needlessly insulting to a respectable citizen. It is obvious that Jamesons's political clout was at work.

In the meantime, Marconi and his friend Solari used their influence in the high quarters of the Italian government and got the head of the Italian Navy to issue the following certificate: 'The coherer has been with good reason baptized with name of "Italian Navy Coherer", as it must be considered fruit of the work of various individuals in the Royal Navy, and not that of one.'

In his lecture before the Royal Institution on 13 June 1902, Marconi presented the results of his two trans-Atlantic experiments and then said,

Other self-restoring coherers were proposed by Prof. Tommasina, Popoff, and others, but one which has given good results, when syntonic effects were not aimed at, was (according to official information communicated to me) designed by the technical personnel of the Italian Navy. ...It consists of a glass tube containing plugs of carbon or iron with between them a globule of mercury. Lieutenant Solari, who brought me this coherer, asked me to call it 'Italian Navy Coherer'.

...It has not yet been found possible, as far as I am aware, to actuate a recording instrument or a relay by means of a self-restoring coherer.

Thus, the circumstances compelled Marconi to divulge what he had tried to keep secret for so long. Surprisingly, nobody, not even his detractors like Lodge or Thompson, bothered to look into what he had actually patented.

In this lecture, Marconi said categorically that this mercury coherer was neither Castelli's invention, nor of any of the other persons whose names were doing the rounds in Italian journals and magazines. It was invented by unknown workers of the Italian Navy. Further, it was not known in which laboratory the work was done, making this, on the whole, a most artificial claim. The rest of the lecture was a masterful effort in creating confusion by dropping many irrelevant names; one such was D. E. Hughes's, who had discovered electric waves long before Hertz, but did not know how to interpret his findings.

Further, Marconi's statement, in the second paragraph of the above excerpt—that an autocoherer could not actuate a relay—is an outright lie, for we know that in his experiments on the ship, an autocoherer was used to actuate a relay to work the Morse key. Marconi made contradictory statements about the coherers, both auto-recovering and tapped. His claim at the Royal Institution that many different coherers were used in his experiments was in variation with what he had said in America at the annual dinner of the AIEE, before a most distinguished audience. In hindsight, it becomes obvious that he was trying to create a smokescreen and a diversion, so that all concerned should keep looking at distant Italy, instead of close-by England. In this game, Solari was his willing partner. Although he was an officer in the Italian Navy and the carrier of the coherer to Marconi in England, he seemingly had no clue who had invented the device. A fantastic example of stonewalling!

These revelations made it abundantly clear that Marconi was not the inventor of what he had patented in his own name. His application for the patent is given below:

Improvements in Coherers or Detectors for Electrical Waves

I, Guglielmo Marconi, of 18 Finch Lane in the city of London, Electrician, do hereby declare the nature of this invention as follows:

Coherers made according to this invention consist of a drop of conducting liquid lying between two conductors. I employ a glass tube having in it two plugs whose distance apart can be adjusted with the liquid between them. Preferably, one plug is of steel and the other is of carbon, whilst the liquid is mercury. Dated this 9th day of September 1901.

Marconi attached a diagram of the device with his patent application, as mandatorily required, which is shown in Fig. 6.4. He later had to suffer the humiliation of having to admit plagiarism, and amended the patent application to give ownership to the Italian Navy.

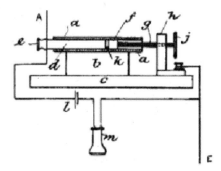

Fig. 6.4: Diagram of autocoherer, attached to Marconi's patent application, British Patent No. 18105.

Marconi's friend Solari always kept on the right side of the law and declared categorically that he was not the inventor. On 10 July 1903, in a letter titled, 'The Real Inventor of the Mercury Coherer', published in *The Electrician,* Solari informed that he had learnt about the 'mercury coherer with a telephone detector' from English literature, but could not recall the exact source. He then tried to mislead the reader by citing irrelevant publications, as indicated by Vivian J. Phillips in 'The "Italian Navy Coherer" Affair'.

In spite of the Solari hint, Lodge and Thompson, the British inquisitors of Marconi, did not or could not locate the true source of the 'mercury coherer with a telephone detector'.

In 1902, Marconi patented his magnetic detector, which thereafter became the standard receiver for wireless communication for many years. In December the same year, the first complete message was sent by Marconi from Glace Bay, Nova Scotia, Canada, to Poldhu in England. His scientific adviser, John A. Fleming invented and patented the thermionic valve (popularly called vacuum tube) in 1904. This was a great help to the Marconi company. The valve remained a piece of standard electronic equipment all over the world for many decades to come. On the whole, the Marconi company was thriving during the first decade of the century.

At that time, Karl F. Braun was leading the parallel development of wireless telegraphy in Germany and accused Marconi of using his British patent on tuning in some of Marconi's own patents. In 1909, they were jointly awarded the Nobel Prize for pioneering work in wireless communication. In his Nobel lecture, Marconi said, 'Part of my work regarding the utilization of condenser circuits in association with the radiating antennae was carried out simultaneously to that of Professor Braun, without, however, either of us knowing at the time anything of the contemporary work of the other.'

Thus, Marconi claimed that he had independently invented similar devices around the same time as Braun. If Braun had gone to court, he would have won the case, since the dates on the patents would have given him priority.

Braun was recognized by the Nobel committee for his improvement of Marconi's transmitting system. Unknown to the Nobel committee, it was really Fleming's transmitting system which Marconi's company was using, and Marconi had no hand in designing it. This meant that the Nobel committee gave credit to Marconi for both the receiving and the transmitting system.

Such a sorry thing could happen because Marconi never acknowledged Fleming in any forums, public or otherwise, and Fleming, as a paid consultant, had given word that he would never claim credit for any of his work for the Marconi company, which he honoured as long as Marconi was alive. In reciprocation of Fleming's agreement, Marconi had promised to transfer 500 shares of the Marconi company to Fleming, if the trans-Atlantic project became successful. He never fulfilled this promise, and Fleming was bitter about it. After Marconi's demise in 1937, Fleming broke his silence about their mutual pact, and is said to have referred to Marconi as ungenerous.

Later Statements

One of the inventions that fetched the Nobel Prize for Marconi was the mercury autocoherer, which had made the trans-Atlantic experiment possible. Marconi confirmed the use of the autocoherer in his later statements. In 1903, Marconi wrote an article, 'Marconi's Own Story of Trans-Atlantic Signals', in his weekly publication *Marconigram,* 25 June,

> In view of importance of all that was at stake, I had decided not to trust entirely to the usual arrangement of having the coherer signals record automatically on a paper tape through a relay and Morse instrument, but to use instead a telephone connected to a self-restoring coherer. The human ear being much more sensitive than the recorder, it would be more likely to hear the signal.

This statement is at considerable variation with what Marconi had said in the Royal Institution lecture. In 1936, Nobel Laureate Marconi's authorized biographer Dunlap quoted Marconi as saying,

> I ran my wire through a window in the barrack, thence to an old telephone pole, where it was attached to the kite. For this special experiment I had devised an especially sensitive coherer of a new type and instead of depending on the ordinary Morse Inker for printing the signals, I had substituted a telephone receiver, believing

that I could then detect much fainter signals, should the wave effects be very light.

There is an admission in this quote that the 'especially sensitive coherer' could either be used with a Morse key or a telephone. Marconi had not only authorized this biography, but also proofread it. He is, once again, manipulating facts, by claiming to be the inventor of the autocoherer, with no mention of the Italian Navy's contribution. Marconi's assistant Vyvyan (1933) wrote thirty years after the trans-Atlantic experiments,

> The kite was rising and falling in the wind throughout the experiments and varying the electrical capacity of the aerial. It was impossible to use, therefore, any form of syntonic apparatus and Marconi was obliged to employ the next best means at his disposal. He therefore used a highly sensitive self-restoring coherer of Italian Navy design, simply connected in series with a telephone and the aerial, and with this simple receiving apparatus on Thursday, December 12, 1901, he and one of his two assistants heard the faint S signals.

The True Inventor

Marconi passed away in 1937 and, until his death, maintained secrecy about who the true inventor of the 'mercury coherer with a telephone' was; his authorized biographer Dunlap and assistant Vyvyan had, of course, no clue. In fact, for a long while, no one succeeded in identifying the true inventor. Even V. J. Phillips, who investigated the scandal surrounding the Italian Navy coherer as late as in the 1990s, failed to detect the self-restoring detector's true inventor. However, he did expose the deceptive and scandalous behaviour of the Marconi–Solari duo thoroughly.

Finally, it was Probir K. Bandyopadhyay who followed up on the Solari hint, about the presence of the 'mercury coherer with a telephone' in English literature, and zeroed in on Bose as the true inventor. He completed Phillips' investigation by connecting the scandal to Bose's paper in the 1899 *Proceedings of the Royal Society*. It is he who compared Marconi's Italian Navy coherer patent to Bose's description of the mercury autocoherer; and exposed the trivial nature of the changes made by the Italian twosome.

It is most surprising that, in spite of the Solari hint, Lodge and Thompson failed to connect the mercury autocoherer with Bose's publication of just two years vintage. It is also amazing that during the summer of 1902, when most of the sordid drama of plagiarizing by the Marconi–Solari duo and covering up by the Royal Italian Navy was playing out, Bose himself was in London, but remained supremely unconcerned.

Bose must surely have known about Marconi's success in achieving trans-Atlantic telegraphy in January 1902—it just could not be otherwise. Yet he remained completely aloof when the terms, 'mercury autocoherer' and 'Italian Navy coherer', were agitating the print media and the learned circles, and Marconi suffered a complete loss of face. Perhaps, Bose was too pre-occupied with defending himself against the attacks of Dr Waller. It is also probable that Bose thought it was against his principles to talk about any patents or attached falsehoods. Bose and his wife set sail for India in October 1902. It is to be noted that Solari's admission about sourcing the coherer in English literature, and Marconi's article in *Marconigram*, came several months after Bose had returned to India.

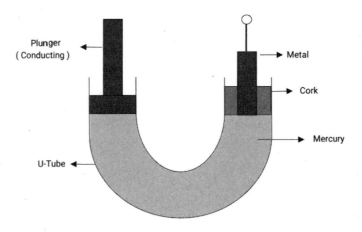

Fig. 6.5: Schematic diagram of the mercury autocoherer or
self-restoring coherer invented by Bose.

One of the self-recovering coherers described in Bose's paper was the mercury autocoherer coupled with a telephone detector. Following Bose's description, a schematic diagram of his autocoherer has been prepared and given in Fig. 6.5. His apparatus had a U-tube filled with mercury, with a plunger in one limb and a metal piece in the other, as shown. The plunger or piston was used to vary pressure in the contact between mercury and the metal in the second limb. Bose found out that by varying pressure and the applied voltage, he could bring a coherer to its most sensitive state. He placed different metals in the second limb to test their auto-recovering properties, and found that a large number of metals with mercury contact worked as autocoherers. Since carbon is a conductor, he tested a carbon–mercury contact in this way and found that this too was an autocoherer. Bose's test circuit was the same as Branly's, shown in Fig. 3.17(a), with Branly's glass tube replaced by Bose's U-tube. It is to be recalled that both Branly and Bose were using a galvanometer. He wrote in this paper,

> Another coherer was found apparently irresponsive to radiation, there being the merest throb (sometimes even this was wanting) in the galvanometer spot, when a flash of radiation fell on the receiver. Thinking that this apparent immobility of the galvanometer spot may be due to response followed by instantaneous recovery, the galvanometer needle being subjected to opposite impulses in rapid succession, I interposed a telephone in the circuit; each time a flash of radiation fell on the receiver, the telephone sounded, no tapping being necessary to restore the sensitiveness. The recovery here was automatic and rapid.

Thus, Bose discovered that a telephone was a more sensitive instrument than a galvanometer, in this situation. It may be observed that the action of Bose's autocoherer was close to that of a diode detector; however, the diode was invented some forty years later.[51]

Solari was not as inclined as Marconi towards engineering inventions. Given his profession as a lieutenant in the Italian Navy, it is most unlikely

---

[51]K. L. Groenhaug has rebuilt and tested Bose's mercury coherer. He confirms that it has characteristics similar to a diode rectifier.

that he, on his own, surveyed the English literature, discovered Bose's paper, and then designed the so-called Italian Navy coherer. The whole thing carries the imprint of Marconi, who was the real actor, with Solari as proxy. Marconi likely had the coherer constructed in Italy in the interest of secrecy. It seems that Solari, under instruction from Marconi, made certain trivial changes in Bose's invention, and put together the so-called Italian Navy coherer. In spite of such a cloak of secrecy, information did leak out in Italy and then arrived in London.

As per Marconi's patent diagram, Fig. 6.4, he replaced the U-tube by a horizontal tube and placed a drop or globule of mercury between two plugs of conductors. In Fig. 6.4, d is a carbon plug, f is an adjustable iron plug and k is the mercury globule; on close examination, we find that he has drawn f as a plunger, although he calls it a plug. He knew that the difference between these two instruments, his and Bose's, was trivial and therefore, wished to maintain secrecy about his patented autocoherer.

After several months of Bose's departure from London, Solari felt it safe to drop a hint about the source of the device—some unknown English literature. It is possible to speculate that he was afraid of getting entangled in future litigation and was playing it safe. The irony is that, had it not been for Banti's chance accusation, there would have been no scandal and no print media spotlight on Marconi's act of plagiarism. Even then it took a whole century to follow the clues back to Bose.

Since 1909, the year of Marconi's 'Radio Nobel', a few generations in India grew up hearing rumours that Marconi had somehow made use of Bose's ideas, without acknowledgement, while constructing his device for wireless communication. As mentioned earlier, rumours had almost attained the status of folklore in eastern and northern India and 'informed' that Bose was denied proper recognition by the western world in an unjust manner. In one variation of this lore, Bose's diary was stolen from his hotel room in London by a man visiting him.

At this point it may be appropriate to recall the incident where a notebook was stolen from Bose's table, during a Friday Evening Discourse at the Royal Institution, and Bose pointed a finger at the representatives of the telegraph companies, who had swarmed his table at the end of the lecture.

There were two main telegraph companies in London, each competing with the other. One was Dr Muirhead's company and the other was Marconi's. Muirhead was on friendly terms with Bose and used to consult him informally, as we are informed by Bose's letters to Tagore. It is now possible to speculate that the stolen notebook, which had drawings of Bose's devices and instructions for his assistant, changed hands and somehow ended up on Marconi's table. There is no evidence that Marconi himself was present at Bose's lecture. There is no evidence to the contrary either. However, no doubt, his telegraph ccompany's men were there.

So, the theory that Marconi had used Bose's invention, without acknowledging Bose, turned out to be true. As for the stolen notebook, whether or not it made its way to Marconi, will remain a rumour for all time to come, for lack of evidence.

Bose and Marconi in London

We have seen that while Bose was on his second scientific visit to London in 1900–1902, Marconi too was mostly in London. Even during his first scientific trip in 1896–1897, Marconi was present in London. There is evidence to suggest that Bose knew about his activities. An American popular science reporter H. J. W. Dam interviewed both Bose and Marconi in London in 1897. An excerpt from his very long essay in *McClure's Magazine* is given below (italics mine):

A year has elapsed since Röntgen gave us the new photography. Today, on the same general lines, we are confronted with something more wonderful, more important, and more revolutionary still—the new telegraphy. Two gentlemen have come to London at the same time from different countries to tell the same story, namely, that telegraphy needs no wires, and that through walls, through houses, through towns, through mountains, and it may possibly happen, even through earth, we can send dispatches to any distance with no other apparatus than a sender and receiver, the communication taking place by means of electric waves in the ether....

But the electrical advance in the last 20 years has been most extraordinary. Invention and experiment, have daily, if not hourly, thrown open *new doors in the electrical wing of the temple of truth.* And now, at the close of the 19th century the great mass of new facts concerning light, electricity, inaudible sound, invisible light, and the Lenard and Röntgen rays; the eager enquiry, based upon new discoveries, into the properties of living matter, crystallization, the transference of thought, and the endeavour to establish scientifically the truth of certain great religious concepts—*all special sciences thus represented, marching abreast of one another along the old Roman road of science, which leads no one knows whither, have come upon a great high wall blocking the way.... And upon the wall, as upon the wall of the palace of Babylon, is a strange and as yet unintelligible inscription—the mysterious word 'ether'. What new and great discoveries lie beyond this wall no one knows; but more than one high authority believes that these discoveries will startle the twentieth century more greatly than the nineteenth has been startled.*

To suggest in the crudest possible fashion, how the ether is at present regarded by the scientists, imagine that the whole universe, to the uttermost stars is a solid mass of colourless jelly; that in this jelly the stars, the solar systems and space-worlds are embedded like cherries in a mould of fruit jelly....

In short, this jelly or ether is a universal substance so thin that it permeates everything in space and earth. Only by its quivering, only by the waves in it which light rays, electric rays excite...are these rays enabled to travel and produce their various results.

Strange to say, however, considering the number of brilliant electricians in the more western countries today, and the enormous amount of interest in and experimental investigation of electrical phenomena therein, it has been left to a young Italian, Guglielmo Marconi, to frame the largest conception of what might be done with electric waves and to invent instruments for doing it....

Before introducing Marconi, however, the attention of the reader is called, for several good reasons, to his immediate predecessor in London, Dr Jagadis Chunder Bose[52]. Dr Bose is a

---

[52]Anglicized spelling of Bose's name, which he himself often used.

Hindoo, and at present the Professor of physics in the Presidency College, Calcutta. He is a graduate of Cambridge...and has been honoured with the degree of Doctor of Science by the University of London, as a recognition of certain inventions regarding electric waves which have won him the highest praise in the Royal Society, the British Association, and elsewhere. It should be said at once that Dr Bose has no interest in the new telegraphy. Though he has been named as its discoverer, he has done little more....

Dr Bose, as he sits in the drawing room of his temporary London home in Maida Vale, is a man of medium height, 36 years old.

Dr Bose says,

'My special work for last three years has been the study of electrical radiation.... My results were represented in the complete apparatus...for the verification of the laws of reflection, refraction, selective absorption...of these waves. ...These have been duly reported and discussed in scientific journals, and I fear would not be appreciated or understood outside of their circle.'

This is too evident a fact to be disputed and the conversation is turned to the wave-telegraphing in Calcutta.

'That,' says Bose, 'was simply an incident in the course of a popular lecture, an illustration of the ability of electric rays to penetrate wood and brick. ...My receiver was in a room 75 feet distant from the radiator, with three walls of brick and mortar, 18 inches thick, between them. The electric wave thus induced penetrated the walls and traversed this distance with sufficient energy, when it was converted, to fire a pistol and ring a bell, these being the simplest and best evidences of its reception that I could devise.'...

'Instead of firing a pistol and ringing a bell, could a telegraph message be sent with it and received through the walls?'

'Certainly; there would be no difficulty about that.' ...

'How far could this ether dispatch, so to speak, be sent?'

'Indefinitely. That depends on the exciting energy. At Salisbury plain, I am told, electric rays were sent, with a parabolic reflector a quarter of a mile through the ether in the air, and then reproduced as Morse signals by a relay.'

'But in telegraphing through houses—across a block of houses, for instance.... What would stop the rays?'

'Metals stops the waves I have been working with. Also, water. They would penetrate wood, brick, glass, granite, rock, earth, and retain their properties.'

'How far have they been successfully sent?'

'Through the air, I believe a mile. Through the walls, a distance of 75 feet, so far as I know.' ...

'What is your opinion with respect to thought transference?'

'I must decline to express it. There is no experimental basis upon which to make a satisfactory statement'.

Dr Bose would say no more for publication.

The reporter underestimates Bose's age by about three years. He interviews Marconi next and writes in the same dispatch,

Guglielmo Marconi, whose name would doubtless be often heard in the years which lie before us, is a young Anglo-Italian. ...He is a tall slender young man who looks at least thirty, and has a calm serious manner.... He is completely modest, makes no claim whatever as a scientist, and simply says that he has observed certain facts and invented instruments to meet them. Both the facts and the instruments are new, and the attention they are at present exciting is extraordinary.

The attention is largely due to the enterprise and shrewdness of Mr W. H. Preece., the able chief of the electrical department of the British postal system. ...He expressed the fullest faith in Marconi, describing his inventions as new and beautiful, scientifically speaking, and added that [Mr Preece] had been instructed by the postal department to spare no expense in testing them to the fullest degree....

Marconi was educated in Leghorn, Florence, and Bologna, and has more recently been following his special study at his home in the last-named city. He speaks English perfectly and said,

'...For ten years past I have been an ardent amateur student of electricity, and for two years or more, have been working with the electric waves on my father's estate at Bologna. I was using the Hertz waves from an apparatus which you may photograph, a modified form of the apparatus for exciting the electric waves as used by Hertz. My work consisted mainly in endeavouring to determine how far these waves would travel in the air for signalling purposes. In September last year, working a variation of my own of this apparatus, I made a discovery.'

'What was the discovery?'

'I was sending waves through the air and getting signals at distances of a mile, or thereabouts, when I discovered...that the waves were going through or over the hill.'

'Do you believe that the waves were going through the hill?'

'That is my present belief, but I do not wish to state it as a fact. I am not certain. The waves either went through the hills or over it. It is my belief, based on many later experiments, that they went through.'

'And what was the thickness of the hill?'

'Three-quarters of a mile.'

'And you could send a dispatch with Morse signals through this hill or over it to someone on the other side?'

'With ease.'

'What followed?'

'What followed was the conception and completion of my special invention...I find that while Hertz waves have but a very limited penetrative power, another kind of waves can be excited with the same amount of energy, which waves, I am forced to believe, will penetrate anything and everything.'

'What is the difference between these waves and Hertz waves?'

'I don't know. I am not a scientist.... I have a vague idea that the difference lies in the form of the wave. I could tell you a little more clearly if I could give details of my transmitter and receiver. These are now being patented, however, and I cannot say anything about them.'

'How high an alteration were you using?'

'About 250 million waves per second.'

'How far have you sent a telegraphic dispatch on the air?'

'A mile and three-quarters. ...This was at Salisbury plain, across a valley between low hills'....

'Did you use a reflector?'

'Yes, it was a roughly made, copper parabolic reflector.... I shall not use one in future, however. A reflector is of no value.'

'Not a lens?'

'Not a lens.'

'Why not?'

'Because the waves I speak of penetrate everything and are not reflected or refracted.'...

'Then you think the waves may possibly be used for electric light houses when fog prevents the passage of light?'

'I think they will ultimately be so used....'

'But would not the fog interfere with passage of waves?'

'Not at all.'

'Not metal?'

'Nothing affects them. My experience of these waves leads me to believe that they will go through an ironclad.'...

Such are the astonishing statements and views of Marconi. What their effect will be remains to be seen. In the United States alone, considering the many able experimenters and their admirable and original equipment, like Tesla's dynamos, the imagination abandons as a hopeless task the attempt to conceive what—in the use of electric waves—the immediate future holds in store....

Prof. Lodge has already stated his belief that electricity is actually matter.... If this be true, it will be a great and startling key to the new fathomless mystery of life.

What is evident from this report is that Bose's Calcutta Townhall experiment before Lieutenant Governor Sir Alexander Mackenzie had attracted wide publicity all over the world and the American reporter, H. J. W. Dam, was well aware of it. Bose had used a pair of elevated aerials in this demonstration, a first in any wireless experiment, and that too was widely reported.

Dam said that Bose had no interest in the new telegraphy, though he had been named as its discoverer. It is true that Bose performed the spectacular experiment in the Calcutta Townhall and signalled to his residence from his college, a distance of a mile. It is also true that he had no interest in developing it further. That would mean collaborating with a businessman and taking out patents, to which he had an aversion.

Bose's Calcutta Townhall experiment had made its mark in the global print media. Marconi, who was so interested and conversant with the latest developments in wireless communication, must have seen the reports in the English newspapers and magazines, if not also in the Italian ones. Given his track record of non-acknowledgement of predecessors, his claim of independently inventing the elevated aerial becomes highly suspect. It should be recalled that Marconi's first patent included this item. Since Bose had not patented his elevated aerial, Marconi's patent was nominally valid.

Marconi, by his own declaration, was using waves of frequency 250 million cycles per second; he also claimed that these waves would penetrate even ironclad. We now know that waves of this frequency cannot go through metals. It is obvious that Marconi was making unsubstantiated and extravagant claims.[53] Bose's statement that metal stops these waves remains true even today, when we know so much more.

From Dam's account, it becomes obvious that Bose was well aware of Marconi's experiments in the Salisbury plain; he brought up the topic by himself without being prompted by the reporter, though he did not take Marconi's name. Both Bose and Marconi said that a metallic reflector of a parabolic shape had been used. None made any mention of an elevated metal plate aerial. Had it been used, Marconi would certainly have spoken about it.

Marconi's explanation about the ineffectiveness of the metallic reflector—the wave simply penetrated the metal instead of being reflected—was in the realm of fantasy. It is obvious that during the first experiment on the Salisbury plain, in March 1897, Marconi was

---

[53]Today, wireless communication with submarines is established using very low frequency (VLF) waves, generated by special apparatus, that can go through the sea and the ironclad of the submerged vessel. However, this form of communication has several severe limitations, compared to the conventional one. With the kind of oscillator that Marconi was using, generating such waves was absolutely impossible.

not convinced about which one would perform better—the reflector or the elevated aerial, and he used the former. Later he used the elevated aerial in the same location.

There is also a discrepancy about the range. As per Bose, it was a quarter of a mile, about 400 metres, but Marconi claimed a mile and three quarters, almost 3 kilometres. Bose's source must have been a news report, since the experiment was well publicized by Preece and Jameson Davis. Marconi's habit of exaggeration is again apparent.

Marconi Plays his Last Card

Dunlap in his authorized biography of Marconi, first quotes an associate about how persistent and industrious Marconi was, '"Marconi's success may be summed up in patience and infinite persistence plus a great deal of natural ability", said one of his early associates, "I have seen him work thirty hours at a stretch...."'

Then Dunlap quotes Bose regarding how valuable Marconi's contributions were:[54]

> Marconi, himself was credited with 'opening new doors in the electric wing of the temple of truth'. Dr Jagadis Chunder Bose, the Hindoo, Professor of physics in the Presidency College at Calcutta, and distinguished student of electrical radiation, foresaw, 'all the special sciences marching abreast along the old Roman road of science which leads no one knows whither.' And he espied an obstacle—a great high wall blocking the way in all directions. Upon the wall, as upon the wall of the palace of Babylon, he perceived 'a strange and as yet unintelligible inscription—the mysterious word "ether".'[8]
>
> 'What new and great discoveries lie beyond this wall no one knows,' said Dr Bose, 'But more than one high authority believes that these discoveries will startle the twentieth century more greatly than the nineteenth has been startled. To suggest in the crudest possible fashion, how the ether is at present regarded by

---

[54]The relevant pages of Dunlap's book (pp. 35–36) are given in the appendix to this book.

the scientists, imagine that the whole universe, to the uttermost stars is a solid mass of colourless jelly; that in this jelly the stars, the solar systems and space-worlds are embedded like cherries in a mould of fruit jelly....

In short, this jelly or ether is a universal substance so thin that it permeates everything in space and earth. Only by its quivering, only by the waves in it which light rays, electric rays excite, are these rays enabled to travel and produce their various results.

'Strange to say, considering the number of brilliant electricians today, and the enormous amount of interest in the electrical phenomena, it has been left to a young Italian scientist, Marconi, to frame the largest conception of what might be done with electric waves and to invent instruments for doing it.'

One ship drives east, and another west,
...And not the calm or the strife
Rebecca Williams.
[8]McClure's Magazine, March, 1897.

The poem by Rebecca Williams is an embellishment added by Dunlap, and is not part of the original article. This section in Dunlap's book ends with a footnote appearing below the poem by Rebecca Williams. This footnote is the only reference to the source, from where the quotation is lifted. Bandyopadhyay examined the original *McClure's Magazine* of March 1897 to connect the quotation to Dam's article. There are several quotation marks in the excerpt and some of them are inconsistent, as presented in the book.

This quotation is a garbled, inaccurate, and deceptive piece, most unfit for any biography, authorized or not. The selected portions of Dam's very long article, from which this quotation has been lifted, have all been italicized (see p. 230), so that the reader can verify easily.

The entire quotation, as in Dunlap's book, consists of statements attributed to Bose; whereas, in the actual article these are all part of the introductory preamble written by the reporter himself. Bose has nothing to do with them. In the interview, as published in *McClure's Magazine*, Bose never takes Marconi's name, let alone praise him to the heavens.

Ironically, the foreword of this authorized biography was written by Marconi himself, and Dunlap wrote the following acknowledgement in response:

Appreciation

It has been the good fortune of the author to have had Guglielmo Marconi's friendly interest in the writing of this story. For his kindness in thoroughly reading the final proofs that the book would be accurate in facts about wireless and historically correct in personal detail, the author is deeply indebted.

The inescapable conclusion is that these selected quotes were deliberately 'doctored' and misattributed, and the responsibility lies with both the author, Dunlap, and the proofreader, Marconi. Perhaps, Marconi wished to tell the future generations that, while Lodge and Thompson criticized him, Bose applauded his achievements. The fraud has now been detected, partially by Bandyopadhyay and fully by this author. Tragically and ironically, the biography came out in print in 1937 and in the same year Marconi breathed his last.

The Radio Nobel for Physics and Bose's Calcutta Townhall Experiment

It is well known that the Nobel Prize for Physics in 1909 was shared between Guglielmo Marconi and Karl F. Braun. Right from the beginning, the award for Marconi generated controversy. There were certain questions raised by contemporary physicists. Did Marconi, who was not a physicist, whose only claim to fame were a large number of patents, and who had never written a research paper, deserve it? In contrast, his fellow awardee Braun was a renowned professor of physics, with an excellent record of research publications.

Did other people substantially contribute to Marconi's achievements? Should the prize have been shared with a larger group? The answer to these two questions is an emphatic 'yes'. But did Marconi deserve the prize?

Bose had invented the crucial mercury autocoherer, repackaged as the Italian Navy coherer, that received the signals of the first trans-Atlantic wireless message from England to Newfoundland, Canada. The same autocoherer also received the signals during the experiment that followed, on board the ship SS *Philadelphia*. Bose also invented the elevated aerial, which proved so pivotal in all of Marconi's attainments.

Bose's Calcutta Townhall demonstration took place in early 1895, perhaps a little before Marconi started his amateur tests at his home in Bologna. According to Marconi's own declarations, he performed some preliminary experiments in the attic, and found that Branly's coherer was erratic and unreliable. Marconi then proceeded to innovate a better coherer, and succeeded to produce his coherer with nickel–silver filings. He continued to work in the attic to test his equipment and send signals to distances measured in metres.

All this took a fair amount of time before Marconi advanced to outdoor experiments. And then he started using elevated aerials. It would be a good guestimate to say that roughly a year had elapsed after Bose's demonstration, before Marconi started using aerials. However, Marconi gives a more accelerated timeline and puts the start of his aerial experiments in August 1895, which still gives priority to Bose by several months. It cannot be overemphasized that this timeline and all descriptions of experiments are as per Marconi's own claims; they are not supported by journal publications or public demonstrations.

Marconi's claim that he came up with the idea of the elevated aerial, independent of Bose, is not trustworthy. Bose's Calcutta Townhall demonstration of 1895, which had used a pair of elevated aerials, had been widely publicized in Europe and America; evidence for this can be found in Dam's news report, which has been quoted from extensively in the previous section. Marconi was proficient in English and Italian and kept abreast with English publications relevant for his subject, and might have read about Bose's Townhall demonstration in the magazines and newspapers in either of the two languages.

Further, it can be proved that Bose's work on radio-telegraphy was known of in Italy. On 30 August 1901, Bose wrote to his friend Rabindranath Tagore, from London: 'An invitation letter has arrived from the International Congress on Wireless Telegraphy, Rome. They have written, "We expect much advancement from your work. Please enlighten us with your new investigations."'

The following correspondence, between Dr Federico S. Bassoli of Modena, Italy, and Bose, provides evidence that Bose's Calcutta Townhall experiment attracted wide media attention in Italy also. On 11 October 1923, twenty-eight years after the event, Bassoli wrote to Bose, in slightly stilted English,

> Sir, I am collecting materials for a book on 'radio-dynamics', the wireless control of mechanisms I am now writing, no literature [books] existing at the present, as I know on this subject matter. For this, and because I desire to do a conscientious work, I address me, when possible directly to the inventors and experimenters asking for help in any documentation.
>
> In the book 'Wireless Telegraphy and Hertzian Waves' by S. R. Bottone (Whittaker Co., London 1910) on p. 50, I have found a very interesting information about your work; that is to say a little report about your experiments about 'the possibility of discharging a pistol or firing a mine from a distance without any intermediary but that of the atmospheric medium' made by you.
>
> You can easily understand the great importance that have historically for me your experiments, as they would be the 'first radiodynamical' experiments in the world, and the 'embryo' of this marvellous branch of radio-dynamics.
>
> As Bottone's report is not much large and detailed, and I have not been able to found any other part more particulars about the experience you have done, I shall be very grateful to you of every information, document or bibliographical notice or other, you will be so kind to send me regarding the subject matter.
>
> Hoping that you will, do me the great favour, in expectation of your answer I beg to agree Sir warmest thanks and very best regards.
>
> Very truly yours,
> F. S. Bassoli.

It should be understood that 'radio-dynamics' refers to the subject concerned with remotely operating a mechanical device with the help of radio waves; Bose had operated a pistol. European scientists in the 1920s considered Bose as the pioneer of this subject. Only in the 1980s, when literature of the 1920s faded from public memory, questions were asked about who the first was—Bose, Popov, or Marconi. This amnesia about Bose's work occurred because there was no mark of commemoration for Bose in physics. Be that as it may, Bose wrote to Bassoli in reply,

Dear Sir,

Your letter dated 11th October has been redirected to me in London. I have been lecturing in Europe on my new discoveries.

As regards your enquiry, the short account given by Bottone is substantially correct. The public demonstration was given in 1894-95 at the Calcutta Townhall .... It was reported in the press, and I saw some account of it given in Italian Journals also. I am sorry that I have no other papers with me on the subject.

You will find some of my researches described in 'Hertzian Waves and Wireless Telegraphy' by Poincaré, also in the proceedings of the Royal Society, London, 1895-1900. My invention of receivers made of Galena rendered transmission to a distance possible. This invention would be found among the list of patents issued in Great Britain and America.

Yours, J. C. Bose

Here, Bose is on record saying that he saw some reports of his Calcutta Townhall experiment in Italian journals also, and it is unbelievable that Marconi, who was focused on radio-telegraphy in 1895, did not come across any of these.

Marconi's mentor, Augusto Righi was a contemporary of Bose. Both were able to generate microwaves and were trying to verify Maxwell's theory and predictions, and the completion of Hertz's unfinished task was engaging the attention of both.

Early in 1895, Bose shot to fame, owing to his sensational Calcutta Townhall experiment. The publication of his three papers in *The Electrician* in quick succession followed in the same year. The Townhall experiment showed for the first time that electric waves could penetrate thick walls of brick and mortar, a result extremely significant even for a physicist interested only in the fundamentals. Righi, who was then ardently pursuing microwave research, must have read about this experiment. This was particularly likely, because Bose's field was extremely close to his own and he would have paid careful attention to all of his contemporary's work.

Righi was sure to have discussed Bose's Townhall experiment on wireless telegraphy with his pupil, who was then wholeheartedly engaged in the same subject. The telephone had become a ubiquitous presence in all offices, laboratories, and wealthy homes by 1895, and all that Righi had to do was to pick it up and talk to Marconi.

Another piece of evidence, about Marconi being in the know of Bose's Calcutta Townhall experiment, comes from the obituary of Admiral Jackson, quoted earlier. In 1895, about a year before Jackson and Marconi met, the former had succeeded in establishing wireless signalling from one end of his fairly large ship to the other.[55] One can safely say that this distance would likely be, at least, a hundred metres, if not more. Besides, in between the two ends of a ship are placed housing for personnel, laboratories, workshops, the communal kitchen, etc., which pose as barriers for the waves to cross. Hence, signalling would be impossible without a pair of elevated aerials, since the standard transmitter in those days was the Hertz or Righi oscillator or its variation, which was not sufficiently powerful. Jackson likely gathered his ideas from Bose's Calcutta Townhall experiment, where for a distance of only 23 metres, Bose had needed a pair of aerials.

Jackson had told many around him that he owed his ideas to Bose and might have written to the higher authorities to acquire funding for his experiments, and therein mentioned Bose's name and papers. Whatever may be the case, the Bose connection to Jackson's experiments had been fairly well known in the navy, wherefrom the *Nature* magazine came to know about it (as mentioned in Jackson's obituary).

According to this obituary, Marconi and Jackson met at least once, in September 1896, when both of them were in England. And they remained in close touch for several months thereafter. Marconi then

---

[55]It should be a matter of historical investigation if Jackson's attainments happened before Popov's St Petersburg experiment.

was a novice of hardly any standing, and had just arrived in London; there is no record of Jackson visiting Marconi. Most probably, Marconi had heard of Jackson's successful experiments and visited him.

It would be in Marconi's interest to visit Jackson on his ship, so that he could see with his own eyes wireless signalling in situ. Hence, the ship was the most likely venue of their meeting. If that is so, Jackson would surely have shown Marconi the most prized of his achievements, that is, wirelessly signalling from one end of the ship to the other, involving a pair of elevated aerials. If they met elsewhere, Jackson may have discussed his methods and equipment, and that would include a pair of elevated aerials.

They were in a relationship of 'much mutual assistance'. It is unbelievable that an experienced officer like Jackson would not tell the young beginner anything about the efficacy of the elevated aerial and Bose's Calcutta Townhall experiments. It should be noted that they were in 'close touch' for several months.

We observe the following sequence of events:

1. In June 1896, Marconi submitted a faulty application for a patent which got rejected; the application included a metallic reflector but had no mention at all of the elevated aerial.
2. Starting from a visit in September 1896, for several months Marconi remained in 'close touch' with Jackson.
3. In March 1897, Marconi filed a revised application for the same patent, with a significant change—now the elevated aerial replaced the metallic reflector.

The only conclusion we can draw is that, until then, Marconi was undecided between the two instruments, namely, metallic reflector and elevated metallic aerial. This means that his Bologna experiments were not conclusive.

It is possible to speculate that Jackson's work convinced Marconi that an elevated aerial was the right instrument for his purposes. But this conviction, it seems, took time to sink in, for we find him experimenting with the metallic reflector again on the Salisbury plain in March 1897 (see Dam's report given earlier). His final choice, of course, was the elevated aerial. Even then, Marconi never acknowledged Jackson, let alone Bose. Jackson remained unaware to the end that Marconi had been claiming to be the inventor of the elevated aerial.

Often in his life, Marconi showed a propensity for usurping other people's inventions by declaring that he hadn't known of the earlier work, and had made the invention independently. He did this twice with Lodge: when Marconi filed his first patent claiming priority for the use of Morse code in wireless telegraphy, and the automatic tapper device (Patent No. 12039); later, patenting the tuned or syntonic apparatus (Patent No. 7777). He did the same with Braun, but only once. He usurped Bose's mercury autocoherer and patented it as the Italian Navy coherer, then claimed the elevated aerial as his own invention.

About the explanation of how the aerial worked, Marconi had the following to say:

> The practical value of this innovation was not understood by many physicists for quite a considerable period, and the results which I obtained were by many erroneously considered simply due to efficiency in details of construction of the receiver, and to the employment of a large amount of energy. Others did not overlook the fact that a radical change had been introduced by making these elevated capacities and the earth form part of the high frequency oscillators and receivers.

It is amazing that while physicists were, for years, expressing scepticism or trying to find an explanation for the aerial phenomenon, Bose remained indifferent. However, his indifference is no reason for the Nobel committee to ignore his contributions. Be that as it may, Marconi deserves credit for the idea that the receiver aerial should be tuned with the transmitter aerial. He 'borrowed', without acknowledgement, the idea of tuned or syntonic apparatus, in general, from Lodge. In other words, he combined the idea of Lodge's tuned apparatus with Bose's elevated-aerials. This combination brought about a revolution in wireless transmission.

Had the Nobel committee investigated a little, they would have also discovered Marconi's science adviser Fleming's crucial contribution. It is a matter of regret that they did not. Unearthing Bose's receiver, the mercury autocoherer, deep inside the layers of secrecy with which

Marconi had shrouded his receiving system, posed a much more difficult task for the Nobel committee, no doubt. In any case, they should have paid attention to the scandal of the Italian Navy coherer, and Marconi's reputation of non-acknowledgement of predecessors.

However, perhaps a greater share of responsibility lies with the community of physicists in Britain. It is obvious that some of them knew the truth and remained silent, but did spread a rumour. The needle of suspicion points towards the trio of Lodge, Thompson, and Fleming.

It should be recalled that Lodge had advanced the theory of 'contact-soldering' in the metal filings of Branly's receiver to explain its behaviour; this theory had engendered the name coherer. Bose then published a paper which overthrew Lodge's theory. Lodge could not have forgotten the content of Bose's paper in just a couple of years. He was not only present at Bose's presentation before the British Association in Bradford, but also was the principal participant in the discussion that followed. Lodge was then accompanied by his friends, as per Bose's letter to Tagore; therefore, his friend S. P. Thompson also was likely present in that meeting. Lodge's attitude then to his opponent was most magnanimous, and Bose called it 'John Bull's love of fair play'.

Requested by Sir William Crookes, Bose spoke on the same subject in a Friday Evening Discourse before the Royal Institution. Among the audience again were a large number of physicists. Thereafter, he was invited by the Royal Society to speak on a kindred subject, with greater emphasis on the physiological aspects. Lodge, Thompson, and Fleming were Fellows of the Royal Society, and therefore, likely to have attended this meeting as well.

Thus, Bose had the opportunity of presenting his findings, accompanied by live experiments, no less than three times before a learned audience. It is most likely that each one of the trio heard Bose speak at least once. Yet none of them pointed out that Bose was the true inventor of the mercury autocoherer.

The last named of the trio, Fleming, received a letter from Marconi when the scandal of the Italian Navy coherer surfaced. It was a request for support, in the face of attacks by Thompson and Lodge. Fleming's reply included a promise to support generally, but with a quid pro quo that Marconi should acknowledge Fleming's contribution. It also had the following sentence, 'I did not consider it advisable for me to say anything on patent questions apropos of Thompson's articles because I feel that these very delicate matters may have to be discussed one day in a Court of law and the less said about them now the better.'

Did Fleming know that Bose, who was then in town, was the true inventor and apprehended that the Bengali scientist might take Marconi to court? This question arises because, on an earlier occasion, Bose and Fleming had presented their respective papers in the same meeting of the Royal Society. Working in the same field, Fleming must have followed Bose's work thereafter.

Even if we ignore Bose's lectures in England before learned audiences, his paper in the *Proceedings of the Royal Society* was there for all to see. The physicists who were active in the same field, such as Lodge and Thompson, had no reason for not looking.

A few questions naturally arise. Would the British trio of physicists, named above, have kept quiet if Bose were a fellow countryman? Were the European scientists and the Nobel committee limited by a Eurocentric attitude and world view? In this context, the following information is significant: although Marconi received the Nobel award in 1909, he had been nominated for it in 1901, 1902, 1903, 1908; also, in 1929 and 1933, many years after receiving the prize. It is not difficult to guess that these nominations arrived mainly from two countries, Britain and Italy. Bose also worked in two countries, India and Britain, but he had none to nominate him.

Why did the Nobel committee overlook Marconi's unscrupulous track record when it came to his patents? Was it because of political pressure from the British establishment? This question is relevant because a Member of the British Parliament, Henniker Heaton, had written in favour of Marconi, when the Italian Navy coherer scandal broke (quoted earlier). The Royal family, too, was favourably disposed towards Marconi, thanks to the impression he made on them through his messaging service in the summer of 1897. It should be noted that two powerful well-connected families were supporting Marconi from behind, in two different countries.

Whatever the reasons, the fact remains that the Nobel committee did not take into consideration Marconi's persistent unprincipled conduct.

This question is salient, not on the grounds of morality alone, but also for the true assessment of a person's scientific achievements.

Was the Nobel committee unduly pressurized by public opinion? This seems to have been the case. A few months before the declaration of the Nobel award, an astonishing rescue operation of hundreds of passengers in a shipwreck took place; this has been detailed at the beginning of this chapter. The rescuing vessels were called to the wreck's location in the middle of the ocean, enveloped in dense fog, by means of the ship's wireless apparatus supplied by the Marconi company. Subsequently, Marconi was catapulted into the centre of media attention and received much public adulation.

In this author's opinion, if his practice of usurpation of other people's work can be ignored, then Marconi deserved the Nobel award. It is because, sometimes, research driven by commercial interests can produce a breakthrough in science. Marconi's trans-Atlantic experiments were part of one such case. These tests should be viewed as physics experiments at a gigantic semi-global scale, which no physicist of Marconi's times could even conceive of.

Marconi's findings were two-fold and of great significance for physics. First, he proved beyond doubt that electric waves could reach thousands of miles and were not deterred by the curvature of the earth. Second, the waves reached much further during the night than during the day. The second finding compelled physicists to look at the sun and the upper atmosphere for explanation, where they found the answer for both the phenomena.

However, the bottom line is that both Bose and Fleming too deserved a share in the prize. The American reporter, R. S. Baker, who interviewed Marconi after the Newfoundland experiment, said it the best, 'He took the coherer of Branly and Calzecchi, the oscillator of Righi, he used the discoveries of Henry and Hertz, but his creation like that of the poet who gathers the words of men in a perfect lyric, was nonetheless brilliant and original.'

In all frankness, we can amend and improve upon his statement as follows:

He took the elevated aerial of Bose, but didn't give him priority; also, Bose's 'mercury coherer with a telephone' and assigned it to the Royal

Italian Navy; he used the powerful transmitter designed by Fleming, but did not acknowledge him; he used the discoveries of Henry, Hertz, Bose, and Righi; he created music by tuning Bose's aerial in the way of Lodge; but his creation like that of the poet who gathers the words of men in a perfect lyric, was nonetheless brilliant and original.

Father Lafont, a Jesuit priest of Belgian origin and a renowned professor of Physics in St. Xavier's College, where Bose had studied, made a comment in the context of the Nobel Prize and the rumour about Marconi's wrongdoings. His statement, made in a public meeting, suggested that if Bose had taken out a patent on his wireless apparatus, he would have forestalled Marconi, and was widely reported in the newspapers. If Bose had patented the mercury autocoherer in Britain, the one usurped by Marconi and Solari, would Marconi be deterred? Looking at Marconi's persistent record and the limited capacity of the patent office to assess priority, one can safely say that the end result would still be the same. For instance, Marconi had used Lodge's patented ideas on tuned telegraphy, been taken to court, but still got the Nobel Prize, long before the case was settled. Even a court case, filed by a British physicist of renown, made no difference. Additionally, unknown to anyone, except Mrs Sara Bull, Nivedita, and Abala, a patent had been taken out by Bose for one of his self-restoring receivers, the artificial eye. Although this patent was in America, it found a place in the list of patents in Great Britain and America (see Bose's letter to the Italian academic, Bassoli). Thus, people in Britain were also aware of this patent. It made no difference to Marconi's dishonourable conduct and the final outcome.

The only thing that would have forestalled Marconi was if Bose had taken a little more interest in radio-telegraphy and spent a tiny fraction of his time on it. There was a golden opportunity begging at his door—Dr Muirhead, an academic turned businessman well known to Bose, had requested him and promised to facilitate patent applications—but Bose spurned his offer. If Bose had accepted Muirhead's offer and, explained to him the function of a pair of aerials, Marconi would have been forestalled. Muirhead was a friend of Lodge's and was aware of

Lodge's patent on the tuned telegraphic apparatus; he too would have tuned Bose's aerials, just as Marconi had tuned his own. In the end, it was Bose's quixotic aversion to patents and his refusal to come to terms with the mores of an industrial age, that was the decisive factor.

7

BOSE TURNS TO PLANT PHYSIOLOGY AND TAGORE WINS THE NOBEL

One wintry evening in 1898 or 1899, Abala and Jagadish had a surprise visitor in their Circular Road house in Calcutta. A coach and a pair arrived and a gentleman in full European attire alighted. For a few seconds Abala was foxed and could not recognize the visitor, and then she burst into a hearty laugh—the visitor was none other than Swami Vivekananda. He was a fun-loving soul, very fond of the spicy Eastern Bengali cuisine which his hostess cooked. The hostess knew well the purpose of the visit and promptly invited him to stay on for dinner.[56]

On such visits, the Swami usually regaled his host and hostess with experiences from his travels in the West. In the visit recounted here, he talked about his stay on an island in the Thousand Island Park on the St. Lawrence River, in the summer of 1895.

It was here on this island that he met Christine Greenstidel for the first time. Christine, of course, had heard the Swami speak quite a few times in her native city of Detroit; in this, her friend Mrs Mary Funke was her companion, but they never approached him personally. Later, they had an urge to seek him out and get to know him better. When they heard that the Swami had gathered a small band of followers in the Thousand Island Park, they could not resist the temptation to meet him.

Christine and Mary turned up unexpectedly on a rainy evening. Though weary after a long journey, they did not rest but plodded up the hill to the residence of the Swami. On meeting him, Christine said, 'We have come to you just as we would go to Jesus if he were still on

---

[56]Abala, later Lady Bose, who outlived Sir Jagadis by many years, reminisced to P. Bhattacharyya, about such visits by Swami Vivekananda, including this particular one. Once earlier, the Swami had appeared unannounced in western dress at the Belur monastery, to the surprise and amusement of his brother monks and juniors.

earth and ask him to teach us'.

The Swami looked at them kindly and replied gently, 'If only I had the power of Christ to set you free.'

According to Christine's memoirs, the Swami had planned to initiate a few of the gathered disciples. He said to Christine and Mary rather shyly, 'I don't know you well enough to feel sure that you are ready for initiation. I have a power which I seldom use—the power of reading minds. If you permit me, I shall like to read your mind, as I wish to initiate you with the others tomorrow.'

They assented joyfully. Satisfied with the result of the reading, he gave them the mantra and made them his disciples. Later, on being quizzed about the reading, he revealed that one of them would travel extensively in the countries of Asia and would be intimately connected with India. He described the very houses she would live in and the kind of company she would keep. Christine continued in her memoirs, 'Important as well as minor events about both of us were foretold, nearly all of which have come to pass.'

The few weeks at the retreat in the Thousand Island Park was like heaven on earth for Christine. She was to reach India, some seven years later with the Swami's consent, when she was thirty-six years of age. In the meantime, she had resolved to become a nun. She was received at the Bombay port by Nivedita and Josephine MacLeod and brought to Calcutta on 7 April 1902, about three months before the Swami breathed his last. She stayed in the American consulate and went to meet the Swami at the Belur monastery; he welcomed her and, in view of the impending summer, advised her to leave the plains and stay in the Advaita Ashram in Mayavati in the Kumaon Himalayas for a few months.

Joe and Sara left for America via England in May, while Christine, Nivedita, and the Japanese artist Okakura went to Mayavati. Nivedita and Okakura left Mayawati after some time. Christine was still in Mayavati when the news of the Swami's death reached her, and she calmly mourned his passing. She came to Calcutta in the autumn and joined Nivedita's school in Baghbazar. Here, she stayed for eight long years, and became known as Sister Christine and provided steady assistance to Nivedita.

The schoolhouse came to be called the House of Sisters; Abala and

Jagadish were frequent visitors and Christine got to know them quite
well. The Boses occasionally invited the two sisters to their Circular
Road house for dinner. Christine was not as animated a personality
like Nivedita. Rather, she was a serene person, wholly engaged in her
school duties and otherwise absorbed in spiritual practices. The two
became good friends. Christine's arrival greatly relieved Nivedita, and
she was all praise for Christine:

'She is absolutely staunch. She is gentle and clinging, and not too
dominant, but she is loyal and sympathetic and generous. Perfect in
sweetness and perfect in trustworthiness and so large in her views.'

And again,

'Christine is, beyond words, soothing, gracious, lovely.'

Here in the same lane, a few years later, Christine met a spiritually-
inclined boy, about twenty years of age, named Basiswar Sen, and
became a mother figure to him. He would later became a devoted
assistant to Bose.

Saradananda-swami, who was then the secretary of the Ramakrishna
Math and Mission, arranged for a monthly subsistence allowance to
Christine through the generosity of Mrs Sara Bull. So, from now on
Sara became a mother to Christine, in addition to Nivedita and Bose.

Sara the Mother: I

In early 1903, Sara was planning to go to Japan to help Okakura start
organizing a conference on religions, then go to India and return in
good time to participate in said conference. She arrived in Japan in
mid-April and stayed with Okakura and his family. Setting sail for India
via Hongkong, she reached Calcutta in early June, at the height of the
Indian summer.

Unfortunately, Sara had contracted dysentery on board. Nivedita
brought a very sick Sara to the Boses's home, where they stayed until
Sara recovered. Their planned departure to the cool hills of Darjeeling
with the Boses had to be postponed for several days. Besides, Sara had
to cancel the return trip to Japan and now decided to go to England
instead. She had brought many teaching aids: books, slides, learning
toys, maps, etc. for Nivedita's school.

When the monsoon rains arrived, all four returned to Calcutta. Sara and Nivedita mainly came to help Christine reopen the school, since the latter was new to Calcutta and knew no Bengali. They lived in a house adjacent to the school, which had been acquired for its expansion. From there, Sara wrote to her friend Mrs Briggs, 'Margot is here, hard at work upon her book. We hope that she will complete it and I will be able to take the manuscript with me to England.... Dr Bose's original work goes on.... I may also have a manuscript of his to take with me.'

Mrs Sara Chapman Bull

On 31 July, Sara wrote to her daughter Olea, regarding Nivedita and Bose,

> I always enjoy [when] I have had time to see my friends and learn more concerning the plans for future work which various people in whom I am interested are undertaking, all satisfactorily and successfully....
>
> [Nivedita] and I attended the mass for the Pope yesterday in the morning.... It was very impressive and will be memorable as an historical and as well as devotional incident. We return to Darjeeling on Monday probably.

It is noteworthy that Sara and Nivedita lived up to the Swami's ideal of respect and acceptance of all religions; they were both Protestants and the Pope is the head of the Catholic Church, and yet they attended the Mass held in Pope Leo XIII's honour. Two years later, Nivedita would write in a letter, dated 20 July 1905, 'Christianity is so beautiful that I cannot understand being really cut off from it.... The Christianity that I love is of convent cells and Christian souls, and no other.'

In August 1903, Sara and Nivedita went back to Darjeeling and Sara wrote to Mrs Briggs from there,

Margot's work goes on apace. She is in her last chapter for which I am very glad. She is very tired, and needs to have time to recuperate before October. If all goes well, Dr Bose comes to us with a mass of demonstrations on his recent plant research, ready for putting in form for publication....

[That] an original research is going on, at the same time very exacting duties, seems a miracle; and we desire to have it all ended as rapidly as possible to ensure its safety.... We have a fire in our sitting room and Margot's little study faces the great snow range. No life could be quieter.

Here, she expresses her concern for the back-breaking work that Bose had been doing to meet the dual demands of his college duties and research. While in Darjeeling, she wrote almost fortnightly to Mrs Briggs. She wrote on 8 September:

The heights have been glorious these two mornings and we chanced to see the full moon and dawn blended this morning....

Dr Bose's work goes on at the most wonderful pace. He comes to us the end of this month [for vacationing] with enough material for a new book on plants. They have a friend's villa in the town.

Margot's book was finished yesterday! To our joy. And now it remains to revise, make footnotes etc. and then she will be ready to act as secretary [to Bose]. ...While Margot writes, I read history and sew. I am just starting Mr Dutt's *Economical History of India*.

Darjeeling reminded Sara of her beloved Norway and she was charmed by its natural beauty. On 22 September, she wrote poetically:

The past week has given us most lovely days and evenings, mystic, picturesque and brilliant, for the rain has fallen mostly at night and the heavy mists given way to [fleecy] clouds moving past the face of the mountains, or piling themselves up at sunset in masses more impressive than the heights they conceal.

Our own supply of flowers cultivated are dahlias: crimson, are single, the plum double, and the loveliest mauve iris, a Japanese sort, which finds its way through clumps of its own grass, and which remains in bloom two days within doors when I pluck them quite fresh....

I find myself able to type one chapter of Margot's book, over which I am very pleased. Mrs Ratcliffe has typed some six chapters. Both she and her husband are best friends to Margot.[57]

Margot is taking a retreat of three days, rejoining us tomorrow. She is tired and I hope it will do her much good.

On 7 October, she wrote,

The past week has been devoted to Dr Bose's work. He comes as early as possible, five miles walk or ride, and stays until afternoon tea. Five papers have been written thus far, and you can imagine what this means of intense application for Nivedita....

I am typing some chapters of Margot's book for the publisher and enjoy the practice very much. It is good on my part to have something to do requiring steady application. We go to Calcutta at the latest on the 21st and this will give me a week there.

A week later, Sara wrote joyfully about the progress of Bose's work in these idyllic environs,

Dr Bose will have nine glorious papers by the end of this week! I am sorry to say he is so tired he can hardly move and has no vacation.... We go down to Calcutta Sunday next instead of tomorrow, as the papers need more time. Dr Bose has to take a day's rest off.

They returned to Calcutta with the Boses on 21 October 1903. We can only imagine how merry the party was during the long train journey, with so much accomplished! Sara stayed with Nivedita at her school, the House of Sisters. On 2 November, a new section was opened for the education of illiterate adult women, mostly married, the Pura Stree Vibhag. Bose's sister Labanyaprabha agreed to teach there. Sara wrote to Mrs Briggs before leaving Calcutta,

I shall be your Christmas present!

Being here, I have been of help in typing Dr Bose's papers: a most wonderful accomplishment, as it really means another book,

---

[57]Mr Ratcliffe was the editor of *The Statesman*, Calcutta.

equally new and important in improving and extending previous
work. I am taking Margot's original manuscript to read to you.

Sara and Nivedita wanted no name or fame for themselves, just the pure
joy out of serving and helping others accomplish great things. Sara set
sail for England in November 1903 and had a nice and quiet voyage,
and on reaching London, took up residence at the Sesame Club. She
took Nivedita's manuscript for *The Web of Indian Life* to her publishers
and submitted Bose's scientific papers to the Royal Society. These were
the series of papers, which were initially accepted and then refused by
the Royal Society, in the winter of 1903–1904.

Plant Life and Its Response

As mentioned in an earlier chapter, Bose, after his failure in getting
his papers published, decided to write a new book—*Plant Response as
a Means of Physiological Investigation*. This was published by the well-
known publisher of Longmans, Green, and Co., in London in 1906.
Within a year, another book, titled *Comparative Electro-physiology*,
followed. These books would later do much to help Bose regain the
confidence of the world's scientists, and the Royal Society resumed
publication of his papers after a long interval.

But all that was still in the misty uncertainty of the future. No
longer satisfied with only writing journal papers, Bose made the decision
to consistently put down work in books—*Research on Irritability of
Plants* (1913), *Physiology of Ascent of Sap* (1923), and *Physiology of
Photosynthesis* (1924) were some of his next works.

Nivedita was an invaluable help to Bose. She offered both secretarial
and scientific assistance: preparing manuscripts, revising papers, drawing
diagrams, verifying calculations, editing, and proofreading. Often the
language and sometimes even the handwriting of the manuscripts were
hers. Her hand is visible in the entire manuscript of the book *Plant
Response*. Either Bose came to 17 Bosepara Lane or Nivedita went to 93
Circular Road. They were together in the hills of Darjeeling, Mayavati,
or Mussoorie in the summer vacations, working on his papers or books.
This continued as long as she lived.

We shall now provide a context to Bose's botanical research, which the Royal Society refused to publish. The birth, growth, and death of plant life, quite similar to that of animal life, is a matter of common observation. Despite this all-important starting point, physiologists believed that there was little in common between plant life and animal life, that plants in general are life without any sensitivity or capacity to respond. Bose's experiments, therefore, came as a jolt to most of them, and as it happens with the advent of all new ideas, an alternative consensus took time to emerge.

While in England, Bose had demonstrated the similarity of responses (to a stimulus) of animal life, plant life, and non-living inert matter. These responses were obtained by recording a trace of the variable current in a magnetic lever recorder (see Fig. 5.3); that is to say, by the electrical method. In fact, there were two electrical methods involved—one by measuring the voltage difference in the specimen; the other by sensing the change in conductivity. In these experiments, the stimulus was applied in different forms—mechanically by striking or twisting, electrically by connecting to a battery, and chemically by treating with various compounds. Bose now extended the scope of these experiments to a much wider field of plant life. Application of heat was also one of the stimuli.

Since plant life was closer to animal life than inert matter and since the electric responses of plant and animal tissues were similar, Bose hypothesized that the mechanism underlying the response was also likely to be one and the same. Bose had observed that, regarding the life processes of the plant, different speculative theories had been put forth. They were not backed by any direct observation, because it had not been possible to observe what goes on inside the body of a plant, as it had been for an animal. He surmised that the need of the hour was to invent new, sensitive instruments for direct observation of different aspects of plant life. Thus, the inventive genius of our scientist found a new avenue of expression in probing into the secrets of plants.

While it is impossible to detail all the research conducted by Bose in the confines of this biography, we shall attempt to discuss some of his most important work to create a holistic view of his life's work. To start with, we shall take up one of the topics that was initially accepted by the Royal Society, then archived, regarding the mechanical response of a plant in the form of the movement of its leaf, stalk, and other organs.

Something puzzled our scientist a great deal—all plants and their organs, when subjected to excitation or stimulation, exhibit electric responses just like animal tissues; but plants, in general, do not show any visible movement, as animals do. Only a few exceptions, such as the mimosa, telegraph plant, and little tree plant, and insectivorous plants like the Venus flytrap, exhibit visible movement. The mimosa, locally known as lajjavati, telegraph plant, known as bon-chandaal, and little tree plant, called joloi, were available in Bengal.

When a mimosa leaf is touched, it responds by visibly contracting, then drooping, as shown in Fig. 7.1. The leaflets of the little tree plant go into visible rapid movements on being touched. The telegraph plant does not need any stimulus—its smaller leaflets keep on gyrating up and down, very slowly but visibly; each leaf completes a cycle in about three minutes, under normal conditions. The Venus flytrap responds when an insect sits on it, by trapping it between two opposite leaves. Then, it slowly digests the insect.

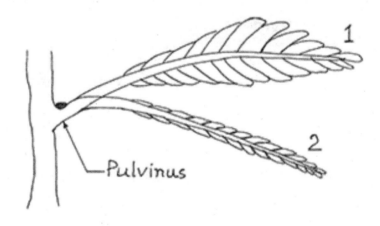

Fig. 7.1: Leaf of mimosa plant;
1. Appearance before touch;
2. Appearance after touch.

Ordinary plants show no visible movement even when subjected to vigorous stimulus, such as a strike by a rod. Bose noted that the drooping of the mimosa leaf was due to the contraction of the lower half of the cushion-shaped and joint-like leaf base, called pulvinus. The contraction of the pulvinus is very small, yet it produces a fairly large fall of the tip of the leaf, as shown in Fig. 7.1. He, therefore, reasoned that contraction due to excitation might be present in ordinary plants also, but might have escaped the attention of other investigators, because it was too small to be visible. During his research to artificially magnify this movement, he invented the optical pulse recorder.

To understand how this instrument works, let us first do a simple experiment in a large room with a forester torch or any other torch that produces a strong light beam, consisting of parallel rays. Place the torch on a table, kept at the furthest point possible from a wall. Position the torch in such a way that its beam of light is horizontal and falls perpendicular to the wall.

Now place a large screen, parallel to the wall, at the halfway point between the wall and the torch. Mark the light spot on the screen with a pen, then turn the torch by a small angle, say 10 degrees, with the help of a protractor, taking care that the light beam remains horizontal all the time. You will notice that the light spot has moved only sideways, neither up nor down. Mark the changed position of the light spot and measure the distance it has travelled from the original location on the screen. The spot will have travelled a large distance for a slight change of only 10 degrees in the angle of the torch.

Next, remove the screen, and let the light beam fall on the wall, which now serves as the 'new' screen. Repeat the experiment exactly as before, and measure the travel distance of the light spot on the wall. You will find that this distance is double that on the screen. We observe that the larger the gap between the torch and the screen, the larger the travel distance of the light spot. Hence, any tiny movement of the source (the torch) can be magnified by placing the screen at a large distance.

The optical pulse recorder works in a similar fashion. In this instrument, a lever, called optical lever, plays a key role. A lever by definition is a rod or bar, hinge-supported somewhere along its length, so that it can freely rotate on that support. The hinge support is called 'fulcrum'. For instance, the see-saw device in a children's park is a lever with its fulcrum in the middle. If you plant your elbow firmly on a table, the forearm becomes a lever, with the elbow as its fulcrum.

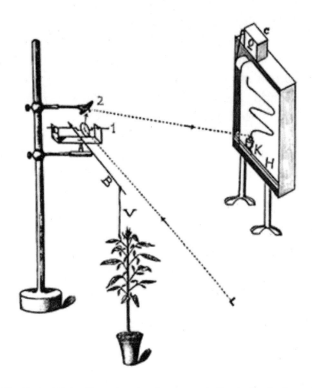

Fig. 7.2: The Optical Pulse Recorder. 1, mirror-on-spindle; 2, tilted mirror; B, arm of optical lever, attached to moving leaflet, via V, a vertical link; L, ray of light, which after reflections from the two mirrors falls on screen of the recorder; C, clock-work, which keeps twin-drum—on which is wrapped the recording paper—revolving; H, horizontal guide bar; K, ink-well with projecting sponge.

Fig. 7.2 gives a schematic diagram of the optical pulse recorder. A ray of light (L), shown by a dashed line, is reflected upwards by the mirror on the spindle (1). The ray is then reflected a second time by a tilted mirror (2), and turned sideways by a right angle, more or less, as shown in the figure. The ray falls on the recording screen, which is placed at a distance from the twin mirror. The slightest shift in the angle of the lower mirror produces a large shift in the position of the light on the screen, the magnification being proportional to the screen's distance from the mirrors. In other words, one can adjust the magnification by increasing or decreasing the intervening distance. The light beam and the angles of the mirrors are so adjusted that any rotation of the lower mirror shifts the light spot only sideways, i.e., horizontally.

In Fig. 7.2, the vertical link (V) connects the arm of the optical lever (B) to the spontaneously pulsating leaflet of a telegraph plant. The other end of the optical lever (B) is supported on the spindle of the lower mirror, the spindle acting as the fulcrum. The up–down movement of the leaflet swivels the optical lever and produces a to-and-fro rotation of the lower mirror. This results in sideways movement of the spot of light on the screen.

The screen consists of a vertically rising paper strip, wrapped around a rotating pair of drums, one unwinding (releasing) and the other winding. The left end of the upper drum is clearly visible in the figure. The drums are kept rotating by a standard clockwork device (C), located on top of the recorder. Near the bottom of the screen, where the light beam is incident, there is a horizontal guide bar (H) which carries a sliding inkwell (K), from which projects the ink sponge. The sideways excursion of the spot of light is tracked by moving the inkwell manually by hand (not shown in the figure). Since the leaflet moves slowly, at the rate of one cycle in 3 minutes, the light spot can be tracked easily. Thus, a magnified record of the leaflet movement is generated.

How can a small leaflet shift the weight of a lever up and down? Does it have sufficient strength to do that? The old-fashioned balance for weighing gold in a goldsmith's shop gives us a clue. If a piece of gold is placed on one pan and some carefully chosen known weights are placed on the other, we obtain a perfect poise. Now, even the weight of the smallest ant is enough to tilt the balance bar to one side or the other. Our optical lever, when properly balanced by a counterweight (not shown in Fig. 7.2), is comparable to the goldsmith's balance-bar; this is explained with the help of Fig. 7.3.

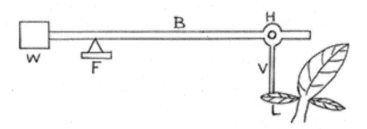

Fig. 7.3: Balancing a lever with a counterweight; B: Optical lever;
W: Counterweight; F: Fulcrum of the lever; H: Hinge;
V: Vertical link rod; L: Leaf of telegraph plant.

The figure shows the optical lever (B), supported on the fulcrum (F), about which it can rotate. The vertical link rod (V) is connected by a hinge (H) to the right side of the lever, and a counterweight (W) is attached to the extreme left. The magnitude of the counterweight is so adjusted that the whole system is perfectly poised and the lever maintains a horizontal position. Now, the leaflet (L) of a telegraph plant is attached to the bottom of the link rod, as shown in Fig. 7.3. It is tied to the link rod by means of a silk thread passing through a hole in the rod, which is not shown in the figure.

In order to move the lever, the leaflet has only to overcome the friction of the fulcrum and hinge; it is strong enough to overcome this force and move the lever (B) up and down. Moreover, to minimize friction, Bose used expensive gemstone bearings for the mirror's spindle and the hinge and also made the optical lever as light as possible, by using lightweight construction material.

Bose gradually perfected the apparatus working with a telegraph plant. Then ordinary plants were investigated with much greater magnification, and of course, after application of some form of stimulus or excitation. Bose's intuition turned out to be correct. The leaf and other organs of ordinary plants also showed movements on being excited. Comparison with muscle curves, familiar to physiologists, proved that the plant contraction curves were analogous.

The filaments which make up the corona or 'glory' of the passion flower evinced large contractions, about 30 per cent of their length.

Other organs of the flower too exhibited sizable contractions, but this was an exceptional case. Other flowers produced relatively small contractions that were only visible on magnification, as Bose expected. The phenomenon of course varies from plant to plant, and is dependent on environmental conditions, age, season, temperature, etc. Bose repeated the experiments with chemically induced depression and exultation to get results analogous to the muscle curves.

The concept of the optical lever was first developed and used in the optical pulse recorder. It would be further refined and put to good use in a truly astonishing piece of equipment, over a decade later. At this time, he showed that application of a stimulant leads to contraction of the diameter of the trunk or main stem of a plant. In order to demonstrate this, he invented a device, using the optical lever, and named it Kunchan-graph (Kunchan means contraction in Sanskrit). Initially, the nationalist in him wished to give Sanskrit names to all his inventions. But noticing how difficult it was for the Europeans to pronounce the name and understand its meaning, he abandoned this idea.

Apart from mechanical response, electrical response was also studied copiously for different plants with various forms of stimulation. All the results were concomitant and showed similarity with muscle curves. Further, he discovered that plant response, under repeated excitation, initially showed gradual increment, and then signs of fatigue, much like animal muscle.

The graphs of plant behaviour, recorded by the optical pulse recorder, can be found in *Plant Response,* and are not reproduced here. The same results would be obtained later by using a completely automated instrument.

Sara the Mother: II

We shall now try to capture the human drama that unfolded around the time Bose started making headway into the field of physiology. After the Royal Society refused his papers in the winter of 1903–1904, Bose and Nivedita worked at a feverish pace to publish his work in the form of a book, before his detractors had time to steal his ideas and claim priority.

Referring to the events of that winter, Nivedita wrote to Sara that when Bose learned about the objections of a group of physiologists led by Dr Waller to his papers submitted to the Royal Society, he was at first thunderstruck. She continued in the same letter,

> After a while, with a flash, he broke the spell. 'Telegraph to Mrs Bull! She will set it right!' 'How selfish you are!' said his nephew, 'Do you know that she is far away, in America? Fancy her leaving home again! And why should she be troubled anyway?' 'Hmm! How much you know! (Scornfully) Doesn't she look upon me as her son?' ...He had despaired of finding all the Waller documents. And suddenly he found that you had made them into a bundle and put them in one place!

As long as Sara was with Bose in England, she took care not only of his health, but also of his research by proofreading, occasionally typing up his research, and acting as a secretary maintaining his papers, particularly when Nivedita was not present.

Bose wrote to Tagore on 29 June 1904, 'I have been feeling rather low lately. I have written nineteen papers, but they are all being denied publication. I am thinking of writing a book, but do not feel like re-visiting the old matter.' This letter has been quoted from earlier. Motivated and assisted by Nivedita, Bose started writing the book *Plant Response* after June 1904; the book took nearly two years to finish. On 1 March 1906, Bose sent Sara the manuscript of his book, *Plant Response*, which was entirely in Nivedita's handwriting; he knew that Sara would read the book, then convey it to the publishers Longmans, Green and Co., and cover any costs. A letter was enclosed in which he wrote,

> You will see from the contents, the scope of the book, and also the list of illustrations. It has been a very severe strain, but well worth the effort.
>
> Do you know that I have actually isolated nerve in plants, and the records obtained with them cannot [be] distinguished from those from animal nerves? This is a very wonderful discovery, and will, I think, enable me to obtain rational clues to various nervous diseases.

Bose was talking about the possible medical application of his research.

He dedicated the book to 'The Mother', but did not mention Sara by name. He made up for it by ending the enclosed letter with,
'Do you know when I was little, I used to bring in a shamefaced way some trifle for my mother. And now I bring this book for you. Your own son.'

Why didn't Bose mention Sara by name in the dedication? Do we see an emerging pattern of behaviour? It is obvious that Bose did not want Sara's name to appear in print. At the same time, he did not mean to hurt her and so, hid his true intentions behind a story from his childhood days. It seems that he was following his policy of not leaving any trace of his personal connection with Sara in writing that might see wider circulation, just as he had done in Nivedita's case.

Bose wrote two more letters to Sara in the same month; in the first, he wrote that his paper, submitted to the Royal Society, had met with adverse criticism on purely personal grounds, rather than on scientific merit. In the second, he said that he discovered one of the laws of human society,[58]

The same jealousy would be found everywhere in the world. As long as you work moderately good things, you are patronized, but when you are above that, you cannot exhort anything but hostility. I have therefore to complete the work and bring out a book. No clique can suppress that.

There is an allusion to a new book in the letter. Nivedita and the Boses went to the cool hills of Mussoorie in the summer of 1906. There, assisted by Nivedita, Bose worked on a new book, *Comparative Electrophysiology.*

In May, Sara was taken ill but the cause was not diagnosed for quite a long time. On 24 May, the Boses and Nivedita celebrated Sara's birthday in her absence. Nivedita wrote to Sara on the same day, 'We are having a lovely birthday, with your picture decorated on the mantelpiece. Presents to everyone.'

Soon, Nivedita became keen to write her version of a biography of

---

[58]The primary source of this letter and the one before is the Sara Chapman Bull Collection of the Vedanta Society of Northern California.

the Swami, *The Master as I Saw Him.* Since she needed to give it all her attention, she had to find a way to extricate herself from the commitment of helping Bose write his scientific books. When in a similar situation in Paris in 1900 as Geddes's secretary, Nivedita was rescued by Sara with an invitation to come to Brittany. Now, at the beginning of 1906, Sara offered to meet her anywhere in Europe and rent their accommodation, where she could write Swami Vivekananda's biography in seclusion. Nivedita suggested that Sara tell Bose that she (Sara) needed her—that would make it easier for her to disengage from his work. Then Sara would send Nivedita a ticket for Europe.

Even then, she was concerned about monetary support for Bose's scientific work and wrote to Sara in 1906, 'To science. The remaining 3000 pounds of the bequest.... This is to be at the disposal of my friend and to be used by him, preferably for two I shall name. But according to the best of his ability for Indian science.'

It is apparent that Sara sent such largesse Bose's way from time to time, and left no records of her own. We get a glimpse of them only from these letters.

In a year's time, when the proofreading of the book *Comparative Electro-physiology* was in its final stages, Nivedita wrote a review of it and requested her friend, W. T. Stead, editor of *Review of Reviews*, to publish it. Stead had some other work on his desk and forwarded it to Sara so that she could publish it in an American journal. The publication of this book was also financed by Sara.

Nivedita was constantly writing to Sara to come to India. Before planning her trip to India, Sara went to stay, in April, with Joe and the Leggetts in England and then visited Nivedita's mother at Wimbledon. Nivedita wrote to Sara on 17 May 1906, 'Mother writes to us, full of anxiety. She says you are white and thin, with dark circles under your eyes, and lonely. And the Bairn[59] says if a letter comes showing that you need me, he won't rebel in the least....'

Sara had to go back to America to properly close up her house, if she wished to go to India for any length of time. There, she was diagnosed with a benign tumour and needed an operation immediately.

---

[59]Meaning a small boy, her nickname for Bose.

The surgery went well and Joe went to Cambridge to live with Sara for a month in December 1906. Sara took several months to regain her full vigour and strength.

On 2 May 1907, Nivedita wrote to Joe, 'I had a telegram of 15 words from Saint Sara yesterday, commanding me to leave for Europe at once.'

Did Sara write any letters to Bose? It was natural for her to have written a few. However, we do not know for sure, for none of Sara's letters to Bose have come to light so far.

Automatic Records

Bose learnt from Nivedita about Sara's illness and recovery. He was affectionate towards the saintly lady, who was such of a mother figure to him, and felt a pang of initial anxiety and then relief. Meanwhile his scientific work was progressing apace. Now that we have described the optical pulse recorder, we can pinpoint the cause of mistrust on the part of British physiologists; or, perhaps, the pretext for the mistrust. They doubted the functioning of the optical pulse recorder. Their contention was that the human hand, tracking the spot of light, could manipulate the response curve, and therefore, the results were not trustworthy; only a completely automated record could be trusted. This was a direct assault on Bose's integrity, whose record of research and its reporting had been unimpeachable heretofore.

Bose knew there was a credibility gap between him and his European counterparts. He knew his options were limited—he could either invent an automatic recorder that, once set into motion, would not require any human intervention, or give up this line of research. Proving his mettle, he decided to meet the challenge by trying to invent an automatic recorder.

He deferred travelling to Europe for later. He would silence his opponents by inventing new instruments, performing an exhaustive series of experiments, and by publishing them as books. The five years from 1902 until his next sojourn to Europe in 1907 were very productive indeed.

But before starting on a new invention, Bose had to race to rewrite the content of his large number of papers, rejected by the Royal Society, for the book *Plant Response*. Once the manuscript was sent to the publishers, he turned his attention to the new instrument and set the following requirements for it:

1. The experimental plant should be excited by uniform stimuli at definite intervals, by the new automatic instrument.
2. The response of the plant should be automatically recorded, without any human intervention.
3. The cycle of applying stimulus and recording response should repeat over and over again.

Keeping the above criteria in mind, he invented a device called a resonant recorder, before embarking on his third scientific mission or trip abroad. In this respect, our narrative is slightly different from Geddes's, who places the invention of this device after the third scientific trip. The resonant recorder served another purpose, that of measuring speed of transmission of excitement in a plant.

If a long steel reed, clamped at one end, is struck at the free end, it vibrates at its natural frequency, much like one of the two arms of a tuning fork. The frequency of vibration of the steel reed can be varied by adjusting its length and thickness, within certain limits. In the resonant recorder, this frequency could be varied from 10 cycles per second to 200 cycles per second.

If left to follow the natural course of things, the vibration of a steel reed gets damped out gradually, in a few seconds. Bose devised an elaborate electromagnetic arrangement to assist the natural vibration so that it could be continued for as long as one chooses. This is the primary electromagnetic arrangement of the instrument. Fig. 7.4, drawn by Bose, has two assemblages of solid objects on two sides, connected by a pair of broken lines. The assemblage on the right gives a schematic diagram of the primary electromagnetic arrangement, where C is the steel reed. This is the coercing reed, because it is used to coerce the recorder strut with a bent tip (V) to move in sympathetic vibration (resonance).

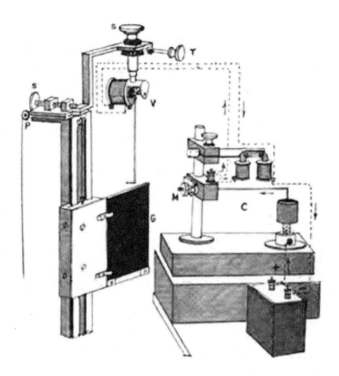

Fig. 7.4: Upper part of the resonant recorder. Thread from clock, not shown, passes over pulley (P), letting down recording smoked plate (G) under gravity in a controlled way; C: Coercing reed which by its vibration coerces the recorder strut (V) in sympathetic vibration. The axis of the recorder strut (V) is supported perpendicularly at centre of circular end of electromagnet. S, S': adjusting screws; M: micrometre, T: tangent screw.

This resonance of the recorder strut is coerced by a second electromagnetic arrangement, which is activated by the same current that supplies energy to the coercing reed. Hence, the coercing reed and the recorder strut vibrate at the exact same frequency. The secondary electromagnetic arrangement is shown in the upper-left portion of the figure. The dashed lines are the current carrying wires, connecting the two assemblages.

The recorder strut (V) is suspended vertically by means of pivots supported on jewel bearings, in order to minimize friction. The bent tip of the vibrating recorder strut taps regularly on a smoked plate, which is allowed to fall vertically under gravity, at a speed controlled by a clockwork device (not shown in the figure). This implies that in an 'idle' run, when no plant is attached, the recorder would create a straight vertical line. The number of dots per second can be found from the frequency of vibration of the recorder strut.

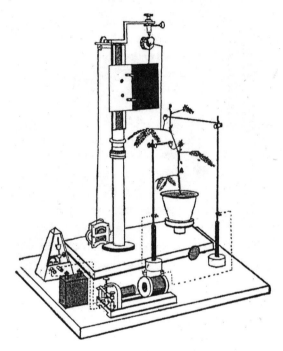

Fig. 7.5: General view of the resonant recorder, attached to mimosa plant, and the electrical connections by which excitatory shock of a definite duration is given to the plant; duration of shock determined by metronome, which completes electrical circuit.

The resonant recorder is shown in use in Fig. 7.5. The stem of a leaf of the mimosa plant is connected to the vibrating recorder strut by means of a silk thread, which can be seen running vertically next to the smoked (black) plate. A mild electric shock (as stimulus) is given near the tip of the leaf. When the stimulus is transmitted to the leaf root, the leaf droops and the recording rod is pulled sideways.

Fig. 7.6 shows a record wherein the successive dots are at intervals of 0.005 seconds. The vertical line marks the time when the shock was given; the leaf movement began at the fifteenth dot after the shock.

Therefore, the perception time of the plant is 0.075 seconds. This is the time span between the shock and the leaf drooping. Since the distance between the tip and leaf root can be measured, the speed of transmission can now be determined. Note that there is an additional advantage with such a recorder. It eliminates friction since, in this device, the recorder tip does not continuously press down on the smoked plate.

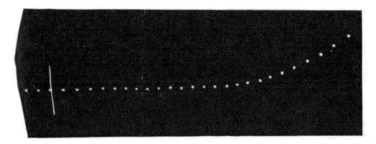

Fig. 7.6: Record for determination of the perception time of mimosa.

Nerves in Plants

Going contrary to prevailing theories, Bose intuited that the transmission of the excitement seen above took place by means of nerves, as in animal life.

Certain facts about transmission of excitement in animal life were well known. The animal has nerves which carry an electric impulse, from the point where the stimulus is applied to the nerve centre, and bring it back; the animal feels a sensation and knows its location simultaneously.

In a standard experiment, mild electricity was passed by connecting the two terminals of a battery to two points on an animal limb, some distance apart. As soon as the current is switched on, the animal feels a sensation at the point connected to the negative terminal of the battery. After a while, all sensation vanishes, as if the body has come to an adjustment with the passing of electricity. When the current is stopped by breaking the circuit, sensation reappears, but at the other connection point, which is joined to the positive terminal of the battery. This pattern of events is thought to be a typical property of nerves. This experiment can be done on a human limb just as well, since humans belong to the class of animal life.

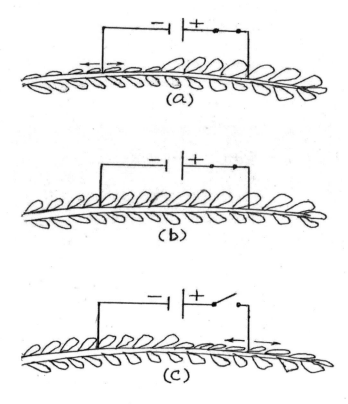

Fig. 7.7: Terminal-dependent excitement due to electrical stimulus of a mimosa leaf.

Bose now performed a similar experiment with the mimosa plant. Fig. 7.7 shows a battery connected to two points on a mimosa leaf; the schematics of the figure are similar to one figure given in *Acharya Jagadish Chandra Bose*. As soon as the current is switched on, several leaflets contract, on either side of the point connected to the battery's negative terminal, as shown in (a). After a while, these leaflets restore themselves to their original shapes, as shown in (b). When the circuit is broken by lifting the switch, contraction of several leaves occurs again, but at the other point, the one connected to the battery's positive terminal, as shown in (c). This was a confirmation of Bose's hypothesis that a plant has nerves for transmitting excitement.

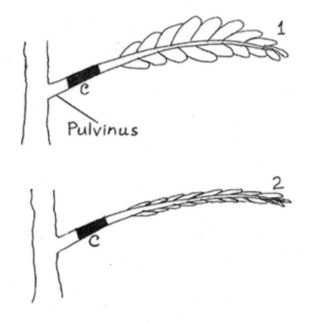

Fig. 7.8: Obstruction to transmission of excitement due to application of cold.

Bose gathered another piece of evidence that plant excitement is transmitted through nerves. It was well known that if something cold is applied at a point on an animal body, it hampers transmission of excitement in that area. Bose wrapped an ice pack (C) around the stem of a mimosa leaf, just above the pulvinus, as shown by a black patch in Fig. 7.8. The diagram marked 1 is the normal appearance, before the leaf is touched. The diagram marked 2 is the appearance after the leaf is touched at the tip, with all leaflets contracted. However, what is remarkable is that the excitement has not reached the pulvinus (the leaf root) and since there is no contraction there, the leaf does not droop (compare with Fig. 7.1). This means that the application of the cold wrap has hampered transmission of the excitement to the pulvinus. This obviously is behaviour analogous to that of animal nerves. Bose also showed that if, instead of cold, a chemical depressant is applied, the result is the same.

It is noteworthy that the two experiments described above could be demonstrated in Europe if the mimosa plant could be transported there.

Bose was determined that for his next scientific trip abroad, he would carry sensitive plants from India, along with all his delicate instruments.

Bose had determined the speed of transmission of excitement with the help of the resonant recorder, as described before. Now he did the same by another method. Taking the circuit present in Fig. 7.7, he replaced the battery with an Einthoven galvanometer and an electric shock was applied to the tip of the leaf. The excitement travelled towards the leaf root and when it passed a connection point, the galvanometer registered a negative voltage spike. Thus, Bose got two successive spikes from the special galvanometer separated by a certain measurable time lapse. Since the distance between the two connection points was measurable, the speed of transmission could be determined. This turned out to be the same as that determined by the resonant recorder.

Bose further showed that, depending on the environmental conditions, the speed of conduction of excitement can vary from 15 mm/s to 400 mm/s in the mimosa plant. In comparison, the speed of the movement of water in plants is never more than 2 to 3 mm/s, even in the most favourable of conditions. Physiologists generally believed that plants transmit excitement from one part of their body to another by transporting fluid. This theory was, therefore, demolished.

There was an alternative notion that excitement is conducted by variation of water pressure. This had a very feeble experimental basis. Bose invalidated this theory as well through careful arguments and experiments. His experiments left no doubt that excitement conduction in plant life is a nerve-dependent phenomenon. Nobody could disprove him at the time, but nobody followed up on his research either for a long time. Modern researchers in the field of plant neurobiology, such as Prakash Narain Tandon[60], acknowledge his pioneering contributions. Bose's findings were substantiated thirty-one years later by Dr K. S. Cole and Dr H. J. Curtis of Columbia University, New York. Their work was reviewed by the *New York Times* in 1938 and Paramahansa Yogananda has quoted two passages verbatim from this review in *Autobiography of a Yogi*.

---

[60]Tandon is a National Research Professor, All India Institute of Medical Sciences, New Delhi.

If the stem of a mimosa leaf, with four leaflets, is cut transversely (perpendicular to the length), one gets the cross section for microscopic inspection, as shown in Fig. 7.9, which is based on a similar figure in *Acharya Jagadish Chandra Bose*. Bose could observe four distinctly separate vascular bundles in the cross section. In Fig. 7.9, they have been numbered 1 to 4, in an anti-clockwise direction. At the leaf root, four corresponding sides have been identified and numbered by projecting the vascular bundles backwards, shown by dashed lines.

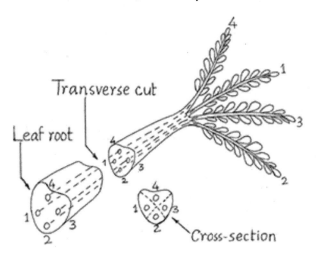

Fig. 7.9: Presence of four vascular bundles connecting
each leaflet separately to the leaf root.

Armed with this knowledge, another intact mimosa plant with a stem with four leaflets may be subjected to experimentation now. When any one side of the leaf root is separately stimulated, one particular leaflet shows contraction, the other three remaining unaffected. This proves that each side is connected separately by a vascular bundle to a leaflet. The dashed lines show the vascular bundles, and the numbering of the leaflets makes the connections amply clear.

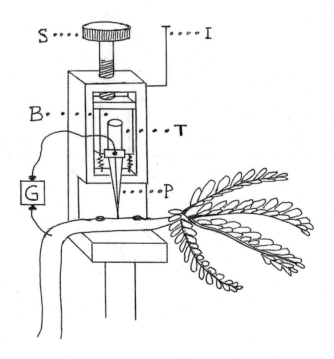

Fig. 7.10: Determining the location of the nerve-fibres with the help
of the electric probe; figure based on *Acharya Jagadish Chandra Bose*.

Bose then wanted to study the properties of different layers in the stem
of a mimosa leaf, leaving it more or less intact. An instrument called the
electric probe was designed, as shown in Fig. 7.10. A glass tube (T) was
heated and drawn into a very fine tapered end. An equally fine platinum
wire was inserted into the tapered end, while still hot. Once the glass
cooled, it contracted and the platinum wire was firmly embedded into
the glass. This glass tube with the platinum wire is the probe (P). It is
mounted on a sliding block (B), which is supported by springs at the
bottom and can slide up and down inside a box-like structure, actuated
by a micrometre screw (S). The probe (P) is mounted in such a fashion
that it hangs outside the box-like structure.

The stem of a mimosa leaf is held horizontally on a platform, right
under the probe, as shown in Fig. 7.10. The tip of the probe is inserted
into the stem; glass being an insulator, it is only the platinum that sends

an electric current to the nerve fibres inside the stem. A conducting wire connects the platinum to the galvanometer (G), the other terminal of which is joined to an electrically-inert part of the plant to complete the circuit.

The probe penetration is gradually increased by turning the micrometre screw, while a stimulus is continuously applied at the tip of the overhanging mimosa leaf, and the galvanometer reading is recorded. A scale is provided alongside the box-like structure and indicates the depth of insertion. Later, a cross section of the stem is taken and different layers are identified. The record of the electric response of the galvanometer is given in Fig. 7.11.

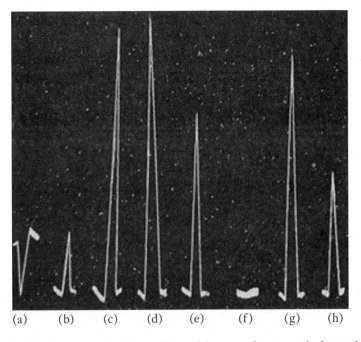

(a)   (b)   (c)   (d)   (e)   (f)   (g)   (h)

Fig. 7.11: Electric response in different fibres of the stem of a mimosa leaf, recorded by the electric probe. From the left (a) small positive response in the epidermis, (b) small negative response in the cortex, (c, d, e) large response in the phloem layers, located on the outside of xylem, (f) response vanishes in the xylem, (g) large response re-appears in the phloem layer on the inside of the xylem, (h) response diminishes in the pith.

Bose discovered that the phloem cells inside the vascular bundle are especially capable of conducting excitement. The phloem layer is present both outside and inside the xylem. The external phloem layer carries excitement from the tip of the leaf inwards to the leaf root; whereas the internal layer carries excitement reflected from the leaf root outwards.

These were significant discoveries, when all other physiologists of the world were completely unaware of the existence of a nerve-like mechanism in plant life, so much so that they did not believe these experimental results to start with.

Similarity with Special Behaviour of Animal Muscles

Bose discovered to his delight that the response of a plant is not merely uniform; it shows progressive increase under repeated excitation, much like what is called the 'staircase effect' of animal muscle (see Fig. 7.12). Further, when the stimulation is carried on for too long, the plant response shows progressive diminution as a sign of fatigue, again quite analogous to that of animal muscle (see Fig. 7.13). This is true not only for the sensitive mimosa leaf, but also for the undemonstrative radish.

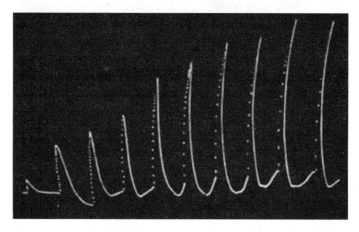

Fig. 7.12: The 'staircase' enhancement of response in plant.

Another remarkable comparison was made between the spontaneous pulsation of the telegraph plant's leaflet and the beats of an animal heart. The comparison was worked out in considerable detail and an astonishing similarity emerged. It would not be possible to discuss here all the intricate details of this, but one of the most interesting points of comparison is the effect of poisons. A poison which stops the heart in its phase of contraction also arrests the telegraph plant in its contraction phase; whereas, another poison which stops the heart during relaxation does the same for the telegraph plant. Further, it has been known that for the heart one poison may act as an antidote for another poison, and so they did in the case of a telegraph plant as well.

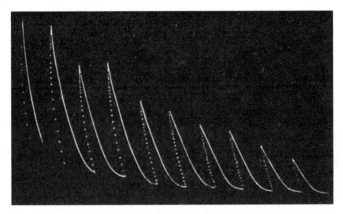

Fig. 7.13: Fatigue depression of response in plant.

Bose's study also revealed that when a plant is fatigued by repeated application of stimuli, its perception slows down considerably. When excessively tired, it loses its power of perception temporarily; then it requires absolute rest of at least half an hour to recover normalcy.

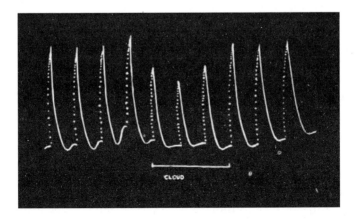

Fig. 7.14: Depressing effect of a passing cloud on the response of mimosa.

There was also a chance discovery while experimenting with a mimosa plant. On an autumn afternoon, Bose found the plant responding unpredictably—behaving normally one moment and then slightly depressed soon after, its behaviour changing much too swiftly. Initially, he was quite confused and checked and rechecked his instruments. Finally, it dawned on him that small clouds had dotted the otherwise blue sky, and were following one another in quick succession, as it often happens during autumn in Bengal. Shadow and sunshine were alternating and the mimosa was so sensitive to its environments that even a passing cloud depressed its response, albeit temporarily. Fig. 7.14 gives an interesting graph of this behaviour, in which the depressed central portion of the signature is underlined.

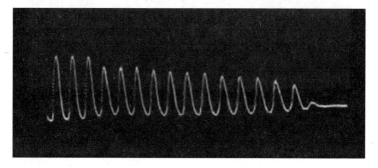

Fig. 7.15: Abolition of pulsation at the death of a plant.

When subjected to gradually increasing heat, most plants evinced inertness above a certain temperature and registered a death spasm around 60°C, just before death. A device called the death recorder was developed, and the mechanical death spasm (see Fig. 7.15), and the corresponding ones caused by two electrical methods were recorded. The death spasm was found to be simultaneous for all three methods, and its autograph or signature turned out to be analogous to that of an animal tissue.

While investigating electrical responses, Bose discovered that the death spasm of a vegetable being heated often generated a large voltage— for instance, in each half of a green pea it could be as high as half a volt. This caused Bose to remark with wry humour, 'It is well that the cook does not know the danger she runs in preparing the particular dish; it is fortunate for her that the peas are not arranged in series!'[61]

In this manner, the general thesis that plant and animal physiology—despite all obvious differences of habit of life and constituent organs—are profoundly analogous was confirmed again and again.

Preparation for Another Journey Westwards

After the publication of *Plant Response* in 1906, American physiologists showed much interest in this new line of research. The book served another purpose—that of establishing the priority of Bose and forestalled any possibility of plagiarism. The next book *Comparative Electro-physiology* was expected to be published towards the end of 1907.

There was now a demand in America for Bose. The British, however, stuck to their mistrust and wished to see his experiments performed right in front of an audience. Investigators of different countries desired to take a closer look at the practical workings of his instruments. Sensing this, Bose too became eager to undertake another scientific trip abroad, with America also in the ambit this time. The Indian government was not unaware of his growing reputation in the West. Fortunately for Bose, a more sympathetic lieutenant governor in the person of Sir Andrews Frazer had taken over from Lord Bourdillon.

Directed by Sir Andrews, Bose wrote a formal letter to him, describing in brief his previous and current research and a request for aid for future investigations. Perhaps, as a result of this, he received a promotion with an increased salary in December 1905.

Bose applied for leave and started preparations for going to Europe in the second half of 1907. Although Bose had applied for leave, the government, in view of his past records of successful scientific missions, decided to send him on deputation. The final approval from the secretary of state would take some time to arrive, and therefore, a leave was sanctioned for the time being to expedite his trip.

On 3 September, Bose delivered a popular science lecture, titled 'Curves of Life and Death' in a meeting in the chemistry department

---

[61] If the peas are arranged in series, their respective voltages would add up. Therefore, 400 peas together would generate 400 volts, which is lethal for a human being.

of the Calcutta Medical College, presided over by Sir Andrews Frazer. Father Lafont and Rabindranath Tagore were also in attendance. In his concluding speech, Sir Andrews congratulated Bose for his attractive lecture, said that Professor Bose was going to Europe to present his latest investigations before the scientists there, and wished him complete success in his mission. Just two days hence, on 5 September 1907, Bose began his journey to Europe.

Since our scientist would be cooling his heels for a few weeks aboard a ship, it is time to turn our gaze towards the other developments that took place in his life.

Bose's Discovery of India

Bose reciprocated the filial love he received from Sara and tried to make her comfortable whenever she was in India insofar as possible. Whenever she happened to be in India during the hot season, he offered to take her to the cool mountains, even if only for a few weeks. Even otherwise, he was in love with the Himalayas, and often took Abala and Nivedita there. He would frequently travel during the two vacations he received in a year. He kept this up even while under tremendous pressure to write books because he loved to explore the vast geographical and historical expanse of India.

Bose's love for his native semi-rural Faridpur township had gradually expanded to embrace the whole of Bengal, as he gained in experience and age; and further, it had enlarged into a yearning to discover the real India. The nationalist in him wished to feel the pulse, first-hand, of a civilization that had continued uninterrupted since prehistoric times. The Vedantist in him thought a spiritual unity, underlying all the countless sectarian differences, in India was to be discovered and realized. So, he made it a point to travel to the pilgrimage centres primarily, and then to the other historic sites. His life partner, Abala, was always his partner in this lifelong quest for discovery. Sometimes, Nivedita and Tagore were also his travel companions.

Wherever they went, they always forayed into the villages around them, away from pilgrimage sites and crowds of tourists, for they knew that it is in the life of a common villager that the ancient culture lives.

In 1904, the Boses took Nivedita to Silaidaha, the village on the bank of river Padma where Tagore had a spacious house. The Boses, as usual, mingled with the villagers. This was the first time Nivedita had an opportunity to come in direct contact with the rural folks of India, and she was very happy. Observing her interacting with the people there, Tagore remarked, 'We had not seen before an embodiment of the spirit of motherhood which, passing beyond the limits of the family, can spread itself over the whole country.'

The Bose couple travelled to numerous temples, caves, pilgrim centres, palaces, stupas, etc. in all parts of India. We can but mention here only a few significant and interesting visits.

One of Bose's first visits was to see the Sanchi Stupa in the Central Province (now Madhya Pradesh). It is a Buddhist pilgrim centre, where a relic of the Buddha is buried and from where Emperor Ashoka's son and daughter, Mahendra and Sanghamitra, went on a spiritual expedition to Ceylon. There is an Ashoka Stambha, one of the pillars of Ashoka, near the main gate, with an edict inscribed on stone and an amalaka symbol in the shape of a segmented stone disc. This symbol is derived from the shape of an amalaka fruit, which has a slightly segmented shape. Legend has it that in his old age, Ashoka went away to the forests, with only an amalaka fruit in his possession, leaving the kingdom to his son. Later, he gifted half of it to a Buddhist sangha. Bose was affected by that symbol immensely, because it meant sacrifice and renunciation.

Sometimes, Bose would pen accounts of his travels in Bengali. One such account is 'Yuktakar' (meaning folded hands), written in the form of an essay about the history and art of the Ajanta caves. It was published in 1894; the Boses must have travelled to Ajanta around that time. The essay became famous for its high literary quality and is contained in the collection *Avyakta*.

Once, on a trip to Nainital for their summer holidays, the Boses visited Lucknow on the way. After this, leaving the rest of his party behind, Bose went to the Pindari glacier alone on an adventure trip. Both his hired guide and himself had a narrow escape during a steep climb. Rich with this experience, the next year he guided his wife and several friends to the same glacier.

Later, when he had become quite well known, they visited the Sri

Rangam temple in Trichinapally in the south of the country, where he was invited by the priest to enter the sanctum sanctorum. Bose knew well about the strictness of the caste restrictions there and informed the priest that he was not an orthodox Hindu and that he was not a Brahmin by birth. Whatever caste he had, was now lost in foreign travels across the sea, and therefore, he had no right to enter the holy precinct. 'No, no,' said the priest, 'Come in. You are a sadhu'.

In the summer of 1904, the Boses, with Labanyaprabha, accompanied by Sisters Nivedita and Christine, went to the Mayavati ashram of the Ramakrishna order. This centre had been set up in the Himalayas, according to the Swami's instructions, by two of his British disciples, a couple called the Seviers. What attracted the Boses was that there was no idol or image worship allowed in this centre, called the Advaita Ashrama. The Swami wished to have at least one such centre, so that the totality of the Hindu tradition could be represented by the Ramakrishna order. It should be noted that though Bose and Tagore had known the Swami well, they never set foot in the Belur monastery near Calcutta, because idol worship was a regular practice there.

On 23 June, the party returned to Calcutta. Nivedita immediately got busy with giving a series of lectures based on their travels. The most successful ones were three lectures, arranged by Bose and given in his home, on Ellora (in Bombay Presidency), Conjeevaram (in South India), and Bodh Gaya (in Behar); all were temple complexes rich in art. She delivered two talks on Indian art at the Government School of Arts, Calcutta.

Tagore was well aware of his friend's wanderlust. He wrote to Bose in September 1900, 'Hope you remember your promise to make me a fellow-traveller with you wherever it may possibly be, to Kashmir, Orissa, Travancore, or anywhere else. On the merit of such a trip, I wish to secure my place in a chapter of your life, without having to do much.'

Tagore's wish was fulfilled in October 1904, but this was slightly more than the usual trip for the Boses. Adjacent to India, there were two other British colonies, Ceylon and Burma, which were predominantly Buddhist. Within India, too, there was a sizable Buddhist population. There were signs that nationalist stirrings in India would trigger similar movements there.

For all Buddhists, the site of Buddha's enlightenment at Bodh Gaya has a special religious significance and is the holiest of all sites. The temple there had been traditionally under the control of a Hindu mahant, but there was absolutely no restriction on people of any faith and all were welcome. The British rulers sensed an opportunity here to apply their famed 'divide and rule' policy, and instigated a demand among a section of Buddhists that the temple needed to be handed over to Buddhist control.

Nivedita, as taught by her guru, held that Buddhism is but reformed Hinduism and as such it is a branch of the Sanatana Dharma[62]. Buddhism was India's greatest gift to the outer world, according to her. She wrote many articles against this divisive agenda of the rulers, and also organized and led a visit to the site by a large group of eminent persons. This was her third visit to Bodh Gaya. Her party included the Boses; Rabindranath Tagore; Sister Christine; Sadananda-swami; Brahmachari Amulya of the Ramakrishna order; Mr Ratcliffe, editor of *The Statesman*, and his wife; famous historian Sir Jadunath Sarkar; and Professor Mathuranath Sinha of Patna. The mahant welcomed them and brought them to the guest house.

She had lengthy discussions with the mahant, who was a person well versed in the Hindu shastras. Regarding the place of Bodh Gaya in Hinduism, the mahant told her that his order of monks was placed in charge of the temple by Adi Sankaracharya himself. The long history of the place, as retold by the mahant, included the story of a seventeenth century sannyasi who tried to restore the place from falling into ruins by gathering different pieces of scattered sculptures and building them into the walls. The order of monks, with their meagre resources, maintained the place through the centuries, until modern archaeologists came to their aid. They then gave their full cooperation to the restorers.

Nivedita wove all this information into an article with the basic tenet that Bodh Gaya must be held for the synthesis known as Hinduism—it must never become the plaything of sects. Her piece was published in almost all Indian newspapers in different parts of the country. Then the controversy gradually died down. Sir Jadunath Sarkar later wrote in great

---

[62]Sanatana Dharma means eternal religion and is considered to be the original form of Hinduism.

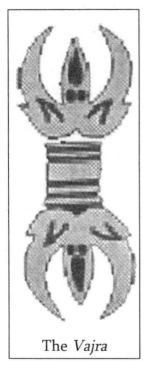

The *Vajra*

Fig. 7.16: The Vajra
(the thunderbolt weapon of
God Indra).

appreciation of Nivedita's interpretation of Indian history.

In this temple complex, Nivedita saw the image of vajra, a symbol of sacrifice, equally important in Buddhism as it is in Hinduism. She heard the story of sage Dadhichi, who died voluntarily so that his ribs could be used to make the vajra, Indra's thunderbolt, for slaying the demon Virittasura. She went into raptures hearing this tale because it reminded her of the life of her guru, Swami Vivekananda, whose life had been one of continuous sacrifice. She said, 'The selfless man is the thunderbolt'. Later, she made a sketch of the thunderbolt, shown in Fig. 7.16.

She put forward a design for the national flag incorporating the motif of the vajra. This flag was not widely accepted, but did spark the imagination of a few eminent people, Bose being one of them.

The party stayed at Bodh Gaya for a week. From Sarkar's recollection we learn that every morning they strolled through the temple complex; then Nivedita read out from Warren Hastings's *Buddhism* or Edwin Arnold's *Light of Asia*, and while doing so she seemed to get transported to the days of the Buddha. Sometimes, Tagore would sing a song in his mellifluous voice, or recite one of his poems. In the evening twilight, they sat under the Bodhi Vriksha[63], a giant peepul tree. Here, they met a poor Japanese fisherman named Fuji. He spent his life's savings to come to the holiest site in his faith, the place of Buddha's enlightenment. Every evening, he chanted a Sanskrit hymn, starting with,

Namo Namo Buddha Divaakaraaya,
Namo Namo Gotama-Chandrikaaya,

---

[63]*Bodhi Vriksha* in Sanskrit means the tree of enlightenment.

Namo Namo Ananta-guna-naraaya,
Namo Namo Saakya-nandanaaya.

His deep voice and Japanese accent made it sound like the 'tolling of a low bell'.

The Boses, as was their wont, were keen to visit a village in the vicinity and decided to visit the village of Uruvela. It is said that this was the village of Sujata, who once revived Buddha by offering payasam. The coupled joyously spent some time here with Nivedita. Today, the village is called Urbel and looks the same as any non-descript Indian village, with no relic or ruin there.

Nivedita and Sadananda-swami

The whole of 1904, Nivedita received numerous invitations to speak from different parts of the country and constantly travelled around India, delivering lectures. Sadananda-swami, as per the Swami's instructions to him on Nivedita's arrival in the country for the first time, accompanied her everywhere as her interpreter and assistant.

During the summer months of 1903 and 1904, when education institutions were in recess, Sadananda-swami undertook another arduous task to fulfil the Swami's wishes. It was a constant refrain of the Swami that a strong mind could reside only within a strong body; first, the nation's young men had to be made truly robust and manly. To that end, the importance of adventure was stressed.

In 1903, Sadananda organized a band of youths, drawn from the well-to-do families of Calcutta, for an adventure trip to the Himalayas. In the following summer of 1904, he organized another batch of young men for a similar but more strenuous trip. Tagore's son, Rathindranath and a nephew Dinendranath

Young Sadananda-swami

were part of the group.

Being a monk, it was natural for him to combine adventure with pilgrimage and so, he chose Kedarnath and Badrinarayan in the Garhwal Himalayas, and also the Pindari glacier, as his destinations. Each of the destinations was more than 150 kilometres from the plains via the narrow walking tracks, which were the only means of travel once you left the plains at Kathgodam.

For infirm pilgrims, sure-footed mountain ponies were available on rent that could negotiate such narrow paths, often with the steep hill on one side and a deep gorge on the other. To guide untrained Calcutta boys, used to cosy urban life, up that long route and then bring them safely back down, proved too much even for the stout constitution of Sadananda. He was completely exhausted upon his return and had to take a long rest at Nivedita's residence. Bose saw him in this fatigued condition.

Bose wrote to Tagore, in a letter dated 29 June 1904, quoted earlier in a different context, 'Sadananda has returned totally exhausted, more dead than alive. What changes did you perceive in [Dinendranath and Rathindranath]? Sadananda is waiting eagerly for an encouraging letter from you.'

Bose was concerned about the much younger Sadananda, and thought that an uplifting letter from someone like Tagore might do him good, particularly since two of the Tagore boys had benefited from Sadananda's tremendous efforts. He continued in the same letter,

An American has arrived in Mayavati. He is an expert in machinery and technical matters. I think, you should do well to invite him to your school in the winter for a few months.

Sisters Nivedita and Christine are quite keen to open a school for teachers' training in your Jorasanko house. How and where they would find so many trainee teachers, I wonder. Besides, adequate funds are also necessary. Nivedita is hoping that much of the requirements would be covered by the sale of her new book, *The Web of Indian Life,* published in June 1904. You would be happy to note that the book has earned high praise in England. Even the jingoistic papers have written that the picture of India sketched by

Kipling etc. may not be true, and the real picture is likely to be what is depicted in the book. Possibly, this book will be widely sold and read. An American edition is already out.

You may do some publicity among your friends. ...The foreign edition is priced seven rupees, and one such is enclosed herewith. Please review it in your *Banga Darshan*.

In this letter, Bose comes across as being keen to help publicize Nivedita's book, so that she could earn some revenue out of its sale. Additionally, he was concerned about the development of Tagore's Shantiniketan along technical lines in parallel to the artistic ones.

In March 1905, Nivedita fell seriously ill; the doctors diagnosed it as meningitis. Sister Christine took care of her for some time while good medical advice was taken. Mrs Sara Bull, who was in America then, sent money for the treatment and for engaging a nurse. But the disease did not show any sign of remission and Nivedita's end seemed near. Since the house was damp and unhealthy, she was shifted with great difficulty to an empty house near the Boses's, who engaged the best doctors. She gradually came around and miraculously passed over the crisis. It is said that a gift of primroses from a friend in Darjeeling arrived at this time, and they seemed to her as flowers from her native Ireland and revived her.

For convalescence, the Boses took her to the hills of Darjeeling in the first week of May. The fresh air of the Himalayas and the tender care of the Boses helped her regain strength. They were in Darjeeling for about two months, until 3 July 1905. Here Nivedita resumed assisting Bose in writing the book *Plant Response*. The beautiful and idyllic surroundings and the salubrious climate brought out the poet in her.

She penned eight poems in all, in the form of an elegy. This collection of poems had a dedication that read, 'Written for a little sister.' It is believed that she was a pupil of Nivedita's school, claimed by the plague epidemic of 1899. Nivedita also wrote a few thoughtful articles. All these were published in the form of a book titled, *An Indian Study of Love and Death*, by Longmans, Green, and Co. This was the same publisher who had earlier carried Bose's books; the financier was also the same, the generous Mrs Sara Bull. In the following year, Sara made her second will for donating $20,000 for translating Bose's dream of building a research laboratory into reality. Sara and Bose stayed quiet about this donation, as they had about ones made earlier.[64]

Sara always supported Nivedita's literary efforts and knew about her thoughts on death. Nivedita had seen the deaths of many loved ones—her grandmother, father, fiancé, and guru. Many plague victims in Calcutta had also died before her very eyes. She was always aware of death, but was least afraid of it. The first poem, 'To be said within the heart', reads as follows,

> Dark is the night,
> And terrible is the storm in the middle of the burning ghat,
> Swift and deep is the river to bear away the scattered dust.
> Infinite is time, into which hurry the passing souls,
> And Love cries out in vain to stay the hand of death.
> For now the hand of the Potter hath shattered the vessel
> That He made
> And the Mother hath hidden from us with a veil, the face of
> Our beloved.

The 'burning ghat' is the cremation ground of the Hindus, often located by a river. The 'Potter' is a Biblical metaphor for the Creator. The female divinity, the 'Mother', could be a Hindu woman with a veil or the Mother of God. Hindu imagery and Christian motifs are thus seamlessly combined in Nivedita's poems.

Jagadish must have read these poems even before they were printed. What impression these poems left on his sensitive literary mind, we can only imagine, for he never said in public or expressed in writing his own impression about Nivedita's literary works, prose or poetry. He mentioned her by name in letters only a couple of times, and only

---

[64]Probir Kumar Bondyopadhyay, a historian of science and technology in Houston, USA, spent years researching and scouring court records to dig out two of Mrs Sara Bull's wills, made in 1902 and 1906. These wills were fully executed during her lifetime and remained totally unknown until April 2021. She made a third will which was contested after her death by her daughter Olea. This legal contest turned ugly and attracted the attention of the print media for several months, and thus, the third will became quite well known.

when his own person was not involved in the discussion. Her books, including *The Cradle Tales of Hinduism*, *The Web of Indian Life*, and *The Master as I Saw Him* were highly acclaimed not only for their content but also for their beautiful prose, bordering on poetry.

Jagadish in his own Bengali writings often used Hindu imagery. For instance, in his *Bhagirathir Utsa Sandhane* ('In search of the source of the Bhagirathi river'), the narrator asks, 'O river, where do you come from?' and is supplied the answer, 'From the coil of hair on the head of Lord Shiva'. So, it could not be that Nivedita's use of Hindu imagery offended his Brahmo sensibilities. Hence, his silence on her writing is puzzling.

On the other hand, Nivedita referred to him freely in her letters. She looked upon him as a little boy and called him 'khoka', an endearing term in Bengali for a little boy. While writing in English, she used 'bairn', a similar term in Scottish and Irish.

The remainder of 1905 and the whole of 1906, Nivedita spent in political activities and writing, while also helping Bose in his research. Bose was a full-time scientist, and, feeling nervous about Nivedita's strident political views, asked her to be cautious.

Nivedita neither took part in underground revolutionary movements, nor was sympathetic to them. In all her speeches and articles, Nivedita's only aim was to rouse nationalism and its flowering in all walks of life, education, science, art, literature, music, economic development, emancipation of women, etc. She tried to dissuade Bhupendranath Dutt, one of Swami Vivekananda's brothers, from such activities, but did not succeed. He wrote in his book, *Swami Vivekananda: Patriot Prophet*, that Nivedita had asked him not to inform her about his secret activities. He was soon jailed for a year on charges of seditious activities. On being released, he went to America and stayed there for quite some time.

During the rainy season of 1906, flooding caused great devastation in eastern Bengal and Nivedita went there for relief work along with the monks and novices of the Ramakrishna Mission. The strain of this relief work proved too much for her and she returned to Calcutta exhausted. There she suffered recurring attacks of malaria. The affliction of meningitis in the previous year and malarial attacks in 1906 completely shattered her health.

Christine and the Boses looked after her during this period of illness.

Brahmadanda-swami and Saradananda-swami of the Ramakrishna Mission came to her place in Bosepara Lane to make necessary arrangements for her treatment. When she improved a little, both Sisters closed up the school and went to live in Dum Dum, in a spacious house owned by Bose's brother-in-law Ananda Mohan. The place was at a fair distance from the bustling city, in a rural setting full of greenery. Bose made all arrangements for their comfortable stay there.

When she gained a little strength, Nivedita resumed writing and also helped Bose in writing the book *Comparative Electro-physiology*. She liked the peaceful environs of her new surroundings, and continued to stay there, absorbed in writing, even after she had fully recovered.

In the beginning of 1907, Mrs Sevier of the Mayavati ashram came to Calcutta and stayed with the Sisters in Dum Dum. At her request, the Boses and Sisters Nivedita and Christine went to Mayavati in the summer. By that time, *Plant Response* had been published; the last chapter of *Comparative Electro-physiology* was being written, according to a letter Bose wrote to Tagore on 7 June.

As has been mentioned earlier, the Boses were poised to travel to Europe for Jagadish's third scientific trip in September 1907. They now invited Nivedita to join them on this voyage. Sara and Joe had been anxious for quite some time on account of Nivedita's failing health and had been continually asking her to come to England. Besides, she had not seen her mother for five years at this point. She now decided to sail for England, travelling alone and ahead of the Boses, so that she could devote all her time on board to working on her guru's biography.

She took a steamer from Bombay on 15 August 1907. When the ship reached Aden, a note from Christine arrived full of good news that the school had reopened, all pupils had returned, and the school was running well; that Sudhira, a young educated devotee of the Ramakrishna order, had joined as a teacher and Christine was delighted to have her as an assistant. This brought great relief and joy to Nivedita.

Third Scientific Mission Abroad: A Partial Failure

The Boses set sail from Bombay, and after a quiet, comfortable journey, docked at Brindisi port in Italy. They proceeded to Germany from here and stayed there for a fair length of time. No other information is available about where in Germany they stayed and which institution or university they visited. It is known that the Boses reached London via Germany by the end of November 1907, two and a half months after they started from Bombay. So, they must have stayed in Germany for at least a month. Geddes, however, makes no mention of Germany at all, and devotes a four-line paragraph to their stay in the UK, 'The Government sent Bose in 1907, on his third scientific deputation, to England and America. After a short stay in England, he visited the United States, and lectured before highly appreciative audiences in the different American Universities.'

Bose wrote to Tagore on 6 December 1907, well after he had reached London,

> I send you my new book [*Comparative Electro-physiology*]. ...I do not get to see any of your recent writings. I was eager to read your article presented at the memorial meeting of Ram Mohan Roy. Please send whatever you write.
>
> We were in Germany for a month, and there I felt much better. But the disease has worsened a little due to the onset of winter. Send me news about your school. My treatment has kept me busy so far. I shall soon start work. ...Yours, Jagadish.

It is known that Bose had been suffering from gout at that time. It is possible to speculate that the book *Plant Response* had not been translated into German even a year after its publication. A few of the German physiologists, who read the book in English, noticed that the book did not contain any material from journal papers—it is mandatory for such papers to go through a peer review—and since the content of Bose's book was not so qualified, they took no interest in the book and its author. His next book *Comparative Electro-physiology* was still with the press when Bose was in Germany.

There might have been another reason for the failure of Bose's German sojourn—the absence of any possibility of live demonstration of his experiments. It should be noted that at that time he was a well-known personality in the world of physics, with the right degrees and significant research credentials, but in physiology he was a newcomer with no higher education. He was, at best, a controversial figure and not a very established one at that.

We come to know from Bose's convocation address years later, at the University of the Punjab, Lahore, in 1924, that he had carried a delicate instrument to London. He said,

> I got into trouble again when I tried to enter the preserves of the physiologists. There was the same pack feeling that resented the intrusion of a stranger who belonged to the fold of physicists. My results were incredible and opposed to accepted theories. I was challenged to show my instruments at work. I had to carry instruments from India; when I landed in London, the porter carried the instrument box upside down, with the result that the heavy base crushed the delicate recording portion beyond recognition. So that the costly visit to Europe was for that time a complete failure.

The ill-fated instrument mentioned by Bose must have been the resonant recorder, which had a heavy base and the recording portion at the top. It could not have been the optical pulse recorder, since Bose had no reason to carry an instrument which was not automatic—the stipulation of the Royal Society had been categorical, that 'Nothing short of the plant's automatic response would carry conviction....'

Most biographers of Bose, including Patrick Geddes, have made no mention of Bose's carrying a sensitive instrument to England and its destruction in this manner. They have glossed over the failure of his third scientific mission to Europe, with some going so far as to paint it as a successful trip. Bose, however, has been forthright and frank, and so, a remarkable gap in the biographical narration is now filled. Although Bose has called this trip a complete failure, we shall rate it as a partial failure or a partial success, because, as we shall see later, the American leg of the trip proved to be very fruitful.

From one of his letters, written on 28 February 1908, more than three months into his England sojourn, we come to know that he had been taken seriously ill, but recovered fully. However, during a stay of about ten months in Britain, he had the opportunity to deliver a lecture only once. This was before the British Association, in its Dublin meeting, towards the end of his stay in Britain on 4 September 1908; the title was 'Mechanical and Electrical Response in Plant'.

It had not been possible for Bose to bring over the sensitive plant specimens from India. The instrument he had brought with great care by train and ship through many ports was ultimately destroyed at London by a negligent porter. Even then a few botanists, who had been personally familiar with the man and his style, trusted and heard him in Dublin, and were surprised by the results.

Bose would have needed at least ten such lectures to summarize the substantive volume of research, contained in those two books he had authored between 1903 and 1907. So, not only had he been denied journal space since 1903, but also a platform to speak from during his third scientific trip. His friends and well-wishers, such as Professor Vines and Professor Howes, who had come to his aid the last time, were either helpless or aloof.

We now turn the clock back by a year and observe that Nivedita arrived in London in early September 1907 and united with her mother Mary, sister May, and brother Richmond. Come November, she went to Germany to meet the Boses and went with them to Paris to meet Joe and Betty Leggett. She was meeting Joe after the Swami's passing away for the first time, and they mourned, wept, and reminisced together for hours. Returning with the Boses to London, she went to live with her mother at Clapham, while the Boses were put up in a house in Pall Mall. Her book *Cradle Tales of Hinduism* came out in print now, and was well received.

Then Sara arrived from America in early December and was received by Nivedita at Liverpool port. When the year ended, Nivedita noted in her diary,

'A wonderful year! Began at Dum Dum. Ends in London. Two books—*Comparative Electro-physiology*, *Cradle Tales (of Hinduism)* out— others proceeding—Oh blessed year! Mother! Mother! Mother!'

She so completely identified herself with Bose's work that she made no distinction between her own book and his. Nivedita got busy with the writing of the Swami's biography while Bose concentrated on his physiological studies; Sara helped Nivedita. They spent happy and creative months together. On 8 April 1908, the government sent the expected sanction for one and a half year's deputation for Bose.

Nivedita's mother Mary was quite advanced in age and the family felt that her assets in Ireland should be sold. Nivedita, accompanied by the Boses, went there for this purpose while Sara returned to America. On 25 August, Bose wrote to Sara,

> How we miss you every day. The mere crossing over the road and you were there; now you seem to be so far away. But we all shall be together soon, and have such a beautiful quiet time of rest and thought. Did you have a good passage?...
>
> I think you must be having a good time back at dear 168, meeting your brother and children.
>
> I hope you are not getting too tired, dear, but having an opportunity to really enjoy your guests.

Nivedita must have noticed that Bose's scientific trip in Europe was a failure. But she kept faith in him, because she understood his science and had witnessed his instruments in action.

In America and Then Eastwards

On 5 October 1908, Nivedita and the Boses arrived in Boston and stayed at Sara's home named 'The Studio House' at 168 Brattle Street, Cambridge. The next day they went to Greenacre, where Sara had a house by the beautiful Piscataqua river, hallowed by several visits by the Swami. From Greenacre, Nivedita and the Boses went to Ridgely Manor to be with Joe and the Leggetts. Nivedita wrote to Sara,

> Today everything is snow.... But it is so beautiful!... Mr Leggett was here when I arrived. He asked most affectionately about you. He is growing so old and slow! I feel sorry! Yet how sweet everything is made round him. Even the man of science joins in the conspiracy to make him happy the moment he enters.

The Boses and Nivedita went back to Cambridge to live with Sara, and Bose's scientific activities started anew. Sara arranged for a sponsorship from the Lowell Institute for a series of lectures by Bose.[65] She also

---

[65]Both Reymond (2017) and Prabuddhaprana (2014) have written that it was a

arranged, through her friends, a special lecture to be delivered by Bose at the Massachusetts Institute of Technology in Boston. This was for about twenty or thirty advanced students from the biological club of the university,[66] and was scheduled for 10 October, at 4 p.m. After the lecture, Sara arranged for a tea party for the students at her home and Bose demonstrated some experiments, as could be arranged at a short notice.

'The Studio House' at 168 Brattle Street.

He delivered lectures at the Universities of Illinois-Urbana Champaign, Michigan, Wisconsin, and Chicago; Colombia University in New York; Boston Medical Society; Botanical Society of America in Baltimore; and Chicago Academy of Sciences, among others. The American scientists trusted him despite the absence of live demonstrations of his experiments, and warmly appreciated his work. He found none of the

scholarship for Bose for several years of study in Europe and America. They must have found some reference to this in the letters of Mrs Bull and/or Sister Nivedita. However, the charter of the Lowell Institute precludes any such possibility; there simply was no provision for offering a scholarship to a foreigner and, of course, not outside America; there was provision for such scholarships for American students for studying in America. However, the Institute often sponsored eminent people from abroad for a series of lectures in America.
[66]Massachusetts Institute of Technology, although named 'Institute' was actually a large and renowned university.

rancour and jealousy that he had found in Britain; most important of all, there was no division between the physicists and physiologists of America.

On 8 January 1909, Bose wrote to Tagore, from Sara's house,

> You will be happy to know that I was specially invited by the American Association for Advancement of Science and went to Baltimore to deliver a lecture. They expressed pleasant astonishment at my findings. In many places, they have started utilizing my [Optical Pulse Recorder] in research. The Agricultural Department of Washington D.C. had also invited me. One thousand scientists are working there and their annual budget is 30 lakhs of rupees. They expect much benefit from my findings....
>
> I reminisce often about your [Shantiniketan at] Bolpur and [home in] Silaidaha. Write quite a few short stories. You have to read out to me one every day [when I visit you next]. We shall together create a dreamland in the twilight days of our life....

Yours, Jagadish.

The letter brings out Bose's love for literature and his friend Tagore.

His lectures abroad and the two books, *Plant Response* and *Comparative Electro-physiology* made quite an impact on the botanists and physiologists of the world. The repetition of his experiments was attempted in many universities. Bose's optical lever started being employed in the University of Cambridge in physiological experiments. Dr Van der Wolk of Utrecht followed with success Bose's line of research. Professor Harper of Colombia University, New York, incorporated Bose's electro-physiological findings in an advanced course. Professor Leno, head of physiology in the Tashkent National University of Tzarist Russia, wrote to Bose seeking permission to translate his works into Russian, 'The great success of *Comparative Electro-physiology* is indivisibly connected with your name. The translation of your works would be of the greatest help to Russian physiologists.'

Nivedita went to New York on an assignment to collect Swami Vivekananda's letters from his many admirers, and Bose travelled with her. She met J. T. Sunderland, president of the *American League*, an organization that advocated the cause of India's freedom. Through him, they met Bhupendranath Dutt, the Swami's brother, who had fallen on hard times. Bhupendranath later wrote in his book, *Swami Vivekananda: Patriot Prophet*, that Dr Bose and Nivedita helped him and made arrangements for his education. It is likely that Bose paid for the expenses involved; he could afford to because his earnings had improved considerably, whereas Nivedita had little money of her own.

Just before Christmas, while they were in Sara's house at Cambridge, Nivedita received a letter that her mother was very ill with cancer. She had plans to leave America with the Boses but now she had to hurry to England. Soon after the Christmas celebrations, Sara took Nivedita to New York, made arrangements for her luggage, and, boarding the ship, spent the night with her, as the ship was due to sail next morning. Nivedita wrote to Sara later, 'The night you went with me to New York. None in the world would have done that but you.'

In Wimbledon, Mary was happy to unite with her eldest daughter and breathed her last in peace. Nivedita spent about a week thereafter with her two siblings. She went to meet the Boses and Josephine, who had arrived in London by then, having sailed from America in early March 1909. Bose wrote to Sara from the boat on 16 March,

> We had a pleasant voyage and hope to reach Queenstown tomorrow morning.... I have been thinking of you in the quiet of the evening.... The thought of the beautiful days comes constantly. The evening light by the riverside at Greenacre, the pines, the seat in the piazza, how beautiful the memory is. Then the quiet of the Studio! Everything has been blessed.

Sara and Joe had planned to meet Nivedita and the Boses in England and go to Wiesbaden, Germany, together. As a cure for Bose's gout, a doctor had recommended baths in the hot mineral springs of Wiesbaden for a month. Sara looked forward to visiting the museums there with the Boses and Nivedita. She left America for Norway in March 1909 but later that month fell ill. Bose feared that she might have to return directly to America, without meeting them in London. He wrote to her on 15 April from London,

How anxious I am on account of your health.... I felt very dispirited when I learnt your thought of returning direct to America. Who can tell what the years might bring, and it would have been a great sorrow if I will not have seen you before I left. I see you must have been ill and wanted to be back home. I am looking forward to your coming here, and if the rest cure in Germany is too tiresome, you will go from here. Of course, I would have liked if it had been possible to be together for a little while....

Fortunately, by late April, Sara had recuperated and came to London and united with them at Clapham Park. All five of them went to Wiesbaden and put up in a house rented by Sara. Sara and Joe helped Nivedita with her biography of the Swami, *The Master as I Saw Him*. The three women collaborated on editing the letters of Swami Vivekananda and reconstructing the conversations with their guru. They began at breakfast on the terrace, where the Boses inevitably joined the trio, and later continued while taking long walks in the nearby forest. After about a month, the work was over. Daily baths in the hot spring benefited Bose immensely.

Then they went to Geneva and saw Mont Blanc, the highest peak of the Alps. In Marseilles, a port city on the south coast of France, Nivedita and the Boses bade goodbye to Sara, who went to Norway, and to Joe, who went to America. They sailed for India on 2 July 1909.

Difficulties and Collaboration

Bose felt rejuvenated after his long rest and started his college duties and research with renewed vigour. Almost immediately his clashes with the college authorities also began.

Bose found that the college authorities had indulged in extremely hostile acts, even more so than before, taking full advantage of his absence. In the same month as of his return from Europe, Bose wrote to Sara of his difficulties,[67]

---

[67]The primary source of this letter is Sara Chapman Bull Collection of the Vedanta Society of Northern California.

I was almost prepared yesterday to send my resignation. But they are yielding a little and there is a possibility in finding things just tolerable. Of course, I will have a bare standing room in the college, the main experiments will have to be done at home. There is another reason which makes me realize how wise you have been in your demand of having this laboratory installed. I have just learned from the assistants that the priceless collection of historical specimens and parts of my apparatus, which I left in a special glass exhibition case, was bundled up and removed by my successor. They made protests of such vandalism, the historical value of the exhibits being beyond price; but this to no purpose. I think I shall be able to restore them to a certain extent. One valuable apparatus worth $40 was wickedly kept in a place where rain showers nearly spoilt the apparatus.

In a letter, dated 5 August 1909, he wrote to Sara,

I have got only one and a half rooms and attempt is made to push me further.... I called in the engineer to give me a plan of adding a laboratory to [my] house.... I do not mean to be downed. Now tell me you are proud of me, because I can fight.

These letters give an account of the harassment he had to suffer in the college; and also show how much he depended on the love and sympathy of Sara, who had been insisting on having a private laboratory for him for quite some time. Fortunately, the land next to his house was up for sale at that time.

Sara gave Bose $4000 for the laboratory. Bose initially was hesitant to accept because he would spend the rest of his life repaying. Sara disarmed Bose by insisting that it was a gift from a mother to a son.

On 4 April 1910, Bose wrote to Sara,

The work in college is often hampered, but I am managing to hold my own. We have to think of the laboratory, which is to be the real place of work. About the adjoining land, I have to proceed cautiously. There is another claimant, so I am buying up his rights in another's name. Then the sale will come off in November, and if everything goes well, I may enter in possession about the end of January.... I am studying some fine type of old Indian architecture, so that the building may be a national one. After all this, by about August or September next we may begin building.

This leads me to wish that you could be in India at that time. This for more reasons than one.... But if you could come in September, we could, after leaving instructions for the building, go together to the hills....

I do hope I shall live to see the laboratory in working order, and that you will come to bless it.

The success of his last two books spurred him on, and soon Bose started writing another book, *Research on Irritability of Plants*. Nivedita, the writer, again gave full assistance to Bose the scientist. An American disciple of the Swami, Miss Laura Glenn (given Devamata as her Indian name) came to stay with the two sisters, Nivedita and Christine, in 1909. She wrote about the two sisters in her book, *Days in an Indian Monastery*, 'The real principal of the school was Sister Christine...an exceptionally unselfish character with a rare spirit of service.'

This description is accurate. Christine stayed in India for about twelve long years continuously and lived a life of poverty and austerity. She sometimes went without footwear and walked through the streets of Calcutta barefoot. About Sister Nivedita, Miss Glenn wrote,

> Literary work absorbed Nivedita too profoundly to enable her to take part to any extent in teaching. She was occupied also in assisting the famous Botanist, Dr J. C. Bose, in preparing a new book on plant life. He spent several hours every day at the school and sometimes lunched there. So, I had a delightful opportunity to know him.

In October 1909, Saradananda-swami, secretary of the Ramakrishna Mission, wrote to Sara about developments in Calcutta,

> Nivedita is well and in Calcutta. She intends [on] going to Darjeeling for a few weeks soon. We are publishing her book *The Master as I saw Him*. Sister Christine is in Darjeeling with the Boses.... The school is being conducted by Hindu ladies whom the Sisters have trained by this time....

As usual, Nivedita and the Boses, and this time in the company of

Christine, spent the autumn vacation in Darjeeling, working continuously on his latest book. Bose wrote to Sara in November 1909, 'I found Nivedita very anxious at Darjeeling and learnt that all her funds had been exhausted. She was expecting your instalment for November, which has not reached yet. She has cut down every possible expense, yet the sum required is for $250 to $300 a year.'

While in London, Sara had begun to feel that Nivedita was taking advantage of her generosity. Nivedita sensed it, felt hurt, but did not bring it out in the open. Sara did not approve of all of Nivedita's activities. The Swami had brought Nivedita to India for working among women, to develop institutions for their education, and also for building a convent. But she spent her time lecturing on politics and nationalism, writing articles and editorials, and was neglecting the work that had to be done for women's upliftment.

Joe too wrote a letter to Sara about Nivedita that forced her to heed her and Bose's pleadings. She remembered that the Swami, her spiritual guru and divine, had entrusted Nivedita to her motherly care. Sara, thus, overcame her suspicions. She soon resumed her periodic remittances to Nivedita, who had only a meagre income from her writings. Initially, Nivedita had felt terribly guilty that she was not fulfilling her guru's expectations. Noticing her dilemma and versatile energetic personality, the Swami had given her the freedom to act. This had happened in Brittany, but Nivedita had felt this was too personal a thing to be shared with Sara.

The school of the two Sisters needed land to expand. Bose rented the piece of empty land next to the school, where there had been a factory earlier. The rent was 12 rupees for a month, and Bose paid the rent for one year. Learning of this, in June 1910, Sara sent Nivedita $100 to relieve Bose. She also kept a bond for $200 at Grindlays Bank, Calcutta, under Bose's name and hers. Bose could draw from it to spend as he needed.

In 1910, Nivedita wrote to Sara in appreciation of her self-effacing magnanimity,

> You know this school is really yours, and my writings are really yours, and the science books [of Bose] are yours, the laboratory [of Bose] will be yours.... Don't you feel that it is a goodly array

of things that you have made possible by your support.... No, I must say that, used as you have used it, money seems to me a great and good thing.

After Nivedita's return from Europe, the editor of *Modern Review,* Ramananda Chatterjee paid a courtesy visit, in July 1909, to Bosepara Lane to greet her and renew their friendship after a lapse of two years. Bose had introduced Chatterjee in 1907 to Nivedita, and ever since then she had been writing continually for his journal. The three often met either at the school or at Bose's residence. About one such meeting Chatterjee remarked,

> Besides writing letters, when we discussed this or that subject, it was she who was the speaker, and I the listener. Professor Bose used to laugh and say to me, 'She wants you to argue and then be defeated in argument by her, and then only she will be pleased.' Nivedita would smile at that remark. Although Nivedita was assertive and wished to press her views to the furthermost point of acceptance, she was always willing to help anyone who came forward to do something for the country.

There is camaraderie and an element of friendly banter in Bose's remark.

Here is an example of how Nivedita helped someone who tried to do something for the country, but of whose methods she did not approve. One of her acquaintances, Sri Aurobindo Ghosh, was the leader of a band of young men who had taken to the path of terrorism in their quest for independence. Sri Aurobindo was also publishing and editing a journal called *Karmayogin.* While Nivedita was away, he had been arrested, tried, and released for want of evidence in a case of some bombings. While in jail he studied the Gita and Upanishads, the main Hindu philosophical scriptures, and his mind turned towards spiritualism.

After release, he returned to his editorial work in the office of *Karmayogin.* In February 1910, he was informed by a subordinate that there would be a police raid that night, in which Sri Aurobindo could be arrested. He escaped to Chunder Nagore, a French enclave near Calcutta, outside the long arm of the British law. Nivedita went to meet him there on 14 February. She visited him a second time within a few days and passed on some money given by Bose, to meet the expenses of travel to Pondicherry, which was another French enclave in South India, very far from Calcutta.

Sri Aurobindo, before his departure from Chunder Nagore, entrusted the journal *Karmayogin* to Nivedita's care. She continued its publication for a few issues until it was suspended in April. She changed the journal's tenor from politics to an enquiry into India's glorious past and drew sustenance from it to arouse nationalism. In one of the issues, she declared her ideology as follows,

> I believe that India is one, indissoluble, indivisible. National unity is built on the common home, the common interest and the common love.
>
> I believe that the strength which spoke in the Vedas and Upanishads, in the making of religions and empires, in the learning of scholars, and the meditation of the saints, is born once more amongst us, and its name today is Nationality.
>
> I believe that the present of India is deep-rooted in her past, and that before her shines a glorious future.

Nivedita, no doubt, took a risk in helping Sri Aurobindo. But Bose, a government employee whose research and academic career depended wholly on goodwill, also took an enormous risk to help someone to whose ways both he and his friend Tagore were totally opposed. Such actions show up an individual's true generosity. No wonder, Sri Aurobindo never mentioned this incident in any of his writings, because it would have exposed his benefactors further. In fact, a few lines that he wrote made it clear that Nivedita had no involvement in his activities whatsoever.

Boshi Sen

The year 1911 saw many additions in and subtractions from Bose's life. One such addition was Basiswar Sen, a tall lanky youth of twenty-three, with a mop of curly hair, who joined Bose's laboratory as an assistant. His name Basiswar gets shortened into Boshi by the Bengali tongue, and so he is often referred to as Boshi Sen. At that point in time, Boshi had

Basiswar Sen at a young age.

an extraordinary past, and was destined to also have an extraordinary future.[68]

Boshi's father Rameshwar Sen, a Kayastha by caste, belonged to a family of great scholarship. He was a graduate of the Calcutta University, a distinguished scholar of Sanskrit and Mathematics, and a school inspector by profession with a good salary. Boshi showed a sharp memory and extraordinary performance in school—once he received a double promotion in class. When Boshi was a boy of twelve, Rameshwar died all of a sudden. While the family was in mourning and busy with the funeral, a servant stole the family gold. A well-to-do family suddenly fell into dire straits. Mercifully, the house they lived in at Bishnupur was owned by them.

Two of Boshi's elder brothers, who had reached adulthood, started doing odd jobs. Two elder sisters had already been married into affluent families. Boshi soon passed the highest class in the primary school, the only one in their small township, and knew that there was no possibility of any further education in the settlement.

Boshi had always adored his father and knew that his father had not been happy with the academic achievements of his elder brothers, and counted on him to fulfil the family tradition of great scholarship. Determined to gain a higher education, twelve-year-old Boshi decided to run away without telling his mother.

One morning, while she was busy in the kitchen, Boshi sped away with tears in his eyes, towards a married sister's home in Bhadul town. That was unfortunately the last Boshi saw of his mother, for she did not live long thereafter. He had to cover a distance of 30 odd kilometres

---

[68]This author has learnt much about Boshi's ancestry and life from the biography of Boshi and his wife Gertrude Emerson titled *Nearer Heaven Than Earth*, written by Girish N. Mehra.

barefoot; by nightfall, he became too tired to walk and sat under a tree, hungry and fearful. After several hours, by a stroke of luck, a bullock cart came that way. He first heard the bell round the bullock's neck and then saw the light of the swinging lantern and called out. The gentleman on the cart turned out to be the father of one of his friends and gladly offered him a lift. He reached his sister's home in the middle of the night

The following morning, Boshi was crestfallen to discover that there was no high school in that township either. His sister was kind enough to send him on to his other elder sister who was in Ranchi. This sister welcomed him warmly and arranged for his schooling. When Boshi was in his early teens in Ranchi, Swami Vivekananda became world famous and a tidal wave of inspiration for the youth. Boshi did not remain untouched by that wave.

He came to Calcutta and secured admission in St. Xavier's College in 1908. His second elder brother Gunishwar, who by then had a steady job, paid for his college expenses. In the past, Gunishwar had always willingly come forward to tutor Boshi with his school lessons. It is not known how Boshi earned his living in the city; it is probable that he was giving private tuition to the children of a well-to-do family, as that mode of earning was popular in Calcutta.

Boshi seems to have met Sisters Nivedita and Christine soon after arriving in Calcutta, and got to know them well, for we find Sister Nivedita reposing great confidence in Boshi within a year. In early 1909, when Boshi was in his second year at St. Xavier's, a friend named Bibhuti Ghosh took him to the Belur monastery to meet an old monk. This was no other than Sadananda-swami, who five years ago had returned from the adventure trip in the Himalayas that had destroyed his constitution.

Even after a long rest on his return, Sadananda never fully recovered. In 1907 or 1908, he lived for some time in Bishnupur, where he came in contact with Boshi's eldest brother Sureshwar. Boshi might have heard of Sadananda-swami from him. We find Boshi entering Sadananda's room following his friend Bibhuti. Before entering the room, he bent down to unlace and remove his shoes, and Sadananda took notice.

The monk, only in his loincloth, was already very ill with asthma and diabetes, and breathed with difficulty. After the routine introduction, the monk said sharply to Boshi,

Oil in your hair which has dripped on to your coat collar, when
you know you cannot afford to have your coat cleaned; paan juice
trickling from your mouth, and you have been wearing foreign
style shoes.... Some people come here as if it is a picnic ground....
Don't you realize that this place was built with the very blood of
Swami Vivekananda?

Boshi kept silent but mused, 'Why should I have come to you, if I were
perfect?' They returned by boat as they had come.

Bibhuti arranged another visit very soon and again Boshi agreed to
go. Someone else in his place might not have agreed to go a second time.
On this occasion, while Bibhuti preceded, Boshi was late in unlacing
his shoes, and overheard, 'Where is that boy who came with you last
time? I am afraid I was too severe with him? I could not sleep all night.'
Sadananda was all kindness to Boshi, 'Brother, do you smoke?' Boshi
confessed shyly that he did a little. The monk handed him his own
hookah. At the time of taking leave, Boshi was simply told, 'All I have
is yours.' An exhilaration surged through his body and mind. He knew
he had found his guru.

During the summer vacation of 1909, while Boshi was in Bishnupur,
Nivedita sent a telegram, 'Can you take care of Sadananda?' Since Boshi
saw him last, Sadananda's condition had worsened and even his bodily
functions had to be taken care of in bed. Those were the early years of
the monastery and it did not have the facility to take care of a bed-ridden
monk. Boshi wired back to Nivedita, 'Yes.' He had no earnings but still
remained positive that he could perform this duty. Nivedita rented a
house for Sadananda at 8, Bosepara Lane, at 20 rupees a month; the
house took some time to be repaired.

In early October 1909, Boshi and his younger brother Tabu
arranged to carry Sadananda in, and the two brothers too moved in
to look after the ailing monk. As Boshi attended college, the night
duty was his. He slept on the floor beside Sadananda's bed. During the
day the monk was under Tabu's care, and sometimes a friend came to
help; often, it was Bibhuti. They cooked for the monk, bathed him,
propped him up with pillows when he had difficulty breathing; they
did everything necessary. Money trickled in from well-off devotees of

the Ramakrishna order.

When able to speak, Sadananda told them about his wanderings with his own guru and various anecdotes from Swamiji's life. He used to say with great pride, 'I became Swamiji's disciple when he was an unknown itinerant monk, not the world-famous Swami Vivekananda.'

Sadananda gave them spiritual lessons by telling simple parables and stories from the life of the Swami or his guru, Sri Ramakrishna. Every now and then, whenever he saw the slightest transgression, he gave them a severe tongue-lashing. Once, after a particularly harsh scolding, he told Boshi, 'Don't you know? I ought to cut my breast open and keep you here in my heart. But I haven't the time to take you up by the easy pleasant way. I have to push you straight up into the line.'

Such sweet words were extremely rare; Boshi had his baptism by fire. Nivedita and Christine used to drop in every now and then to see Sadananda and encourage the boys as they performed their onerous duty. On 25 November 1910, the holy mother of the Ramakrishna monastery, Sri Sarada Devi, came to see ailing Sadananda. She was very pleased to see how the two young boys were ministering to the monk's every need. Returning to her residence, she remarked, 'Blessed are those boys! They are the ones who can be called true sadhus.'

Sadananda-swami breathed his last on 18 February 1911, while Nivedita had gone to America to be with Mrs Bull. Boshi had learned from his guru that beyond the cycles of birth and death, there is immortality. He did not mourn, rather felt a subdued elation that his guru had been released from pain. He had devotedly served his guru for nearly two years and his character was shaped by the guru.

In the same month, Boshi graduated with a science degree, and was qualified to enrol for master's; but he had other ideas—he wanted to join the Ramakrishna order as a monk. He knew Brahmananda-swami, the president of the Ramakrishna Mission and mahant of the monastery, well. Brahmananda-swami, who used to be called Raja Maharaj, was fond of Boshi, and the latter was sure that, if he asked, Raja Maharaj would initiate him. He took a bath in the river Ganges, purchased some sweets and flowers for offering and went to the senior monk.

Brahmananda-swami (alias Raja Maharaj)

As he entered the room, Raja Maharaj asked, 'Well Boshi. What is the latest in science?' Boshi started to talk about Millikan's cloud chamber, in which the motion of electrons could be detected, and so on. The monk allowed him to chatter on for some time and then interrupted to say, 'You stick to this Boshi. You will get everything through your science.' Boshi got the message. He never tried to be a monk again, instead choosing to focus on a career in science and fulfilling his father's dreams.

Nivedita, for quite some time, had been persuading Boshi to join the research team of her good friend Jagadish C. Bose. She had also spoken to the scientist about Boshi. Now that he had a graduate degree in science, Boshi wished to pursue a higher degree, and approached Bose, who readily registered Boshi as a master's student under his guidance. Boshi wanted to retain the house at 8 Bosepara Lane as a hallowed memorial for his guru, and continued to live in the house. Nivedita too wanted to keep the house and kept paying the rent. Outside college hours, Boshi did odd jobs for Nivedita's school and often visited the Belur monastery to meet Raja Maharaj. Whatever he did, he did with full concentration and sincerity, true to his guru's teachings.

The Great Departures

About one year before Boshi joined Bose's laboratory, in March 1910, Nivedita had three European-looking strangers visiting her school. One of them, an English lady, simply said that she heard about a school, run by an Irish woman in the Indian part of the town. Nivedita showed them around and then the visitors started a philosophical discussion. Nivedita told them about the ancient roots of Hindu thoughts and her belief that spiritualism had spread from India to the rest of the world. At the time of taking leave, the English lady revealed her true identity as Lady Minto, the wife of the then viceroy. She told Nivedita that she knew that the police were keeping a watch on her, and advised her to meet the police commissioner. Nivedita was surprised that Lady Minto was moving around incognito without the usual protocol, and thanked her for the reforms Lord Minto had introduced. Later, she did meet the police commissioner, following which surveillance on her was lifted.

In the summer of 1910, the Boses and Nivedita went on a pilgrimage to Kedarnath and Badrinarayan in the Himalayas. In the first week of June, they started the climb from Haridwar. At night the party usually rested in a dak bungalow; when one was not available, they took shelter in dharamshalas or chattis. They saw how pilgrims from all parts of India were coming and mingling together en route to the holy temple of Kedarnath, their ultimate destination. The spiritual unity of the whole nation became apparent to them and they rejoiced in exhilaration. The last four miles were an extremely steep climb, but the view around them was unforgettably beautiful. Badrinarayan was a bit of a disappointment for Nivedita; the temple priests were too orthodox to allow her entry. She remembered what Swamiji had told her about not confronting orthodoxy, so she joined the pilgrims in the parikrama, circumambulation, of the temple. They returned to the plains at the end of June.

Calcutta was waiting with ominous news for the party—Mrs Sara Bull was very ill in America. She requested Nivedita to come over, but Nivedita had returned from a journey west just one year ago and was not in a position to undertake another voyage. She wrote letters, one after another, to encourage the ailing lady, and was hoping against hope that she would turn the corner and start improving.

In the autumn holidays, the Boses as usual took Nivedita to Darjeeling, where they concentrated on preparing the manuscript of Bose's latest book, *Irritability of Plants*. A telegram arrived that Sara's condition was serious and she wanted Nivedita by her side. She took the next available ship to America. It was then late October or early November. When the steamer reached Genoa, Nivedita wrote an inspirational letter to Bose, timed to reach him on his birthday,[69]

> When you receive this, it will be our beloved 30th, the birthday of birthdays. May it be infinitely blessed—and may it be followed by many of ever-increasing sweetness and blessedness. Outside there is the great statue of Christopher Columbus and under his name only the words 'La Patrie' and I thought of the day to come when such words will be the speaking silence under your name. How spiritually you are already reckoned with him and all those other great adventurers who have sailed trackless seas to bring their people good.
>
> Be ever victorious! Be a light unto the peoples and a lamp under their feet! And be filled with peace! You the great spiritual mariner who have found new worlds!

Nivedita reached Cambridge on 15 November 1910, and found Sara very weak, frail, and anaemic. The disease was diagnosed to be pernicious anaemia, which did not have a cure at that time. The doctors were administering palliative treatment by giving serum injections. In Nivedita's care, Sara showed visible improvements. Perhaps, the Ayurvedic tonic that Nivedita had brought from India helped.

In December, Sara and Nivedita went to Brooklyn to live with Sara's friend Judith Swanander and her daughter Siri. News came that Sara's estranged daughter Olea was coming to see her. Sara said, 'When Olea comes, I don't want to see her alone.' When Olea arrived, she saw her mother in the presence of Nivedita and Siri, and the meeting went by

---

[69]According to Pravrajika Atmaprana, the letter was written from Geneva. However, at that time Nivedita had not gone to Geneva. From the description of Columbus's statue, it is likely she was at his birthplace Genoa, Italy, which is a port on the Mediterranean, en route to America.

peacefully. On a subsequent visit, Olea came unannounced and Nivedita was not present. When she returned, she found Sara mentally disturbed and learnt from Judith that Olea had visited. Nivedita cried and the next day went to a nearby church to pray for Sara.

They went back to Cambridge soon. Nivedita found that Sara now was constantly thinking of Sri Ramakrishna and Swami Vivekananda or Vedanta. She was reminiscing about their days in Kashmir. Nivedita tried to keep Sara's mind focused on these subjects. In January, Nivedita wrote to Joe,

> We parted last night on a little wave of Sri Ramakrishna.... She has told me all she did for [Swami Vivekananda], and exactly what she said—and it was wonderful—the real keynote of her life. And of her own accord she said this was to be a new life for her, and she would use her judgement henceforth, not to condemn anyone, but only to protect herself from error.

Sara breathed her last in the early hours of the morning of 18 January, while Nivedita chanted 'Hari Om Ramakrishna'. Nivedita stayed on for a while with Sara's neighbour, the Longfellows, before returning to India. Olea immediately contested Sara's will on the grounds that Sara had been driven insane by a Hindu cult. Sara's household servants were bribed to stand false witness. The case dragged on for some time, and eventually Olea won the case. Sara's will had bequeathed a substantial sum to Bose's future institute and Nivedita's school, but all this was now under question. However, Sara's brother and lawyer, Mr Thorp, knew both Olea and Nivedita well and was trying to save some provisions of the will. It is a tragic irony that soon thereafter Olea died by suicide.

While still in America, Nivedita was further distressed to hear about Sadananda's passing away. She went first to England to see some old friends, the Ratcliffes among them. In Paris, she met with Josephine and Betty MacLeod. They embraced, wept, and mourned the death of Saint Sara together. They also remembered Sadananda-swami and prayed for his soul. Nivedita sailed for India from Marseilles on 23 March 1911.

On her arrival in Calcutta, she met the holy mother, Sarada Devi and they talked about 'Sara Mem', as she used to be referred to by the holy mother. They talked also about Sadananda. The soothing words of the holy mother brought peace and consolation to Nivedita, after the twin losses of Sara and Sadananda.

That summer, the Boses took Nivedita to the Advaita Ashrama at Mayavati in the Himalayas. One of Bose's nephews was also with them. They stayed there for a month and worked together on his book *Irritability of Plants*. Once, Bose even lectured on his latest discoveries to the sadhus at the ashram. They returned to Calcutta in early July.

All along Nivedita had been anxious about the school's finances, since Sara, who had been the main provider, was no more and her will was under contest. Lady Minto had offered the government's help, but accepting help from a foreign ruler was an absolute 'no' for Nivedita. Finally, word came from Mr Thorp that the provisions in Sara's will for the school's maintenance could be retrieved, and Nivedita heaved a sigh of relief.

But more woes were in store. Both Christine and Sudhira withdrew from the school, one after the other. They declared that they no longer wished to live and work with Nivedita. Nivedita had always written and spoken in appreciation of these two companions. Besides, she was a bread earner for the school even if in a small way, thanks to the royalties she earned through the sale of her books; she kept back nothing for her own self.

It is not known what compelled Christine and Sudhira to take such a step. Perhaps, it was Nivedita's political activities and the constant flow of visitors that disturbed them. Perhaps, young Sudhira was influenced by Christine. Christine went to Mayawati and Sudhira joined the Brahmo Girls' School. Nivedita was dismayed and shocked. She had to look after the school; three of her books were nearing completion; she was also assisting Bose in preparing the manuscript of *Irritability of Plants.*

The Boses, Nivedita, and Boshi travelled to Darjeeling at the beginning of the autumn vacation, and stayed in the Ray Villa, a house owned by Dr P. C. Ray's brother. Here, Nivedita had an attack of mountain blood dysentery. Dr Nilratan Sarkar, a famous physician from Calcutta, was also vacationing in Darjeeling. He was a good friend of Bose and began treating Nivedita immediately. The best possible medical facility was arranged but to no avail. She knew that the end was approaching, but was least afraid. Every morning she greeted her hosts with a brave smile.

Bose wrote to Joe stating, 'Nivedita is in extreme danger...in spite of...the best medical aid, the case is getting worse every day.'

On 13 October, at the holiest of all moments for Hindus, the moment of confluence of the receding night and the forthcoming day, Nivedita uttered the 'Rudrastuti shloka' from Brihadaranyaka Upanishad:

Asato Ma Satgamaya (From the Unreal lead us to the Real),
Tamaso Ma Jyotirgamaya (From Darkness lead us to Light),
Mrityor Ma Amritam Gamaya (From Death lead us to Immortality),
Abhiravirma Edhi (Reach us Through and Through Ourselves).

Nivedita said to the Boses, 'The frail boat is sinking, but I shall yet see the sunrise.' It is said that the moment a ray of the crimson-gold sun came streaming into the room, her atman left her worldly body and soared up into the abode of joy. She was cremated in the evening; a monk of the Ramakrishna order performed funeral rites and the ashes were collected in an urn by Boshi. At the very spot of her funeral pyre, the public raised a samadhi. Her epitaph on the memorial stone reads,

'HERE REPOSES SISTER NIVEDITA WHO GAVE HER ALL TO INDIA.'

On 18 October, Bose wrote to Joe,

My dear friend,

We could not keep her. The light has gone out our life. She was conscious to the last, and spoke of continuation of her work.... God has been kind, too kind to us to have given us a glimpse of the divine.

Yours, J. C. Bose

When the news of Nivedita's illness arrived in Calcutta, Sudhira regretted her decision and was preparing to go to Darjeeling. But soon came the news that signalled the end of all news. Christine and Sudhira returned to their beloved school with a feeling of great regret and guilt.

The Boses and Boshi returned to Calcutta with a heavy heart. Jagadish had suffered two great losses in a short span of ten months. His two great benefactresses were gone for ever. He attended to his college duties, yet grieved for a long time. One and a half months later, on his birthday, 30 November, Bose wrote to Josephine MacLeod[70] from his Calcutta residence, using for the first time the endearing name 'Yam' that Nivedita called her,

> My heart goes out to you, dear Yam, because you knew her as she was, because you loved her, and she always rested on your love. Of this she was absolutely sure. Bless you dear friend in standing by her and being true to her. Did we ever realize what privilege it was to know her as a friend!

> Tell me something human. I cannot bear the idea of accepting the loss. She must be living and with us every minute!... Is it possible to work on under the conditions under which I was placed, and under such isolation? Do you know how it kills one to discover a new thing, and then no one to tell?? To all these I was reconciled because she was my pen and public. I could dream and work and wait. Now the last prop is gone. I could live by work but the strength and inspiration are crushed.

> Such a big world of science and discovery opened out! Now there are the results coming, and the one who would have welcomed them is away.

> But I must not be unmanly. Today is my birthday, this day 17 years ago I resolved to put all my strength for science. Five years I worked all by myself, struggling hard. And when my strength was nearly gone, then she came to help me. These 12 years, it has been incessant work, but the hardship was not too much. You know her presence made it so easy to choose all that is great. ...And today I shall try to take up the burden in a worthy way.

> ...Only one thing I see clearly. Her school must be maintained, and all her writings must be published.... But I feel so broken down.

---

[70]A facsimile of the original handwritten letter is displayed on the official web site of the Bose Institute, in a collage with photos of Bose and Nivedita. This is an acknowledgement of Sister Nivedita by the present Bose-Institute authorities. It is welcome, although belated and posthumous. In 1917, when the Bose Institute was inaugurated, there was no world wide web, and nobody knew of this letter. The original letter can be found in the appendix (p. 441) to this book.

Write to me often, and tell me how we could best carry out her wishes. Tell me things she spoke to you. Did she really think us as her own?... God bless you and keep you.

Yours J. C. Bose.[71]

It is obvious that Bose was commiserating with Joe through letters. Nivedita was not only his pen and secretary, she was his scientific soulmate, his inspiration, and light. Being a pupil of all-round brilliance in high school and having an enormous capacity to keep on learning, she could understand his science, and that is how she kept him company through his many discoveries. As long as she was around, he had someone to share his thoughts with, and did not feel lonesome. We do not know how Joe helped Bose through his grief; her letters to Bose have not been found among his papers.

For a long while, Bose kept on visiting Nivedita's school in search of solace. His forlorn demeanour made people around him worried. Two years later, in 1913, Christine wrote to Joe,

Dr Bose is much better physically and mentally, and one no longer has the fear that he may not be with us for long. But life is so dull for him now. He constantly says, 'I do not know how to pass my days'. Margot gave him sympathy, understanding, enthusiasm, inspiration and help in his work. You can imagine what a void she left.

Some of Nivedita's ashes, that Boshi had brought back, were sent to the Belur monastery. A portion was sent to Nivedita's family. On 12 October 1912, it was buried, with a Christian ceremony, amid the honeysuckle in the family grave in Great Torrington, under the sign of the holy cross. Boshi kept the urn of her remaining ashes in his puja room in 8 Bosepara Lane.

Abala Bose wrote of Nivedita, 'As a woman I knew her in everyday life, full of austerity and possessed with a longing for righteousness which shone round her like a pure flame. Others will know her as the great moral and intellectual force which came to us in time of great national need.'

---

[71]All the Bose letters to Josephine MacLeod are preserved in the archive of Ramakrishna-Vivekananda Center, New York, who have very kindly given access to this author.

Tagore called her 'lokamata', the mother of the people. Nivedita's friend, S. K. Ratcliffe, the editor of *The Statesman,* wrote in her memory, 'Those to whom she gave the ennobling gift of her friendship hold the memory of that gift as this world's highest benediction.'

Tagore Wins the Nobel Prize

Nivedita's death landed another person in great difficulty—Boshi Sen. It was Nivedita who had been paying the rent of his guru's last abode, the house at 8 Bosepara Lane. Now Boshi had to find a way of keeping it.

Professor Bose offered to find a good teaching position for Boshi at his personal recommendation. Alternatively, Boshi could join as a full-time research assistant under Bose at a salary of 20 rupees a month. Either way, Boshi had to give up on his M.Sc. He reasoned that with a teaching job, he would earn much more but would need to stop pursuing higher education altogether. But as a research assistant, he would have a window open to on-the-job learning. So, he chose the latter. All his earnings would go towards paying his rent, and he would have to otherwise survive on the charity of friends, since he did not wish to burden his second elder brother any longer. Later in life, when Boshi became a renowned scientist, he would say.

> I owe my science to Sister Nivedita. It was she who placed me under Sir J. C. Bose. It is difficult for me to express in words what I feel about her. In my own little way, I try to express in life some of the dynamic ideas she used to radiate.

In his boyhood, Boshi remembered, his father had described Bose as a great scientist and Tagore as a great poet. He now came to know both of them quite intimately.

Tagore published his book of Bengali poems *Gitanjali* in 1910. Like all poets, he used to sublimate his emotions into poetry and in times of grief, this gave him solace and sustenance. An abiding faith in God and Vedanta philosophy saw him through many a crisis—within a span of five years between 1902 and 1907, he had lost his wife Mrinalini, second daughter Renuka, and youngest son Samindranath. That is when the song offerings of *Gitanjali* were composed. He translated some of them into

English during a retreat in Silaidah on the banks of his beloved river, Padma. The translations were in prose, but they usually took on the character of free verse. Tagore wanted to share these poems with his British friend William Rothenstein, who incidentally was not a poet but an artist. Rothenstein connected with India through his interest in Indian art.

Rothenstein had exhibited his paintings at the Paris Exposition in 1900. One of them, *The Doll's House*, won the silver medal and made him famous. It is extremely likely that he was invited to Betty and Frank Leggett's parties where many prominent luminaries used to be invited. Swami Vivekananda and Sister Nivedita were present in most of these gatherings, and Rothenstein might have met them.

It is not known how he got interested in Indian art. It could be that his friendship with people who were interested in Vedanta philosophy, like the poet W. B. Yeats, attracted him to Indian art and sculpture, or perhaps the stir Swami Vivekananda's speeches created in England a few years earlier had influenced him in this direction.

Be that as it may, in 1910, we find Rothenstein embarking on a seminal tour of prominent sites of Indian art and sculpture. While he was visiting the ancient Buddhist caves of Ajanta, by sheer coincidence, he met a company of visitors, including Sister Nivedita, the Boses, and two young Indian artists, Nandalal Basu and Asit Haldar, who were engaged in copying the ancient frescos in water colour. It is but natural that Rothenstein would wish to become acquainted with such a group.

Later, they met in Calcutta, and Rothenstein was introduced to Abanindranath Tagore, who was then the vice principal of the Government School of Arts, where Nandalal and Asit were students. Rothenstein appreciated Abanindranath's endeavours. He was also made aware of Abanindranath's uncle Rabindranath Tagore and his school at Shantiniketan. A visit to the school left a lasting impression on Rothenstein's mind and he became a lifelong friend of the senior Tagore.

Tagore sailed for England in May 1912, at the invitation of Rothenstein. The latter introduced Tagore to his circle of friends, which included W. B. Yeats, Ezra Pound, Thomas Moore, May Sinclair, Ernest Rhys, Stafford Brooke, and many others. A meeting was arranged to hear Tagore's poetry. He read out the lyrics of *Gitanjali*, whose music and rhythm transported the audience to a world of Vedantic mysticism. The resplendence of Tagore's imagery cast such a spell of enchantment over them that they dispersed silently without saying a word. Later, Yeats suggested minor changes in the translations of the *Gitanjali* songs. His suggestions were especially valuable for Tagore since Yeats had delved deep into Vedanta philosophy. As a member of the Sesame Club, he had been a regular in Swami Vivekananda's Vedanta lectures about a decade earlier.

It is due to Rothenstein's efforts that the English version of *Gitanjali* (titled *Song Offerings*) was published in 1912 by the Indian Society in London, with an introduction by Yeats. He wrote in the introduction,

> These prose translations have stirred my blood as nothing has for years.... I have carried the manuscript of these translations with me for days, reading it in Railway trains or on top of the omnibuses and in restaurants, and I have often had to close it lest some stranger would see how much it moved me.

Yeats predicted that Tagore's lyrics would be sung by wayfarers and boatmen through generations.

A limited edition of 700 copies was printed, among which 250 were for sale. Tagore dedicated the book to Rothenstein. The book was received with enthusiasm in England and the Macmillan Press in London bought its rights, publishing ten subsequent editions within nine months until November 1913. The book received glowing reviews in the *Times Literary* supplement, *Manchester Guardian*, *The Nation*, etc. In America, Ezra Pound and Harriet Monroe published six of these poems in the December (1912) issue of the prestigious magazine *Poetry*, with a note by Pound.

Thomas Moore in his individual capacity, as a Fellow of the Royal Society of Literature of the United Kingdom, recommended Tagore's name to the Swedish Academy for the Nobel Prize for Literature; twenty-seven other academics, poets, and novelists recommended Thomas Hardy for the same.

Initially, the inclusion of Tagore's name was strongly opposed by Herald Hijarne, the chairman of the Academy. Most other members, including E. H. V. Tenger (who knew Bengali) and Carl G. V. von Heidenstam, familiar with Tagore's literary genius, supported his nomination. Tagore's name was finalized because of his profoundly sensitive, fresh, and beautiful verse, expressed in his own English words.

A cablegram from the Nobel committee arrived in Calcutta on 14 November 1913, and the news was communicated to Tagore at Shantiniketan through a series of telegrams. On 19 November, Bose wrote to Tagore in flowery Bengali,

> Friend,
> For so long, you remained unrecognized and without any adornment of victory on the larger arena of the world, and witnessing that I felt intense sorrow and pain, which are now relieved. How do I offer my gratitude to the merciful God for this great benediction! Pray, you grow mightier every day. Be ever victorious. May the God of Truth and Justice ever be on your side.
>
> Yours,
> Jagadish.

A Horrible Mistake

A felicitation committee was formed, consisting of many of Tagore's well-wishers and other eminent people, headed by Jagadish C. Bose. Ramananda Chatterjee, the editor of *Modern Review* and *Prabasi* was also a member. On 23 November, a special train carried the committee and about 500 enthusiasts to Bolpur, the railhead for Shantiniketan. There was an open-air felicitation meeting on a tree-covered ground at Shantiniketan. It was declared that after the garlanding of Tagore and congratulatory speeches, Tagore would sing a song. But instead he delivered a long and severe reprimand in chaste Bengali, ending with the following statement:

'I can only raise the cup of your honour to my lips, I cannot drink from it with all my heart.'

A hush fell over the rejoicing crowd. The ceremony had ended anticlimactically; the invitees dispersed in silence.

It seems that, in the crowd, Rabindranath had spotted several persons, who had made unfair criticisms of his writings, even throwing derogatory comments about him and his family, over the years. One such attack that was particularly vicious needs be mentioned. A book of poems of Tagore, titled *Chaitali*, had drawn adverse criticism that was published in a journal called *Sahitya*. Tagore published a rebuttal.

Then someone named Hemendra Prasad Ghosh published a bawdy and scurrilous story, titled 'Pranay-er Parinaam' ('The Outcome of a Love Affair'), in the same journal. The characters in the story were so skilfully portrayed that anyone, with a slight familiarity with the history of the Tagore family, could easily understand that these were imitations of the prominent figures of the family, some of them long dead. The story was scandalous and full of ugly innuendos and in very bad taste, fit to be classified as 'yellow literature'. One can imagine how upset Tagore might have been. Bose wrote a letter of protest but the editor of the journal chose not to publish it. However, on reading a copy of the letter, the poet felt comfort and solace.

At the felicitation meeting, seeing quite a few of his past adversaries in the meeting—perhaps Hemendra Ghosh was also present—Rabindranath lost his cool. But what could Bose, the chairman of the committee, have done? There was no way of screening people. Tagore's angry reaction singed his friends and foes alike. Bose felt hurt and humiliated. He returned to Calcutta completely bewildered as to the reason for this unexpected outburst.

Later, after the dust had settled, Tagore realized his blunder. He had to go door to door to make amends. A month later, in the general body meeting of the Ram Mohan Library, Rabindranath expressed regrets. Bose has not written anything about this incident, but Ramananda Chatterjee, the editor of *Modern Review* and *Prabasi*, who was also in the committee, recorded his reaction.

It seems the relationship between the scientist and the poet took some time to repair, for at this stage we find a long gap in their correspondence. The next letter from Bose to Tagore is dated 20 July 1918, after an interval of nearly five years, although the rapprochement had come much earlier. In the meantime, much water had flown down the Ganges. Bose had completed his fourth scientific mission to Europe and America (1914–1915). Sister Christine, after twelve long years of austere living in Calcutta, had become physically exhausted and returned to America in 1914; then, World War I broke out and she was detained there because she was of German descent. Bose inaugurated the Bose Institute in 1917.

8

THE BOSE INSTITUTE AND SISTER NIVEDITA

The Diligent Disciple

Boshi started working in Bose's laboratory in Presidency College in February or March of 1911. While working in Bose's laboratory, Boshi eagerly learnt from what he saw around him and what he was assigned to do. On the whole, he was enjoying himself and did not take any days off, except once when his second elder brother was afflicted by kala azar. He even worked on Sundays. Bose, his teacher, leader, and guide, too worked indefatigably and never counted the hours; his assistants and students emulated his enthusiasm.

A good description of Bose's laboratory was given by Boshi. It was confined to a room and a half, where five of his research students jostled for working space. There was also a small space, under the fire escape, which was enclosed by glass panes, and where some of the plant experiments were conducted.

One interesting event from Boshi's early days in the laboratory was an experiment on the comparison of the passage of nervous impulse in a frog's muscle and mimosa plant. He has not named the instrument; however, in 1911, the most likely instrument would be the resonant recorder. Contrary to Bose's theory, the results were not analogous but exactly opposite. Bose had no explanation and was frustrated. The electric connections were carefully checked and the experiments repeated, but with the same disconcerting results. Then, out of desperation Bose asked the experiment to be transferred from the main laboratory to the glass house. Someone dropped the choking coil while shifting and it had to be sent to the repairer. There it was discovered that the terminal markings had been reversed by mistake. All the researchers, including Boshi, congratulated the fellow who had dropped and damaged the component, for his achievement.

Bose did not confine himself to imparting scientific training only. He was also concerned about the personality development of his trainee. He once wrote to Boshi,

> I do not think you need be troubled with being emotional, no one ever did anything fine who had not been deeply impressed by some noble emotion. But it has to be used as a great latent force under check, and finding expression only in action. ...I believe in periodic habit of silence; you should cultivate the habit of listening and not saying much. The quiet dignity and patience only come after long practice, specially to those who are straightforward and frankly speak out their mind.
>
> Every day try to put restraint on yourself, and learn every day till the end. I want you to be constantly growing in every direction.

It has been mentioned that even after Nivedita's demise, Bose visited her school often for a few years. His sister Labanyaprabha was one of the teachers there. It came to their knowledge that Boshi was staying in and paying the rent for the house in Bosepara Lane, where Sadananda breathed his last, for sentimental reasons. Since Boshi's salary was no secret, they quickly gathered that he was living a life of poverty. Bose often invited him to eat wholesome meals in his house and then Boshi reached home late in the evening. When he went to visit Raja Maharaj in the Belur Math, and such visits were frequent enough, he would reach home at one o'clock in the dead of night.

As long as Boshi was in Bose's lab or home, he was engaged in providing one form of service or the other to his mentor. That included secretarial work, besides assistance in research. Boshi has even said that he did certain household chores. Under the expert guidance of Bose, he turned into a talented research scholar. His memory and reasoning had always been sharp, and now he became highly skilled in manipulating sophisticated instruments. He learned physiology and botany, and how to develop and perfect a new device step by step from scratch; in other words, the art of invention.

As hinted in one of his letters to Sara (dated 5 August 1909), Bose had fitted up a laboratory in his house at 93 Circular Road. Once, Bose asked Boshi to continuously record the pulsations of a leaflet, cut off from a telegraph plant and dipped in water. The experiment required observing its movement and changing the smoked plate every four hours, and was carried out in the hall of the third floor laboratory in Bose's house.

The leaflet was normally expected to die in about 7 hours, but this particular one was exceptionally strong and kept pulsating uniformly throughout the night. Early in the morning it showed signs of slowing down and finally at around six o'clock it stopped altogether. Just then Bose looked in and was pleasantly surprised to see the uniformity of the results. He suggested reviving the leaflet by chemical stimulation and examining how long the effect lasts. Boshi applied a stimulant, the plant revived and started pulsating vigorously. He remained at work continuously for 36 hours until the plant mercifully died in the late afternoon.

Bose's summer vacations in the hills were often working vacations, and usually Boshi was a part of the entourage to provide assistance. In the summer of 1913, Boshi accompanied the Boses to Mayavati monastery, not far from Almora, when Mrs Sevier, one of its founders, was still there. They stayed in the monastery guest house for two months. Bose, the Brahmo, was attracted to this particular monastery of the Ramakrishna order because idol worship was not permitted there. To Boshi, the place was the holiest of the holies, because both Swami Vivekananda and Sadananda-swami had set foot there a few times. Bose was then adding the finishing touches to his book *Irritability of Plants*, with Boshi's assistance.

During one such vacation in Darjeeling, Tagore was present, with whom Boshi had already been familiar for a few years and was on friendly terms. During a formal sit-down dinner around a table, Abala kept piling delicacies on Tagore's plate despite his protests. Boshi happened to be seated in between Tagore and Sir Patrick Geddes. Tagore whispered through his mighty grey beard, 'Boshi, if I transfer all these to your plate, will you eat them?'

Boshi cheekily asked, 'What will be my reward, Sir?'

'Every time you come to my house, you will have pitha.[72]'

---

[72]A typical Bengali delicacy, pitha is a kind of stuffed pancake made of powdered rice, filledwith sweetened, shredded coconut or other such fillings.

Tagore kept passing the food to Boshi's plate with great dexterity so that no one would notice. Boshi, then a healthy young man, had his stomach's fill. In the end, he said to Tagore, 'Sir, you have missed your profession. You ought to have been a pickpocket.' Tagore had a hearty laugh.

Boshi adored his scientist guru and used to write in English about Bose's life in *Modern Review,* edited by Ramananda Chatterjee. A passage from one of the essays is worth quoting here, for its literary quality,

> His early love for his own village culminated in a longing to know the whole of India and there is hardly any place of historical importance between the snowy peaks of Kedarnath in the North and Rameswaram in the South that he did not visit. The rock-cut temples of the earliest Buddhist period, the inscriptions of Asoka, the ruins of ancient Universities, the Himalayan glaciers, the Stupa of Sanchi, the excavations of Taxila, the ruins of Rajgir, to these and many other places he came time and after time till he realized India, made one by linked history, from the dawn of civilization to the present day.

Boshi finished his schooling in the provincial district town of Ranchi, in a Bengali-medium school. Then he studied science in St. Xavier's College, Calcutta. Where and how did he learn a foreign language so well? It is obvious that he had an aptitude for language and literature, much like his mentor. This also speaks of the kind of secretarial help he gave to Bose in writing books and scientific papers, for more than a decade.

Slower Movements in Plants

Even before Boshi had joined Bose's laboratory, and soon after returning from his third scientific trip abroad in July 1909, Bose had made much progress in research, undaunted by dearth of space. He had started working on developing a new instrument, because the resonant recorder had limitations for a certain type of experiments. It was good for measuring movements which were extremely quick. There are, however, plant movements which are relatively slow. For instance, the leaflet of a telegraph plant completes one cycle of movement in 3 minutes. Hence, an instrument was required for recording slower movements for hours and, perhaps, even days.

Moreover, there are movements in certain plants which are very feeble and for which friction in the fulcrum of a relatively heavy metallic recorder strut may be too much to overcome—in the resonant recorder the writer was necessarily metallic and, therefore heavy, as it had to be magnetically vibrated.

Hence, instead of the writer strut, Bose now set the smoked glass plate into slow oscillation; the writer strut was only subjected to the pulls and pushes of the plant, and was made of very light non-metallic material. Instead of descending vertically, the smoked glass plate was now made to slide horizontally from left to right. Thus was born the oscillating recorder as described by Geddes. It seems that the same instrument was also called a plant phytograph by Bose. He drew a schematic diagram of the phytograph, as shown in Fig. 8.1.

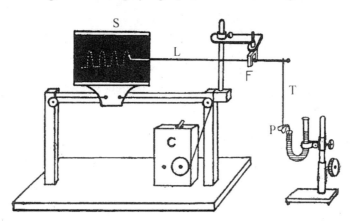

Fig. 8.1: Plant Phytograph: P - Leaf of Telegraph plant placed in the U-tube; T - thin link rod; F - Fulcrum of lever; L - lever; S - Smoked glass plate; C - Clockwork device.

In this instrument, the smoked glass plate is mounted on a horizontal guide bar which also carries pulleys at either end. The thread from the clockwork device goes over the pulleys, as shown in the diagram. The leaf is placed in a U-tube, containing water, and connected to the writing lever by a thin link rod. The glass plate moves from left to right slowly.

It also oscillates, in a direction perpendicular to the plane of the paper, to come up periodically to take an impression from the writer tip.

All this is made possible by the ingenious adaptations of the clockwork device. The travel speed and oscillation of the plate can be varied for recording the movements of different parts of a plant body. For instance, for recording an extremely slow process, it is possible to make the plate travel from left to right in 24 hours and come up for taking an imprint every 15 minutes.

A leaf of a telegraph plant consists of three leaflets, as shown in Fig. 7.3. The central leaflet is large, flanked by two smaller leaflets on either side. It is the smaller leaflets which show autonomous movement without any external stimulus or excitation. Bose recorded this movement with the help of his plant phytograph.

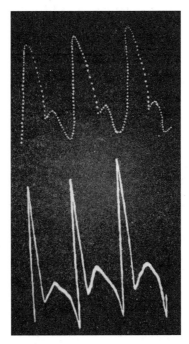

Fig. 8.2: Record of Autonomous movement and simultaneous electric pulsation of the leaflet of a telegraph plant; Upper curve: autonomous movement as recorded by phytograph; Lower curve: Electric pulsation at leaflet root recorded by voltage sensor.

Bose also discovered a simultaneous electric pulsation, at the root of the leaflet, which has certain similarities with the electric pulsations due to the rhythmic heartbeats of an animal. He simultaneously recorded the leaflet's mechanical pulsation with the phytograph and the electrical pulsation with a voltage sensor, as shown in Fig. 8.2. The two autographs were extremely congruous.

They seemed very similar when compared with the electric pulsation produced by the heartbeats of a frog. However, their time periods are different; one cycle of plant pulsation takes about 3 minutes, whereas that of a frog's heart about a second.

Fourth Scientific Mission to Europe

The volume of research conducted by Bose between 1909 and early 1913 is all contained in his book *Irritability of Plants*, which was sent to the publishers Longmans, Green, and Co., London, in the summer of 1913, and got promptly published the same year.

In 1911, during the coronation of King George V, Lord Hardinge, then viceroy of India, decorated Bose with the title of Companion of the Order of the Star of India. In March 1912, the Calcutta University in its convocation meeting, honoured him with the title of Doctor of Science.

That, at the turn of the century, the top echelons of the British bureaucracy were often favourably disposed towards science and the few successful scientists that India produced, we have seen instances of. It is the middle and lower bureaucracy that had been hostile. But from 1910, even that started changing as the liberal attitude percolated down from the top.

In April 1913, Bose sent a proposal to the Bengal government for setting up a laboratory in the Himalayas for studying plants of the temperate climate of Europe, and a botanical garden with a laboratory outside Calcutta. For this twin purpose, he stipulated his requirement for a grant of 24,000 rupees annually for the next five years. In December, the secretary of state for India sanctioned an annual grant of 18,000 rupees for the following three years, with a rider that if the research output was found satisfactory, the grant would be extended for two more years. Thus came up Bose's summertime laboratory in Darjeeling and a garden with a small laboratory building in Sijberia, some 30 odd kilometres downstream of Calcutta on the eastern bank of the Ganga.

In the meantime, Bose was fast approaching the retirement age of fifty-five. In view of his reputation as a teacher and a researcher, he was given an extension of two years and was allowed to work at Presidency College until 1915.

By seniority and distinction in service, the highest appointment in the education service, the post of director of public instruction had been within his grasp, if he had so chosen. That would have fetched him a much higher salary, but taken him away from Presidency College and his beloved research into the realm of administration. Bose was not interested in power and wealth. His only goal had been to put India on the scientific map of the world, which had not been reached yet. So, he chose to continue as a professor of science at a much lower salary.

There was, however, a windfall in his fortune. Bose, with characteristic indifference to personal gain, had never paid attention to the hierarchy of posts in his cadre. It turns out that he had long been entitled to promotion to the highest grade due to seniority, with corresponding rise in pay. The principal and director of public instruction chose to keep quiet and did not inform the government for their own malicious reasons.

There's a Bengali saying that goes, 'the wheel of justice is occasionally turned by the wind'. On the eve of Bose's retirement, there was a review owing to the claim of a junior officer, and this anomaly came to light. The government gazetted Bose to the highest grade with retrospective effect, and he received a large sum as arrears, which he at once invested in his future institute. His salary also rose considerably; from now on, the financial burden for research lessened on him.

Bose's previous books *Plant Response* (1906) and *Comparative Electro-physiology* (1907) had been in the public domain for years now. Many researchers in different universities had been trying to repeat his experiments with some success, and the opinion amongst the scientist community was slowly turning in his favour.

In 1913, Bose submitted a paper to the Royal Society that contained proof of nervous impulse in plant; although quite opposed to the generally held opinion that plants had no nervous system like animals, the paper was so convincing that it was published with alacrity. It was placed in the higher category of *Philosophical Transactions* than the ordinary *Proceedings of the Royal Society*; thus, the Royal Society opened its doors to him after a long interval of eleven years. The paper was titled, 'An Automatic Method for the Investigation of Velocity of Transmission of Excitation in Mimosa'.

Bose's conclusion that plants, like animals, have a nerve-like mechanism for conduction of excitement was not challenged, but for long nobody else could measure the speed of conduction of excitement by another method and confirm Bose's results. Confirmation came fifteen years later due to K. Umrath. It is obvious that Bose was well ahead of his times.

Following the Royal Society publication, Bose received numerous invitations from European and American universities to give lecture-demonstrations. The government, alive to the situation, decided to send him on his fourth scientific deputation in 1914. This time around, Bose was determined to carry his delicate instruments along with even more delicate (for the cold climate) tropical plants to Europe. A special glass case was used for the safekeeping of the plants.

Out of all his students and assistants, he selected Boshi as the custodian of the plants and also as general help. In early 1914, the Boses sailed from Bombay with the instruments, while Boshi took the longer route from Calcutta port via Ceylon, carrying a pair each of the mimosa and telegraph plant. Boshi has given an account of this journey,

> As long as the ship ploughed through [the] Indian Ocean, the plants thrived as though they were on their own familiar soil. During the journey through the Red Sea, they bathed in sunshine and enjoyed the warmth. When we entered the Mediterranean there was a sudden chill, and the plants became depressed and the leaves dropped. As we proceeded further west, the weather became colder and colder, and when we reached the Gulf of Lyons, I was greatly discouraged by the fear that I might not be able to carry my charge alive to the destination. The Bay of Biscay, I was warned, would prove to be quite fatal. The only thing I could do was to wrap the case with blankets, and expose the plants to brief flashes of

sunshine when they appeared. ...The Master had already arrived a few days earlier. ...He had carried with him two boxes of his most delicate apparatus. The one he carried with his own hands was quite safe. The other box had to be entrusted to the care of a railway porter; the result was that these instruments which had survived the perils of the sea succumbed to the rough handling of the British workman.... These extremely delicate instruments... required certain repairs and readjustments.

Only half the plants survived the voyage and were sheltered in the tropical greenhouse in The Regent's Park. Bose now set up a temporary laboratory in his Maida Vale residence where the problems of experimenting with tropical plants in a temperate climate were studied and systematically solved. Many distinguished scientists, including Lord Rayleigh, visited his laboratory and witnessed his experiments.

Fig. 8.3: The two plants (mimosa and telegraph) that accompanied Professor Bose around the world.

Bose was invited to lecture at the universities of Oxford and Cambridge, where the audience was highly appreciative. In Cambridge, Sir Francis Darwin presided over the meeting. Bose presented at the Royal College of Science in London as well.

In May 1914, Bose was invited to speak at the Friday Evening Discourse of the Royal Institution. The special status of these discourses has been described earlier. This was the third time that he was thus honoured. The audience consisted of the most renowned scientists and thinkers in Britain; Albemarle Street was jammed with carriages and automobiles. By convention, the lecture was required to start at nine o'clock and finish not a second after ten, in order to avoid prolonged disruption of the traffic. According to Boshi, this tradition had to be breached on this occasion because the enthusiastic audience demanded that Bose continue for longer.

The title of the lecture was 'Unvoiced World of Plants' and Boshi has left us a first-hand account of this.[73] Dr Raleigh, a respected teacher and well-wisher of Bose, had sent word that he perform not more than two experiments, in view of the extreme delicacy of the instruments and plants, lest something goes wrong and his reputation suffers. Bose knew that his results had been in the public domain for some years and yet they were so startling that the audience suffered from sheer incredulity. This could only be cured by extensive live demonstration. So, he chose to take the more difficult path and perform a series of experiments.

Bose demonstrating 'Plant Autographs and their revelations'.
Boshi Sen sits on a stool (right); J. Sircar is at the far end.

One after another Bose showed how the mimosa revealed its nervous impulse and how the speed of the impulse could be measured by his resonant recorder; how the leaf of the telegraph plant gyrates under

---

[73]Boshi wrote a series of articles in *Modern Review*, edited by Ramananda Chatterjee, under the title 'Around the World with my Master'.

conditions of chemical exultation and depression; how its signature, taken by his plant phytograph, resembles the heartbeat of an animal heart; how both these plants behaved when subjected to mild electric shocks. His death recorder captured the death throes of a locally procured plant, when subjected to intense heat. He made the invisible visible on the screen like a magician, while his commentary captivated the audience. Each experiment was punctuated by loud applause.

His private laboratory at Maida Vale received a stream of distinguished visitors. Whenever a plant-based experiment had to be performed, his plants had to be brought from the green house in a specially heated taxi with its windows closed, and retuned there afterwards. Among the visitors were Sir William Crookes, then president of the Royal Society and the famous dramatist George Bernard Shaw, who was very proud of his vegetarian diet, for the reason that he never inflicted any pain on a living being for his own survival. He watched in silence when a cabbage leaf exhibited violent convulsions as it was boiled. Shaw was known for his quick wit but according to his wife, for the first time in his life, he was at his wit's end and had nothing to say.

A very renowned animal physiologist, whose name has not been revealed by Bose or Boshi, was so impressed that he had a spontaneous confessional outburst,

> Do you know whose casting vote prevented the publication of your papers on Plant Response by the Royal Society? I am that person. I could not believe that such things are possible, and thought that your oriental imagination had led you astray. Now I fully confess that you had all along been right.

Here, then, is proof of the prejudice that existed among British scientists about Indians' 'oriental imagination'. The 'casting vote' belongs to the chairman of the committee and is used to finalize a decision only when there is a perfect tie between the proposing side and the opposing side. Therefore, the mystery physiologist must have been the chairman of the committee in question.

Visits of the editors of leading newspapers and journals were not infrequent. *The Nation* wrote with a tongue-in-cheek tone,

In a room near Maida Vale there is an unfortunate carrot strapped to the table of an unlicensed vivisector. Wires pass through two glass tubes full of a white substance; they are like two legs, whose feet are buried in the carrot. When the vegetable is pinched with a pair of forceps, it winces. It is so strapped that its electric shudder of pain pulls the long arm of a very delicate lever which actuates a tiny mirror. This casts a beam of light on the frieze at the other end of the room, thus enormously exaggerates the tremor of the carrot. A pinch near the righthand tube sends the beam seven or eight foot to the right, and a stab near the other wire sends it as far to the left. Thus, can science reveal the feelings of even so stolid a vegetable as the carrot.

This passage in *The Nation*, by its description of the instrument, is evidence that Bose had carried his optical pulse recorder, as well, along with the other three apparatuses mentioned before, namely resonant recorder, plant phytograph, and death recorder. The *Daily Telegraph* wrote an extensive review of his lectures and called him the 'Darwin of Botany'.

The Royal Society of Medicine invited him to speak and his lecture there was highly appreciated for its potential application in medical science. The secretary of the Society officially wrote to the Government of India, expressing high praise for his work which was so 'entirely new in biological science'.

Sir Lauder Brunton wrote to Bose,

Ever since I began the study of Botany in 1863...the movements of plants had a great attraction for me. For Mr Darwin I made some experiments on digestion in insectivorous plants in 1875. All the experiments I have yet seen are crude in comparison with yours, in which you show what a marvellous resemblance there is between the reactions of plants and animals.

Bose had received invitations from the universities of Vienna, Paris, and Bonn. He first travelled to Vienna, then Paris, before returning to London. In Vienna, amongst his audience of physiologists was the renowned botanist Hans Molisch. They declared, 'Calcutta was far ahead of them in these new lines of investigation.' In Paris, the party learnt of the assassination of Archduke Ferdinand of Austria. At this juncture, Bose decided to honour his invitation from Bonn, Germany, and his party was on its way there on 3 August 1914. They had reached the Victoria railway station and were preparing to take the train to a port on the eastern coast, when Bose had a premonition and suddenly said, 'We'd better not go', and the party turned back. The very next day, on 4 August 1914, World War I broke out. If they had gone to Germany, they would have been detained there for the next four years. Two of Bose's nephews, who had preceded the party, were not so fortunate.

In America Again

Once his engagements in England were over, Bose's next stop was the United States. He reached America on 22 November 1914, and stayed with Mrs Bull's brother, J. G. Thorp, in Boston, whom he had met earlier during his trip in 1908. Thorp, married to poet H. W. Longfellow's daughter, was a distinguished lawyer and an influential citizen; Bose met many eminent scholars and academicians in Boston and Harvard through Thorp.

He lectured at most of the major universities along the American east coast, such as Columbia, Harvard, Clark, and Wisconsin. The American Association for Advancement of Science, Philadelphia, and the academies of science at New York and Washington invited him to speak. At Washington, William J. Bryan, the secretary of state, arranged his presentation before the State Department; the Bureau of Agriculture invited him to speak and the leading men there emphasized the importance of his work for agricultural research. Agronomists in America, during both of Bose's visits there, expressed high interest in his work, whereas, at least on record, we see no such enthusiasm on the other side of the pond.

Bose's lectures were attended by several eminent scientists; among those who expressed their appreciation were Nikola Tesla, the Serbian-born physicist and inventor, and Percival Lowell, the astronomer. Graham Bell, the inventor of the telephone and founder of the Bell Laboratories, held a reception in Bose's honour.

The popular press in America published many reports of his lectures; some even included cartoons. One report had William J. Bryan, the secretary of state and a contender for the presidency, watch a drunken carrot scrawl an illegible autograph. His cartooned face expressed great horror, as Bryan was also an ardent prohibitionist. Another cartoon showed a drunken carrot leaning helplessly against a lamp post.

Since return to India by way of Europe and the Mediterranean was not possible due to the war, it was decided that the entourage would return via Japan. They sailed for Yakohama on 20 March 1915 from San Francisco. Bose lectured at the Wasede University on 1 May. He met Professor Koketsu of the Royal University, who had confirmed some of the conclusions of Bose, after performing his own experiments. They visited temples and other attractive sites in Tokyo and other places, before boarding a ship for Ceylon. There, the party toured the ancient Buddhist temples. On reaching Indian soil, they came to Calcutta by way of Rameswaram, Madurai, and Srirangam, visiting the temples in each place. On the whole, Bose's fourth scientific mission abroad was a resounding success.

The Bose Institute: A Blend of Science and Art

The Boses and their companions reached Calcutta in May 1915. In the same year, the government appointed the Royal Commission of Public Services under the chairmanship of Lord Islington. The Commission consulted eminent public servants and Bose was one of them. He calmly told the Commission, with a straight face, that if the Indian employees were paid salaries as high as those paid to their European counterparts, they were likely to squander money just as foolishly as their European colleagues. The subtle message in what he said was not lost on the Commission; it helped remove the disparity in the emoluments between the two races that had existed so far, in various branches of the public service.

In the next couple of years, Bose's time at Presidency College came to an end as he retired at the age of fifty-seven on November 1915. The government now honoured him by gazetting him as professor emeritus, on full pay instead of a pension, for five years—a unique recognition in the education service of India. Thus, his connection to Presidency

College was extended.

Further, the government decided to appoint him to a special temporary post for five years, starting from December 1916 for a monthly salary of 1,500 rupees. His annual research grant was considerably increased, and three of his assistants were given government appointments and sent abroad on deputation for five years.

The letter from the government to the director of public education, Bengal, announced these decisions and cited certain recommendations of J. B. Farmer and W. M. Bayliss. From now on, the British political establishment started to take pride in our scientist and his achievements, as an example of the success of the colonial administration. Further, in 1917, the government conferred knighthood on him.

A life of true retirement and ease was not in Bose's destiny; he had to draw on his residual energy to go on and on, since his life's mission still remained unfulfilled. Ironically, just on the eve of his retirement, a fully equipped physical laboratory was built in Presidency College. This parting disappointment strengthened his resolve to build a laboratory for his people. He spent two years after his retirement planning, building, and organizing for his research institute. However, his own research was not interrupted; it continued unabated in the laboratory on the upper floor of his house, the garden laboratory in Sijberia, and the summer laboratory in Darjeeling.

Bose wished that the subjects of physics, chemistry, and bio-science would be cultivated in his institute, but their boundaries would be blurred; there would be an emphasis on interdisciplinary research. Scholars of different sciences would collaborate with each other.

The Boses had always been a frugal couple and had been setting aside a portion of Jagadish's salary and his earnings from other projects over the years. These had been invested in securities which trebled in value during his career. The huge sum in arrears that he received with his delayed promotion, when added to his savings, was of great use in the financing of the construction. Geddes mentions that a contribution towards this also came from 'an old and valued friend'. We know that this friend, made anonymous by Bose, was none other than Mrs Sara Bull. It is a mystery why Bose chose not to name her, even after her passing away.

Bose wrote a letter to Professor Vines around this time, dated 15 November 1916, from which we learn about his financial situation. He wrote,

> My wife and I are dedicating all our savings for founding this institute. I should be able to finance the research work here from my own earnings as long as I live. If my work gets full recognition in the west, then I hope that someone would come forward after my death to make this institution successful.[74]

When the construction work for the institute was nearing completion, Bose wrote to a reliable and bright former student, Nagendra Chandra Nag, requesting him to join the institute. The letter expresses his worries of an uncertain future:

> I have recently recovered from an illness. There may be a relapse, if I continue to work too hard. But there is no other way, since the institute must be thrown open for work in the first week of January [1917]. Everyone is surprised on seeing the building's Mauryan era architecture. The interior decoration is also no less beautiful....
>
> The fund in my hand, at present, is just about sufficient for the requirements of the Vigyan Mandir[75]—Rs 12,000 for the land and research building, and 1,00,000 for the endowment. The interest of this deposit will be expended in maintenance, house tax, and cost of electricity. The rest depends on how long I live. In future, when this temple of science becomes a source of immense academic power, then many would be eager to join it for the sake of their own career and fame.

Nagendra Chandra Nag responded to his guru's call and joined the institute as an assistant director; he took much of the administrative workload off Bose, who could then find time to continue with his own research.

---

[74]This is a translation of the Bengali translation of the original letter, which was in English.
[75]The Bengali name of the Bose Institute is Basu Vigyan Mandir (meaning Bose Temple of Science), Basu being the Bengali version of the surname Bose.

In this letter Bose refers to the architecture and interior decoration of the institute building. Apart from Bose's own vision and suggestions, the man who made a great contribution to these was an artist called Nandalal Basu.

Nandalal Basu, a student in the Government School of Arts, Calcutta, was one of the pioneers of an art movement that was gaining force in Bengal in the beginning of the 1900s. This movement sought to revive ancient Indian art in modern idiom. Nandalal as a painter was a practician of the movement, whereas the theoreticians were Sister Nivedita, E. B. Havell[76], and Dr Ananda Coomaraswamy. The Japanese artist and historian Kakuzō Okakura also had an influence.

Throughout the nineteenth century, British art historians and critics had propounded a theory that Indian art was Hellenic (Greek) in origin. Very few, such as Swami Vivekananda, saw through the falsity of this theory.

Nivedita was not an artist, but had an appreciation for the world of art. During her travels with the Swami in 1899, she visited many Hindu and Buddhist sites and at all these places she listened as the Swami spoke on relevant Indian scriptures and history; the interpretation of art and sculpture was seamlessly integrated with his commentary. Later, in Chicago, the Swami helped her prepare a lecture on 'Indian Art and Crafts'. In the Paris Exposition of 1900, Nivedita heard the Swami speaking in the conference on history of Indian religions. It became clear to her that much of Indian art was rooted in Hindu–Buddhist mythology and deeply spiritual in nature.

Nivedita met Havell in 1902 when she visited the School of Art and was glad to know that they had similar thoughts on the matter. However, Havell was not as well versed in Indian mythology and scriptures as Nivedita and often discussed with her in order to grasp the esoteric meaning of certain Indian art forms. She reviewed Havell's and Coomaraswamy's books on Indian art in *Modern Review*. She also

---

[76]Ernest Binfield Havell, a British art historian, was the first principal of the Government School of Arts, Calcutta.

wrote articles and gave lectures, exhorting Indian artists to leave the path of western imitation and create a new Indian style by drawing on ancient heritage. Nandalal, a student of the School of Art, later wrote, 'I do not know whether Havell has mentioned the name of the Sister anywhere in his books, but she made him understand the viewpoints of Indian aesthetics and philosophy of art.'

Nivedita was sometimes invited to lecture at the Art School, where Nandalal and Asit Haldar were students. The two young artists often visited her at Bosepara Lane. When, in 1910, Nivedita came to know that Lady Christiana Herringham, a British artist-copyist and art patron, would be paying a visit to the Buddhist caves of Ajanta, she purchased two railway tickets for Nandalal and Asit, without asking them. Pleasantly surprised when she handed them the tickets and some money for the journey, they gladly joined the party of Herringham. Within a few days, Nivedita and the Boses caught up with them at Ajanta.

That was when William Rothenstein was also visiting the Ajanta caves and met this group. The young students came back with valuable copies of the Ajanta frescos and a life-changing experience. Their master and vice principal of the Art School, Abanindranath Tagore was pleased to see these paintings. Soon after the Ajanta visit, Nivedita wrote an article for the *Modern Review*, titled, 'The Ancient Abbey of Ajanta'. It was art appreciation and Buddhist history skilfully integrated, and created a stir among Indian artists.

Now, influenced by Nivedita and Havell, Abanindranath adopted a new style of painting, recasting the ancient Indian style in a modern mould in which bhava (an idea with feeling) was essential.

Okakura was a friend of Josephine MacLeod. Okakura had been the director of the New Art School at Ueno, Tokyo, and had resigned when the Japanese government made teaching using Western methods mandatory there. He started his own school of art, Nihon Bijutsuin, at Yanaka. The art historian in him wished to see ancient Indian art in all its variety, and prompted him to come to Calcutta with Josephine MacLeod, in early 1902.

In Calcutta, Okakura stayed in the Belur monastery. Mrs Sara Bull held a reception for Okakura in the American consulate, in March.

Many persons from the School of Arts were invited, among them Abanindranath Tagore, who happened to be a nephew of Bose's friend, Rabindranath.

Okakura then went around visiting temples, stupas, and caves all over India, sometimes in the company of Joe, Nivedita and Sara, other times alone. He visited Tagore's Shantiniketan also.[77] Distilling his knowledge and experience of Japan, China, and India, he wrote a book, *Ideals of the East*, which was primarily on the art, and also on the religion and philosophy of Asia; Nivedita edited the book and wrote the foreword. Okakura wrote in the book,

> Asia is one. The Himalayas divide, only to accentuate, two mighty civilizations, the Chinese with its communism of Confucius and the Indian with its individualism of the Vedas. But not even the snowy barriers can interrupt for one moment that broad expanse of love for the Ultimate and the Universal, which is the common thought-inheritance of every Asiatic race....

Okakura further wrote that a 'common thought-inheritance' enabled Asia to produce great religions. This book served to strengthen the revivalist art movement. The movement went on gathering momentum, and a few years later in 1908, culminated in the formation of the Indian Society of Oriental Art in the Jorasanko house of Abanindranath. Other founding members were Sister Nivedita, E. B. Havell, A. Coomaraswamy, Gaganendranath Tagore, Sir John Woodroffe (a judge of the Calcutta High Court) and O. C. Ganguly.[78] Our scientist, Jagadish Bose, was on friendly terms with the two Tagores in this group because of his proximity to Rabindranath Tagore.

Abanindranath and his students Nandalal Basu, Asit Haldar, Venkatappa, etc. produced masterpieces in the new style, derived from ancient roots. Many exhibitions were held and these artists were acclaimed in India and Europe. Thus, the Bengal School of Art was born. The pioneers of this school, Nandalal in particular, played a central

---

[77]Okakura's visit triggered Tagore's interest in Japan.
[78]In many books and websites, Abanindranath has been acclaimed as the sole founder of the Society. That is not true. He was one of the founders.

role in designing the architecture, and the interior decorations of the Bose institute.

Nivedita did not live long after the Bengal School won recognition and fame. After her death, Nandalal wrote, 'The thought of the progress of Indian artists always dwelt in her mind. I can never say enough of the encouragement I received from her mind. When she died it was like being deprived of the presence of a guiding angel.'

Nivedita, even after death, had much influence on the Bose Institute. Geddes, who had known Nivedita intimately, wrote,

> Her fervid faith in the long-dreamed-of Research Institute, its possibilities for science and its promise for India, was no small impulse and encouragement towards its realization; and thus is explained the memorial fountain with its bas-relief of 'woman carrying light to the temple', which adorns the entrance of his Institute.

As one enters the Institute's premises, there is a large water bowl, adorned by a semi-circular lotus-in-stone on one side, and enclosed by an ornate wall on the other. The bas-relief in bronze of a woman with rudraksha prayer beads carrying a lamp is mounted on the wall, overlooking the basin. It was sculpted by a Maharashtrian artist Vinayak Pandurang Karmakar and is modelled after Nandalal Basu's famous painting of Sister Nivedita. The relief is named *Aloka Dyuti*, meaning the diffused lustre of light.

There is no indication that the bas-relief is of Nivedita's; however, in a letter (dated 27 October 1916) to her sister, Mrs May Wilson, Bose wrote,

> Though there are many who are kind to me, I am naturally reticent and cannot make new friends—I mean those to whom you can talk about things that matter. We observed the 13th, her death anniversary, but tomorrow is the birthday. We will think of that day reminding us that her spirit is risen and is among us. Through the strength that is daily coming to me, and the way I am able to carry out more and more...through them I realize more and more of the real meaning of immortality.

The Bose Institute will also be beautiful architecturally. As you enter, there is a large stone lotus on the left – that is the basin in which water lilies grow. Just overlooking that will be a bas-relief of a woman, with prayer beads and a lamp in her hand. The institute is an embodiment of her prayer. On the 13th, the ashes were laid in a receptacle just by the side of the lotus. There will be an overhanging Shefali tree, which sheds every morning lily white flowers, and makes a white carpet on the ground, the seed she brought from the caves of Ajanta.

Nivedita's name is not taken explicitly in relation to the bas-relief, although the letter is an expression of adoration for her. Only through the mention of the death and birth anniversaries, 13 October and 28 October, do we know that Bose is talking about Nivedita. In the second paragraph, there is another clue—'the seed she brought from the caves of Ajanta'—about which only the Boses knew. We are puzzled again and again by Bose's strange silence about Nivedita, as if he does not want anyone else but May Wilson to know that the bas-relief is of Nivedita's. It is clear that he was following his policy of avoiding straightforward acknowledgement of both Nivedita and Sara.

Boshi had kept Nivedita's ashes at his residence. He has said that, instructed by Bose, he buried a little box, containing some of Nivedita's ashes, at the base of the fountain just below the bas-relief. He further said that except Lady Bose, no one else knew about it; the Boses never revealed this as long as they lived. The fact about the ashes was revealed almost a century later, in 2007, after Boshi's biography was published. Bose's letter to Mrs Wilson, quoted above, was brought to light in 2017, and was a confirmation of what Boshi had said.[79]

The institute, made of sandstone, was constructed on about four acres of land with a beautified landscape, variegated by many gardens. A small garden of sensitive plants was planted at the entrance. Paramahansa Yogananda, who attended the inaugural ceremony of the Bose Institute,

---

[79]Reymond has written that, in 1915, when the foundation of the building was being laid, Bose had deposited a part of her ashes underneath the corner-stone. She was not given Bose's letter to Mrs Wilson and might have heard some rumours in the West about the burial of the ashes under the Bose Institute. This is not supported by Boshi, who was in possession of the ashes. There are other authors who have reproduced Reymond's error.

said that near its front gate, 'A small temple in a garden is consecrated to the Noumenon beyond phenomena. Thought of the Divine Incorporeity is suggested by the absence of any altar-image.' True to his Brahmo faith, Bose had not allowed any image or idol on the altar of the small temple. A sundial has been constructed near the temple, which compares its time with an electric clock nearby.

The wooden entrance door of the building was beautifully carved with creepers, flowers, and the vajra symbol[80], which Nivedita had seen at Bodh Gaya and captured in paint on paper; she also got it stitched on cloth (see Fig. 7.16). The door carvings were designed by Nandalal and engraved under his supervision. The door also has the crossed vajra symbol, in addition to the original one of Nivedita. It seems the crossed vajra is an innovation of Nandalal.

Bose chose the crossed vajra symbol as the logo or emblem of the Institute (see Fig. 8.4). It is prominently displayed on the main entrance gate of the premises, and also as an adornment on top of the building. Bose had brought back the symbol of ardha-amalaka (half of the amalaka fruit) from the Sanchi Stupa and had it incorporated on pillars, cornices, and many other places as an added embellishment.

Fig. 8.4: Emblem of the Bose Institute as displayed on its signboard.

The long entrance hall today displays the instruments and devices invented by Bose, lined up on one side in order of chronological priority. Hence, we have near the entrance, the equipment invented in 1895 and used for wireless signalling. Towards the far end, there are highly sensitive and sophisticated instruments for probing into the secrets of plant life. Thus, the importance of inventing new methods and apparatuses for experimental science is emphasized.

---

[80]Vajra is the symbol of the thunderbolt. Crossed vajra is the emblem of the Bose Institute.

We are reminded that the world's greatest inventors, from Galileo and Da Vinci to Bell and Edison, were their own instrument-makers; that civilization advances by the effort of a skilled pair of hands, guided by an intelligent, educated brain; a lesson most important for a country such as India, where the educated are rarely skilled and the skilled rarely educated. Bose wished that the research scholars of his institute would emulate him. They would not only do advanced research, but also acquire hands-on dexterity for creating new devices; well-equipped laboratories and workshops were provided for this purpose.

An exceptional feature of the Bose Institute is its large lecture hall, with the capacity to seat 1,500 people. The institute's inauguration took place here and it was built to be used for holding lectures on the latest and most abstruse scientific topics, but was not restricted to them in any sense. Bose had absorbed from his teacher Father Lafont the idea that science must not be confined to an ivory tower, but had to be brought down to the level of common folk. The term 'popular science' had not been coined then, but Bose was full of its spirit. His plan was to hold popular science lectures, open to all, periodically in this hall. The space, including its size, seating arrangement, and acoustics, had been designed keeping this in mind. In this context, we are reminded of another event which shows just how much Bose cared for the common people. Once in April 1911, Bose was invited to Mymensingh in eastern Bengal to preside over a conference on Bengali literature. Maharaja Kumud Chandra Singha made an additional request—he wanted Bose to lecture on his scientific discoveries before the lay public, to which he readily agreed. But soon the organizers realized that there was a groundswell of interest to hear him, and there would not be enough room in the hall. To restrict numbers, they proposed to institute an entry fee; but Bose would have none of that. Instead, he spoke on two successive days, publicized beforehand, once in English and then in Bengali.

The lecture hall's ceiling decoration is unique and equally appealing to all tastes, whether scientific, artistic, or philosophical. In the centre is a giant radiating lotus, a free adaptation of one of the caverns in Ajanta. Sensitive tropical plants, studied so extensively by Bose, ring the lotus. This attractive and meaningful piece was the creation of Nandalal Basu.

The body of the hall is left plain, so that the attention of the audience remains focused on the arena. Above the stage, on the upper part of the wall, there is a symbolic frieze, named *Anweshan* (meaning the quest), by the same artist. It depicts a man, sword in hand, as if risen from the sacred river in the background, who strides boldly forward, followed by a woman playing on her magic flute. The man symbolizes pragyan (intellect) who cleaves his way through ignorance and the woman kalpanaa (imagination) who plays an inspirational melody.

In the romantic world of the artist, 'intellect' is masculine and 'imagination' is feminine. The latter reminds one of the three feminine figures, Abala, Nivedita, and Sara, who surrounded Bose for so long. One is particularly reminded of the inspiring letter Nivedita wrote to Bose, on his fifty-second birthday, from Genoa (see p. 312); and the letter that Bose wrote to Josephine after Nivedita's death (see p. 316), in which he said, 'Now the last prop is gone. I could live by work but the strength and inspiration are crushed.... You know her presence made it so easy to choose all that is great.'

The artist in Bose located a large garden, behind the main building, where an artificial stream flows below an arched bridge, as a reminder of the stream of his childhood days near their house. The stream imparts beauty and a unique ambience to the garden.

The Bose Institute, when it was first built.

The Institute was officially inaugurated on Bose's birthday, 30 November, in 1917. The lecture hall was full to its capacity with eminent people from all walks of life in Calcutta. The inaugural song was a composition of Tagore, sung by a chorus of young boys and girls, although Tagore himself could not be present as he was travelling in America. An English translation of the song, rendered by Manmohan Ghosh, published in the *Visvabharati Quarterly*, Shantiniketan, is as follows:

> O Hermit, call thou in the authentic words
> Of the old hymn called Sama[81]: 'Rise! Awake!'
> Call to the man who boasts his Shaastric[82] lore;
> From vein pedantic wrangling profitless,
> Call to that foolish braggart to come forth
> Out on the face of nature, this broad earth;
> Send forth this call unto thy scholar band.
> Together round thy sacrifice of fire
> Let them all gather. So may our India,
> Our ancient land unto herself return
> O once again return to steadfast work,
> To duty and devotion, to her trance
> Of earnest meditation; let her sit
> Once more unruffled, greedless, strifeless, pure,
> O once again upon her lofty seat
> And platform, teacher of all lands.

Bose gave a lengthy dedication address wherein he outlined the genesis and purpose of the institute. It was to act as a beacon of guidance for all time to come. A few selected excerpts are presented here.

Bose began with the following words, 'I dedicate today this institute—not merely a laboratory but a temple.' A copper plate with a Bengali engraving was prominently installed; its English translation is as follows:

> This Temple of Science is my humble
> offering to the feet of God,

---

[81]Sama is one of the four Vedas.
[82]Shaastra is Sanskrit for scripture; Shaastric is its adjectival form.

for the sake of India's Glory
and Benefaction of the World.

Shri Jagadish Chandra Bose
14th Agrahayana, Samvat 1327.

These words are meaningful; Bose wished to lift research, beyond its indentity as a profession, to the level of worship. He referred to the 'vast expansion of the perceptive range by means of artificially created organs', thus emphasizing the importance of inventions. After a philosophical preamble, he spoke about his own past struggles.

> Thirty-two years ago, I chose the teaching of science as my vocation. ...There were neither well-equipped laboratories nor skilled mechanicians. This was all too true. It is not for man to complain of circumstances, but bravely to accept, to confront and to dominate them; and we belong to that race which has accomplished great things with simple means.

He talked about his initial days of success followed by his dark years, twelve in all. Redemption came after many years of struggle. Then he turned his attention to the challenges before India.

> What is it that India is to win and maintain? Can anything small and circumscribed ever satisfy the mind of India? ...India is drawn into the vortex of international competition. She has to become efficient in every way...spread of education, civic duties and responsibilities...activities both industrial and commercial. Neglect of these essentials...will imperil her very existence....

Bose pointed out that in the West, competition alone had led to a mad rush for exploitation of science for commerce, with the outcome often being more destructive than constructive. 'In the absence of some power of restraint, civilization is trembling in an unstable poise on the brink of ruin.' It should be recalled that just then World War I was at its peak. Bose continued, saying that this was all because western man had 'forgotten that far more potent than competition are mutual help and cooperation'. He stressed selflessness in research and its applications.

He also spoke about the importance of advancement of knowledge through research and diffusion of that knowledge in the spirit of cooperation. Herein lies the relevance of an unusually large lecture hall, useful for 'the widest possible civic and public diffusion' of knowledge. In the same context,

> Through the regular publications of the Transactions of the Institute, these Indian contributions will reach the whole world. The discoveries made will thus become public property. No patents will ever be taken. The spirit of our national culture demands that we should for ever be free from the desecration of utilizing knowledge for personal gain.
>
> ...It is my further wish that, as far as limited accommodation would permit, the facilities of this Institute should be available to workers from all countries. In this I am attempting to carry out the traditions of my country, which, so far back as twenty-five centuries ago, welcomed all scholars from different parts of the world within the precincts of its ancient seats of learning at Nalanda and Taxila....
>
> These are dreams that wove a network round my wakeful life for many years past. ...The possibility of a fuller expansion will depend on very large endowments. ...I came with nothing and shall return as I came.... What I have I will offer, and the one who has shared with me the struggles and hardships that had to be faced, has wished to bequeath all that is hers for the same object. In all my struggling efforts, I have not been altogether solitary. While the world doubted, there have been a few, now in the city of silence, who never wavered in their trust.

The last but one sentence is a tribute to his wife, Abala. The last sentence obviously was a reference to Sister Nivedita and Mrs Sara Chapman Bull, who were both dead; but curiously, he never named them. Only a few persons like Tagore, Sister Christine, Josephine MacLeod, and Boshi Sen could decipher the meaning of Bose's statement and believed that it was in reference to Nivedita. But as far as Mrs Sara Bull was concerned, only Josephine knew of the silent unseen benefaction. Joe too did not waver in her trust in Bose, and did make some contribution, no matter how small, and she was not 'in the city of silence'.

Speaking about the emblem of the Institute, Bose said, 'It was rishi Dadhichi, the pure and blameless, who offered his life [so] that the divine weapon, the thunderbolt, might be fashioned out of his bones to smite evil and exalt righteousness.' He then touched upon all his main inventions and discoveries. About his discovery of alternate binocular vision of humans, he said, 'the characteristics of an artificial retina gave a clue to the unexpected discovery of "binocular alternation of vision" in man—each eye thus supplements its fellow by turns, instead of acting as a continuously yoked pair, as hitherto believed.'

After the inauguration, Bose handed over the Institute and the endowment, that contained all his savings and a few donations received so far, to a trust created for running the institute. He was conscious of the fact that all available funds and his own monthly earnings would be quite insufficient for running the institute. So, he appealed to the general public all over India for donations.

The Maharaja of Kasimbazar, Sri Manindra Chandra Nandy, immediately promised funding to the tune of 2 lakh rupees today. Maharajas of princely states of Baroda, Kashmir, and Patiala also promised donations. At this time, Bose was invited by the merchants of Bombay city for a lecture tour. He travelled in the Bombay–Puna region delivering lectures in many places, amid great public enthusiasm. Seth Mulraj Khatau and Sri Bomanji contributed substantial amounts to the endowment.

Soon after the opening of the Institute, Bose wrote in his diary,

> Far more important for future success of the institute than all is the character and devotion of the scholars whom I have been able to train or attract to its service. I will only mention a few of them. First, Dr J. Sircar, the nephew of Dr Nilratan Sircar. His professional qualifications are of the highest order and it was expected of him to share and secure the extensive practice of his distinguished uncle. But he did not for a moment hesitate to sacrifice his prospects to join my institute. My own nephew again has been trained in science which he pursued at Cambridge. I have forbidden him any career except that of a scholar. He preceded me in my proposed lecture

tour in Germany and has unfortunately been [detained] there.[83] On his return he will give all the best efforts of his life to the cause of science. There is nice assistant Basiswar Sen, to whom the offer of employment in the Western Universities with great opportunities was no temptation. It is men of such character and devotion that will discover truth, and not those who count on success as maxims of personal advancement.

Bose has mentioned three persons in this note—Dr J. Sircar, his nephew whom he has not named, and Basiswar Sen—for their character and devotion. He understood well that the building, logo, architecture, art, workshops, etc. were all part of the infrastructure and paraphernalia; the soul of the institute was in its research and academic staff. He now focused his energies into recruiting the right people.

Renewed Effort in Advanced Age: The Crescograph

After establishing the institute, Bose, who was then sixty years old, concentrated on his unfinished task of solving the mysteries of plant life. He wanted to find out the reason behind the differences in rates of growth of different plants. Unlike the movement of the mimosa or the telegraph plant, the growth of most plants is extremely slow, almost imperceptible.

We need to form an idea about the extreme slowness of plant growth. During adolescence, a young child may shoot up by 12 centimetres, or 5 inches, in a year. For a human being, this is an extremely fast rate of growth, but is still a fairly slow speed. At this speed, it would take 8,333 years to cover a kilometre or 12,000 years to cover a mile. A tree, at a liberal estimate, grows ten times faster. A snail is the slowest animal on earth, but its speed is about 2,000 times faster than the growth of a tree. An average plant grows by about a five thousandth part of an inch per second, which is equal to 0.0005 millimetres per second. This tiny dimension is comparable to the length of a single wave of visible light. It is obvious that enormous magnification is necessary to make this growth perceptible.

---

[83]His nephew Debendra Mohan Bose was detained by German authorities after the outbreak of World War I.

Plant physiologists so far had been using an instrument called auxanometer, which magnified this growth by twenty, and one had to wait for half a day to get a measurable result. For agricultural research, the effect of a single nutrient has to be observed, keeping all environmental factors such as, temperature, humidity, sunlight, etc. static. Otherwise, the result gets vitiated, and one does not know if the enhanced rate of growth is due to the nutrient or something else. It is not possible to keep these influencing factors constant during the span of half a day. So, an instrument that could provide a greater magnification than the auxanometer was required, and our scientist kept pondering on this problem for weeks.

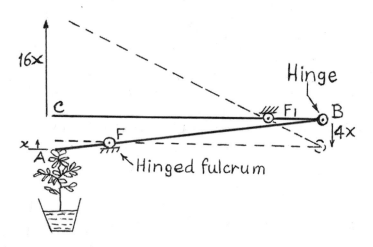

Fig. 8.5: Basic mechanism of the crescograph.

One fine morning Bose, with two small sticks in hand, walked into the laboratory highly excited, according to Boshi Sen. He exclaimed, 'I have got it'. What he had 'got' was the basic mechanism of his new instrument, the crescograph. The name is derived from a Latin root 'crescere', meaning 'to increase'. He, then, proceeded to explain with sketches to his curious assistants how two conjoined levers could be used to magnify movement. His explanation can be captured with the help of Fig. 8.5, which shows a lever AFB, where the fulcrum F divides the lever in the ratio of 1:4; in other words, length AF is a fourth of

FB. The second lever BF_1C is with a hinge to the first lever at B, and fulcrumed at F_1. Again, the fulcrum divides the lever in the ratio of 1:4, as shown. Note the fulcrums are fixed to a larger rigid structure (not shown in the figure) and cannot move. The levers can rotate around them. The balancing counterweights are not shown in the figure, for the sake of convenience

A plant, whose growth is to be magnified is attached to point A. Suppose, it grows by a length x in five minutes and pushes up point A of the lever by that amount. The dashed line shows the changed position of the first lever. It is obvious that point B moves down by 4 times x. Again, the new position of the second lever is shown by a dashed line. It is apparent that point C moves up by 4 times 4x, i.e., 16x. Hence, the movement of point C shows plant growth magnified by 16 (= 4^2). Note this analysis is valid only when the movement of point A is extremely small compared to the length of the lever. Fortunately, this condition is always satisfied because plant growth is extremely small for the duration of this experiment.

In Bose's scheme, the two levers were divided by their fulcrums in the ratio of 1:100. Therefore, the magnification would be 100^2 = 10,000 times. This scale of magnification makes even a few seconds of growth visible to the human eye.

In the process of explanation, Bose must have appeared like a magician waving a pair of magic wands, casting a spell over his assistants. But he was an impatient magician and wanted a rough model of his magical instrument made at once. There were no scientific instrument makers in Calcutta those days, but there were skilled and intelligent technicians in the workshop of the laboratory. The job was entrusted to Noren Sen, the chief technician among them.

The first model, instead of magnifying growth, magnified the defects and distortions arising out of friction in the hinges and bending of the long levers. Bose ideally needed weightless but infinitely rigid levers, and frictionless bearings. But such things are not available in nature, or even in a magician's bag of tricks, because the lighter the lever, the more it bends. So, a long struggle ensued, led by the innovative genius, to design levers as light and rigid as possible employing aluminium alloy used in making aircraft components. Imported gemstone bearings of the Swiss watchmakers were used to minimize friction. But even these were impaired in their function due to deposition of dust. Bose then devised a new system of suspension which obviated the problem. In the end, an almost magical but extremely delicate instrument was invented, named high magnification crescograph (H. M. C.), shown in Fig. 8.6.

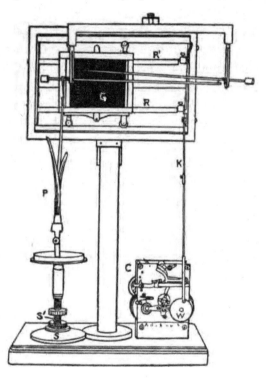

Fig. 8.6: The High Magnification Crescograph.
P - Plant; C - clockwork for periodic oscillation of recording
smoked glass plate (G); S, S' - micrometre screws; K - crank; W - rotating wheel.

The conjoined pair of levers are quite apparent in the figure, along with their balancing counterweights, near the centre of the main rectangular structure. The recording part of the H. M. C. consists of a smoked glass plate (G) moving from left to right and periodically shifting forward to take an impression from the bent tip of the second lever. It is very similar in design to the recording part of Bose's plant phytograph. The H. M. C. not only produced an enormous magnification, it also automatically recorded the growth of a plant and its changes, in a period as short as a minute.

Bose discovered that plant growth is retarded by the slightest touch. Rough handling of a plant arrests its growth altogether for quite some time. This of course is consistent with the common advice of an experienced gardener.

That a change in ambient temperature would result in change in growth was expected. Application of cold water retarded growth, and very cold water brought it to a complete stop. Warm water produces a remarkable increase in growth, but only up to a certain point. Water, hotter beyond this point, retards growth and at about 60°C the death spasm occurs. Application of electric current and chemical stimulants closely paralleled the results achieved with heated water.

The effect of manures, chemicals, drugs, etc. could now be determined in the course of a few minutes. The great advantage in all these investigations over previous methods was the very short duration in which the experiment was concluded, during which all other parameters could be kept constant. The importance of a crescograph for agricultural research cannot be overemphasized.

To detect the effect of an external stimulus, manure, drug, or application of a gas, Bose first had to measure the normal rate of growth; and then measure the changed rate due to the stimulus. The effect of the stimulus could be found by subtracting the normal rate from the changed rate. He wished to eliminate even this last bit of required human intervention—the need for any calculation. This meant that the platform carrying the plant had to descend at the exact rate at which the tip of the plant was ascending, whatever that rate may be. Since the growth rate varied from plant to plant, Bose needed an instrument with the provision of wide adjustments. Fig. 8.7 shows the balancing device, which was now appended to the H. M. C.

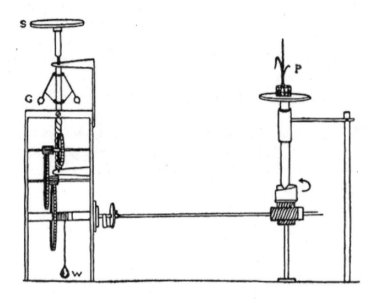

Fig. 8.7: The Balancing Device: Compensation of growth movement produced by equal
subsidence of the holder containing the plant (P). Adjusting screw (S) regulates the speed
of the governor (G). W, heavy weight actuating clock-work.

A train of revolving clock wheels, seen on the left, is actuated by the fall
of a weight, W. This turns a set of gears, seen on the right, that lowers
the plant, P. The exact adjustment is obtained by turning the screw (S)
that regulates the speed of the governor (G) which controls the rate of
descent. In this way, when the rate of growth is exactly compensated,
the recorder dots a horizontal series.

Fig. 8.8 gives a record of the effect of carbonic acid gas on growth,
taken by a balanced crescograph. A jar filled with this gas, much heavier
than air, is emptied over the plant; the invisible heavier gas surrounds
the plant for quite some time, before it gets diffused.

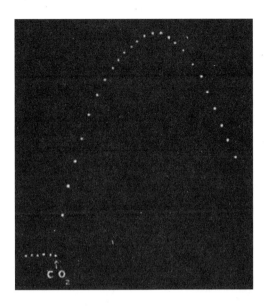

Fig. 8.8: Record showing the effect of carbonic acid gas on growth. Horizontal line in the beginning shows normal growth before the application of gas. As soon as the gas is applied, growth is enhanced, shown by the rising curve. This reaches a maximum in about two and a half minutes, followed by a retardation of growth, shown by the falling curve. Successive dots at intervals of ten seconds.

The H. M. C. was utilized for another investigation. There is a class of movements which is brought about by slight changes in the environmental conditions, such as by variation of diurnal temperature, by radiant heat and light, by the stimulus of gravity, etc. For instance, a plant kept in partial shade would over time bend in the direction of light. These movements are generally called tropic movements. There is a myriad of phenomena in this class that lacked satisfactory explanations. Bose's H. M. C. helped him study these in minute detail and bring out generalized laws.

The fact that a growing plant bends towards light is called the tropic effect of light. It was known that the tropic effect is very strong in the ultraviolet region of the solar spectrum, declining practically to zero towards the yellow and red. On the other hand, it is the yellow, orange, and red which are most effective in photosynthesis of plants.

Since light was known to be an electromagnetic wave, the

following question naturally arose: how would a plant respond to other electromagnetic waves, such as radio waves, which are known to have much larger wavelengths than the visible spectrum?

Animals being completely insensitive to radio waves, it was generally assumed that plants, which are slower and duller in response, would also be insensitive. Bose systematically investigated this phenomenon and destroyed this myth. His transmitting equipment involved a 10 metre lofted aerial. The receiving equipment, positioned at a distance of 200 metres, had a matching aerial whose lower terminal led into the laboratory, and was connected by means of a thin wire with the experimental plant growing in a pot. The latter was then connected to the earth. The mimosa plant showed both mechanical and electrical responses, whereas other ordinary plants evinced only an electrical response.

For the effect of radio waves on variation of growth, the H. M. C. with the appended balancing device was employed. Fig. 8.9 shows the record of growth of a seedling of wheat under stimulation by radio waves.

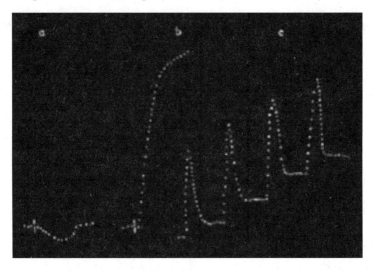

Fig. 8.9: Record of responses of plant to wireless stimulation. (a) Response to feeble stimulus; (b) response to strong stimulus; (c) response to medium stimulation.

A feeble stimulus accelerated growth (down-curve) initially, but after a while it returned to its original steady rate. A strong stimulus produced a huge retardation (up-curve). A stimulus of medium strength produced several cycles of retardation followed by partial recovery, the net result being a trend of retardation.

Thus, Bose conclusively proved that the so-called dull, vegetative life has a much greater range of perception than earlier given credit for.

The Magnetic Crescograph

Bose's first biographer and friend Patrick Geddes was in Calcutta at this time. After seeing the H. M. C. at work, Geddes remarked, 'Surely, the utmost perfection has at last been reached.' Bose's cryptic reply to this profound compliment was equally profound, 'Man is never satisfied'. While many British scientists expressed disbelief at Bose's feat, claiming that such exponential magnification achieved through mechanical means was impossible, he was wise enough to ignore them.

Bose pushed on further to achieve even greater magnification. His first attempt consisted of adding one more lever to the existing two. He soon found out that the penalty of additional weight and friction is too much for the plant's capacity, and an altogether new approach needs to be tried. He then fell back on his own concept of optical magnification, employed on the optical pulse recorder (Fig. 7.2). To minimize friction, he removed the second lever and now employed magnetic pull for transferring displacement, and thus was born the magnetic crescograph. Fig. 8.10 shows the external appearance of the apparatus, with the plant on the left, kept on a platform whose height can be adjusted; the instrument is housed in a long rectangular wooden box, mounted horizontally on a column. On the right, a reflected light beam (shown by dotted lines) creates a spot of light on the screen; the light spot moves from left to right as the plant grows.

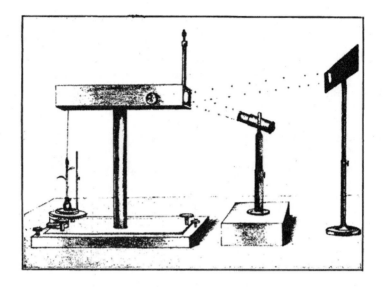

Fig. 8.10: The magnetic crescograph for magnifying imperceptible growth of plants by ten million times.

Fig. 8.11 gives a schematic diagram of the instrument, prepared by Bose, in which the container box has been sectioned in such a way that the parts inside the box can be viewed.

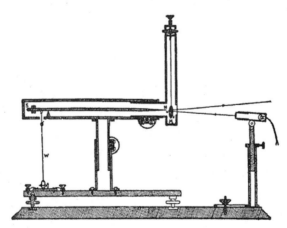

Fig. 8.11: The Magnetic Crescograph; a sectioned view showing internal configuration. Plant (W) is connected to the left of the magnetic lever (SN); Mirror (M) is suspended by a thread, near the right tip of the magnetic lever; a ray of light reflects off the mirror.

There is a single lever (SN) in this instrument that is seen with its counterweight on the left. The lever is magnetized, where the letters S and N indicate south and north polarity. The plant (W) is connected to the lever between the counterweight and the fulcrum, through a hole in the box. The right end of the lever is tapered to a point and has a magnetic north pole (N). A small mirror (M), with two small attached magnets, is suspended by a thread from above, close to the pointed end of the lever. The exact position of the mirror can be adjusted by means of a micrometre screw at the top of the L-shaped box. The movement of the lever, due to the growth of the plant (W) attached to the left, upsets a very delicate equilibrium of the mirror and makes it tilt. A beam of light is then reflected off the mirror. The screen, which receives the reflected light, is not included in this figure, but has been shown in Fig. 8.10.

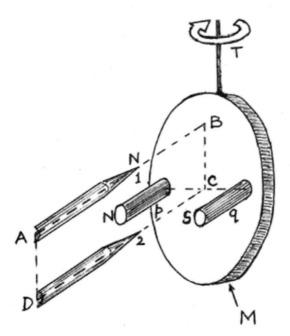

Fig. 8.12: Enlarged view of mirror (M) with small magnets (p and q) and the initial position of the magnetic lever (A1). The same lever takes up position D2 after some time when the plant has grown sufficiently.

Fig. 8.12 gives an enlarged view of the mirror (M) with two small magnets (cylinders p and q), fixed on its rear. The front ends of p and q are of opposite polarity, N and S. The mirror-suspending thread (T) is partially shown in this figure; this thread is very fine so that it offers practically no resistance to being twisted. The tapered end of the magnetic lever is shown in its initial position A1, at the start of the experiment. When the plant connected to the other end of the lever (shown in Fig. 8.11) grows, the tapered end starts descending; it always remains in the central vertical plane (ABCD), which is shown by dashed lines and lies midway between p and q. As the tapered end descends, the pointed N-pole moves closer to and in between the two small magnets, p and q. The lever repels the N-pole of p and attracts the S-pole of q, more and more.

As a result, with the growth of the plant, the mirror M swivels gradually, twisting the suspension thread T, as indicated by the curved arrow. This causes the spot of light on the screen (see Fig. 8.10) to gradually move from left to right. When the tapered end takes up position D2, closest to the small magnets, the rotation of M reaches its maximum limit and the light spot reaches the end of the screen. Thus, plant growth of a few thousandths of a millimetre causes the light spot to move by several metres. Bose showed that maximum magnification achieved by the magnetic crescograph was ten million, when the screen was placed at a distance of only four metres. The simplicity of this instrument is stunning!

Our mind cannot grasp magnification so massive. If we magnify the speed of a snail ten million times, we get 200 million feet per hour. This is equal to 61,000 kilometres per hour. The speed of the NASA X-43, an unmanned experimental hypersonic aircraft, is 12,000 kilometres per hour. Hence, our 'crescographic' snail is more than five times faster than NASA's fastest aircraft. The X-43 aircraft takes about 3.25 hours to go round the earth over its equator, whereas the crescographic snail would take about 40 minutes.

The magnetic crescograph does not have the facility of automatic recording. However, since the light spot traverses a ten-foot scale from left to right, it would have been possible to record growth manually, if so required. Bose submitted a few papers to the Royal Society based on his research with the crescographs, and these papers were quickly published.

Bose was performing such multi-faceted research well into his retirement age, while also managing his new institute. Even at this time, in spite of his extremely busy schedule and signs of deteriorating health, the nationalist in him remained public-spirited. Rural Bengal and Assam were suffering from endemic malaria. The mosquito vectors of malaria found convenient breeding spots in the numerous waterbodies, clogged by an aquatic plant called water hyacinth (kochuri pana in Bengali). Bose spent considerable time in researching how to eradicate that plant and made certain recommendations to the government.

Bose was called upon to preside over the meeting of the Central Malaria Prevention Committee; in his address he said, 'We must ourselves rejuvenate our disease-ridden nation and not depend on the foreign bureaucratic government' and emphasized the importance of general health. He made it mandatory for the employees of the Bose Institute to do physical exercise under the supervision of a famous physical instructor, Pulin Behari Das.

Fifth Scientific Mission to Europe

The World War had ended in 1918, and there was a war-induced economic downturn. The government was experiencing a severe shortage of funds in all spheres. In 1915, the government had sanctioned a substantive annual grant for research to Bose for five years. That was now coming to an end, and Bose wanted an extension. He was also thinking of the financial security of the institute. Familiar with the style of the colonial administration, he, therefore, considered putting his case before the higher authorities in England.

A worried Bose wrote to his administrative deputy Nagendra Chandra Nag, 'I can clearly see an approaching crisis. Within a year, the British government will adopt a policy of curtailing all manners of expenditure to make up for the loss of revenue. To protect the Institute from that economic squeeze, it is necessary for me to go to England.'

It was towards the end of 1919 that Bose felt it was imperative that he visit England, mainly in the interest of the institute, and also to convince the scientific community finally of the value of the Indian contribution to modern science.

But the time did not seem opportune. His friends in England warned him about war-weariness in political and academic life. People were busy with their daily struggles and had little time for science, art, or other such finer pursuits. One year seemed too short a period for recovery for the war-ravaged economy and from the war-inflicted psychological stress. He would find it impossible, they said, to arouse any interest in his work or the Institute. Inherently stubborn that he was, Bose ignored such warnings and persisted in his plans to travel. He reached London in the middle of November 1919; he had financed this trip from his own resources.[84]

But all the naysayers were proven wrong. The scientific circles in England received him with great enthusiasm and he received invitations to speak at the Royal Society of Medicine, the universities of Cambridge and Oxford, University College, London, and a few other places. The plant growth experiments with the crescograph and the discovery of vascular bundles in plants by the electric probe aroused awe and curiosity.

Soon after reaching England, Bose had written a letter of appeal to the Secretary of India, Edwin Montague, for continuing the government grant to the Bose Institute. Montague had been somewhat familiar with the scientist's investigations from his last trip to India in 1917, when he had been able to meet Bose. In collaboration with the India Office, Bose arranged a lecture demonstration there in the beginning of December. This event was the first of its kind in the India Office, and was a great success. Later, Montague visited Bose at his residence and assured him of support.

In February 1920, Bose was invited to speak before the Royal Institution where he made a detailed presentation of his research with the magnetic crescograph. On 23 March, Aberdeen University conferred on him the honorary degree of LLD for reviving the tradition of scientific

[84]There is a general belief in India that all of Bose's scientific missions and trips to Europe were financed by the authorities. Starting with this fifth scientific mission to Europe, all later visits were not funded by the colonial government.

research in India in addition to his own discoveries and inventions.

In the spring of 1920, Bose set up a laboratory in his Bloomsbury Square house, where he received distinguished visitors. Here, his most delicate instrument, the magnetic crescograph was set up. He would charm large audiences with almost magical demonstrations using this instrument, as described below:

A plant is connected and the instrument projects a spot of light on the screen. The growth is magnified ten million times and the light spot is seen to rush across the screen. Cold water is poured into the tub containing the plant. The spot now starts to slow down and finally comes to a stop. This signals that the growth is fully arrested. A thermometer records the temperature of the plant chamber, which is now being gradually warmed up. The growth revives and accelerates. A stopcock turns on a depressing agent, and the plant is paralysed and the growth comes to a stop again. A dose of stimulant instantly revives the plant. The experimenter may then choose to apply poison and make the plant hover between life and death. But he does not allow it to die, for at the critical moment an antidote is given and at once the poor plant is granted a fresh lease of life. The experimenter appears like a magician, and that was exactly the allegation levelled against Bose by his old adversary Dr Waller. Bose later wrote about this,

> I made a portable instrument which I carried myself. It was the now famous magnetic crescograph which produced an incredible magnification of a hundred million times. This was regarded as theoretically impossible. I had a laboratory fitted up open to all scientific men, but a persistent opponent challenged me to exhibit it in a neutral place, the implication being that the performance of my apparatus was due to some jugglery. Of course, my opponent wanted simply to put me in trouble; he well knew that the vital portion of my indicator was suspended by a thread finer than a hair which would break during transport to a new place.
>
> I could not refuse the challenge, all the leading scientific men assembled to test the apparatus at the University College, Gower street [London]. I carried the instrument safely in a motor car but when I got down the slight jerk broke the thread. By the merest

chance I had a seccotine[85] capsular by me, with which I joined
the broken ends of the thread. The seccotine did not dry, and my
delicate indicator was being pulled down by its weight all the time.
But for 15 minutes the thread held together and by that time the
experiments were completed. The excitement in the press knew
no bounds, and it was perhaps my pluck under unfair conditions
that won for me the largest number of friends among the scientific
men and the lay public.

This demonstration took place on 23 April 1920. W. M. Bayliss, V. H.
Blackman, A. J. Clark, W. C. Clinton, and F. G. Donnan stated, giving
a kind of certificate of authenticity to the magnetic crescograph, in
The Times on 4 May: 'We are satisfied that the growth of plant tissues
is correctly recorded by this instrument, and at a magnification of one
million to ten million times.' It is noteworthy that Blackman had been a
persistent adversary of Bose until then. Bose wrote the following letter
the very next day in *The Times*,

> Criticism which transgresses the limit of fairness must inevitably
> hinder the advance of knowledge. ...If the result of my work, by
> upsetting any particular theory, has roused the hostility here and
> there of an individual, I can the more take comfort in the warm
> welcome which has been extended to me by the great body of
> scientific men of this country.

Following this, Bose had a packed schedule. On 13 May, Bose was made
a Fellow of the Royal Society (FRS), the highest honour that the country
could bestow on a man of science. On 20 May, in the evening, there
was a ceremony to welcome Bose to the society; he would affix his
signature in a memorial register, wherein the first name on the list was
that of King Charles.

Consultations on his induction into the society had been going on for
some time and Bose was kept informed of the developments. On 10 May

---

[85]Seccotine is an adhesive that needs a considerable amount of time to dry, before it
is fully effective. It originated in Ireland and was first marketed and patented in 1894
by John Stevenson MA.

1920,[86] he wrote to Boshi,'My name was warmly supported by all leading physiologists including Bayliss and Starling who, I learn, have become my staunch admirers. The plant physiologists as a body supported me.... They are all astounded by the results they saw demonstrated before their eyes.'

The Times announced the welcoming ceremony of 20 May in the morning of the same day: 'Sir Jagadish would be ceremonially elected as a Fellow of the Royal Society today. He is the second Indian to be so honoured....'

Bose himself wrote a dramatic recollection of this event in Bengali,

> Prof. and Mrs Vines had arrived from Oxford to attend the ceremony. We had lunch together and they left for the society venue. For a few weeks previous, I hadn't time to sleep for more than two hours a day, passing every waking moment in alertness and tension. After the mid-day meal, I was overcome with fatigue and tried to catch a bit of sleep; it was agreed that Abala would wake me up at four so that there would be time barely sufficient to reach Burlington house at half past four.

But Abala, who had been accompanying Bose to all his lectures and demonstrations, herself was tired and fell fast asleep. When finally, Bose was woken up, it was four-thirty. They hurriedly put on the selected outfits set aside for the occasion and set forth by a taxi. When they reached the venue, the ceremony which had been in progress, was about to conclude. In Bose's words,

> I found Prof. Vines running here and there in frenzy; we entered the ceremonial hall as quickly as possible. The assembly loudly cheered us in congratulation. When it came to affixing my signature, I discovered that I had rushed without my spectacles. God alone knows how and where I signed.

---

[86]Mehra (2007) has given the date of this letter as 10 March 1920. It could be a misreading of the date in the hand-written letter, or a typographical error. The subject of the letter is Fellowship of the Royal Society, and we know from other sources that the decision to award Bose the fellowship was taken in May 1920.

Just three days before, that is on 17 May, Bose had delivered a lecture at University College, London; he had to speak for one and a half hours more than the scheduled time due to the eagerness of his audience. At the end of his discourse, the president in his concluding remarks said, 'Just like the telescope and microscope, Professor Bose's inventions will bring revolutionary change in the progress of science.'

On 4 June, researchers from the main agricultural research centre in Britain, the Rothamstead Experimental Station, visited the laboratory attached to Bose's residence to see the crescographs in operation.

At the invitation of Professor Carveth Reed of the London University, Bose spoke before the Psychological Society in October; the topic was 'Control of Nervous Excitement'. Interestingly, in his book *Irritability of Plants*, published in 1913, there had been a couple of chapters on psychology.

At this time, Bose's first biography, *The Life and Work of Sir Jagadis C. Bose*, by Professor Patrick Geddes, was published by Longmans, Green, and Co. in London. The lay public of Britain, to whom Bose's name had become well known by then, was curious to know about his life; to them the book came as a great source of enjoyment; it painted for them a holistic picture of a noble life of continuous struggle and sweet victory at the end. Its appearance was opportune and served to enhance his fame in no small measure.

Bose came to Paris at the invitation of the Physiological Congress. He lectured at the Congress and also before the Biological Society. At both places, his opponents were hard at work to discredit him, but had no success. At the Sorbonne University, he demonstrated his magical magnetic crescograph. A renowned physicist, whom Bose has not named, remarked in admiration, 'Monsieur, I see it but my heart still refuses to believe!' He then visited Stockholm at the invitation of the Physical Society and his lecture there was much appreciated.

His experiments and discoveries had overturned the thesis of the leading German physiologist, Gottlieb Haberlandt. It is worth recalling that during his last trip to Europe, Bose had not been able to visit Germany due to the outbreak of Word War I. This time he had received no invitations from Germany. Even then the Boses proceeded there, carrying the two crescographs. In Bose's own words,

> My stay in Europe was drawing to a close and I had less than a week to spare. I therefore went to Berlin without notice and drove directly to the celebrated Physiological Institute at Dalhem, presided over by the eminent and veteran physiologist Haberlandt. I was received with marked coldness and suspicion as having come from the Allied countries; the anti-foreign feeling was then at its highest. I only asked for fair play. Let all the leading scientists be invited and I would be ready to meet the shock of hostile criticisms. A lecture was organised and a miracle happened, for in less than 15 minutes the whole audience gave expression of their warmest appreciation. So complete was the conversion from scepticism that in his subsequent address, Prof. Haberlandt declared that it was no accident that it should have been an Indian investigator who had in so high a degree perfected the new method of enquiry and exhibited such an extraordinarily developed faculty for experimentation.

The Boses returned to England immediately. The only thing that was now left unfinished was the matter of sanction of an annual grant-in-aid by the government to the Bose Institute. Edwin Montague, who had promised Bose his support, had sent a long letter of recommendation to the Government of India and was awaiting their reply. As usual, the lower bureaucracy tried to delay matters. The Boses could not afford to wait any longer and sailed homewards; they reached India in the beginning of January 1921. In the end, Mr Montague prevailed upon the colonial administration and an annual grant of 1 lakh rupees was sanctioned.

Soon after Bose's fifth European sojourn, quite a few of his books were translated into French and German.

Bose Inspires Synergy

Jagadish's fifth scientific mission to Europe was a grand success, grander than that of the one before. Bose's return with new laurels generated tremendous enthusiasm in the institute's researchers. Bose, after a short break, returned to the work table with as much vigour as ever. A flurry of inventions came out of the institute in the next three years, such as, the magnetic radiometer, transpirograph, and a recorder of ascent of sap. This culminated in the development of the photosynthetic recorder, which bears the mark of Bose's ingenuity. Bose wrote to one of his friends in Bengali,

> There have been quite a few remarkable inventions and discoveries since my return from England. One can say with a fair certainty that our laboratory, at the moment, is leading in the quantity of substantive research in the whole world. Eminent scientists of France and Germany wish to document my work in their respective languages. That our contribution would be recognized so widely and in so short a time, I never expected.

Bose's work of the last several years, scattered in various scientific journals and transactions, were consolidated in the next three years, and published by Longmans, Green, and Co. of London. These were the *Transactions of the Bose Institute* (Volume III and IV), *Physiology of the Ascent of Sap* (1923), and *Physiology of Photosynthesis* (1924). The investigations in the institute were continually leading to one general conclusion—there was a fundamental unity between the workings of plant life and animal life.

In the meantime, the Visva-Bharati University, established by Rabindranath Tagore at Shantiniketan, was acquiring an international reputation. Tagore now wished to pass its administration to a public trust and invited Sir Jagadish to be its vice president, which was readily assented to.

Gertrude Meets Bose

In the summer of 1921, Bose was in Darjeeling accompanied by Boshi, working in his summer laboratory on certain plants that could not withstand the sweltering heat of Calcutta. Tagore was also there to escape the heat of the plains. Incidentally, the first reconnaissance expedition to Mount Everest, the tallest peak in the world, had gone up at the same time under the leadership of Colonel Charles Howard-Bury. The famous mountaineer George Mallory was also part of the team.

An American geographer, named Gertrude Emerson, arrived in Darjeeling, hoping to meet the members of the expedition on their return, while collecting materials for an article for the *Asia* magazine, of which she was the sub-editor. Before this she had been a globe-trotting writer who was roped in by Willard Straight, founder of the magazine in New York. Gertrude was known to Tagore, having met him twice before—first when she was an undergraduate in Chicago, and later in New York, when she interviewed him on behalf of *Asia*.

Gertrude Emerson Sen

Gertrude went to meet Tagore and met Bose in his company. As was his wont, Bose invited Gertrude to visit his institute if she were ever in Calcutta. It is possible that Boshi and Gertrude saw each other here, without being formally introduced. She visited Tagore in Shantiniketan as well. It was he who suggested to her the idea of living in an Indian village, if she wanted to know the 'real' India.

Before going to Darjeeling, Gertrude had interviewed the most talked-about Indian leader at the time, Mohandas Karamchand Gandhi, in Lahore. Then travelling around Agra, Rajputana, the Ajanta caves, Mysore, and the Malabar coast, she continued writing about India for the *Asia* magazine. In December 1921, she had a second meeting with Gandhi in Sabarmati Ashram, in Gujarat. She went back to America via North Africa and Europe.

The words that Tagore had said to her kept playing in her mind until, in October 1926, she decided to translate it into reality. She took a year's leave from the magazine and came to India, found through her contacts, a very remote village, towards the east of the United Province, called Pachperwa—the village of five trees. The nearest railhead was a day's walk or bullock cart ride. There was no shop or post office; salt and a matchbox could be purchased in a weekly market 3 kilometres away. She liked the village for its isolation, pitched a tent there till a house could be built for her, and then settled in.

Boshi Sen Leaves Bose

Boshi owed his scientific training and career to Bose. He had been admiring Bose right from his boyhood days; as Bose's assistant, the admiration had changed into adoration, and Boshi had started looking up to Bose for guidance. But since 1922, he had felt somewhat dejected, because of two incidents that occurred in quick succession.

A group of foreign friends were visiting Bose in Darjeeling in the summer. They had planned an overnight horse ride to Tiger Hill so as to reach there at dawn to see the sunrise on the snow-capped peak of Mount Kanchenjunga. The peak is only slightly lower than Mount Everest and looks majestically awesome at sunrise. It appears so close and so tall from the Tiger Hill observation post atop it looks like it is reaching the zenith of the sky. Boshi was looking forward to the trip.

Bose had a paper almost ready for publication in the *Royal Society Proceedings*. During those days, there used to be a home mail steamer going out to England at regular intervals on a fixed day of the week. He asked Boshi to stay back and type up the paper so it would be ready to post the next day. The paper was written entirely on Boshi's research, supervised by Bose, and Boshi worked on it all night. But when the paper appeared in the next edition of the journal, much to Boshi's dismay, his name was missing; it had been credited to Bose and another student, who had nothing at all to do with it. Boshi felt extremely hurt, but kept his own counsel. The idea to start his own laboratory began to take root in his mind from that day.

The second incident, as narrated by Boshi, seems innocuous enough for the time in which it happened. At this time, Bose appointed a relation[87], who was a biscuit manufacturer, to an administrative post in the institute at a monthly salary of 500 rupees, whereas Boshi had risen

---

[87]Boshi refrained from naming this relative. We do know that Bose appointed Abani Nath Mitra, a cousin, in the administrative post of a superintendent at the Bose Institute.

from 20 to 150 rupees after having worked with Bose for twelve years.

In early 1923, an American couple, Glen and Marguerite Overton, arrived at the Bose Institute and approached Bose with a letter of introduction from a common American friend. The letter had a reference to, 'that joyous soul Boshi Sen'. Bose thought that they were interested in visiting his laboratory, and sent word accordingly through Boshi. While delivering the message, Boshi read disappointment in the face of the visitors, who did not seem interested in science. He enquired about their expectations and was told, 'We want to meet Indians and learn about their thinking—the real India.' They eagerly accepted Boshi's suggestion that they meet the monks of the Ramakrishna Mission at Belur. After a visit to the monastery, with Boshi as escort, and a formal dinner together at the Great Eastern Hotel, they got to like 'the joyous soul Boshi Sen' so much that they asked him, 'Couldn't you take two weeks off from Bose, and go around India a bit with us?'

When Boshi asked Bose for permission, he said, 'Well, it seems you are losing interest in your work.' Boshi was hurt, since he had not taken a single day off in his many years with Bose, except when his brother had fallen ill. He chose to escort the Overtons on their short trip, feeling entitled to a leave. When it was time to part, the Overtons sprang a surprise on him, 'Why not come back to America with us? You can visit all the universities, and study and see everything. For you, everything will be first class.'

Boshi decided to take them up on their offer. He went to Bose and said, 'Sir, I am going to ask for a long leave, maybe a year.' Bose replied, 'If this place does not suit you, go and look elsewhere.' Bose's indifference and curt reply gave freedom to Boshi; he felt no moral obligation to stay on.

When Boshi's ship reached San Francisco, he learnt that Overton's business had floundered and he was not in a position to fulfil his promise. Boshi went to New York and met an old acquaintance, Patrick Geddes, who pushed him to meet with Leonard Elmhirst.

The son of a poor Devonshire clergyman, Elmhirst had arrived from England as a deck passenger, and secured admission in Cornell University to study agriculture. He worked as a part time waiter in a restaurant to supplement his income. He was sent by his department to

Dorothy Straight, belonging to the Whitney family, to collect donations for the university. Dorothy's husband Willard Straight, the founder of *Asia* magazine, had died in 1918. It so happened that Elmhirst and Dorothy fell in love and were engaged when Boshi approached him. Geddes had furnished him with a letter of introduction with the line: 'This is to introduce Boshi Sen, a live wire'.

Geddes, an old friend of Bose, had known Boshi as Bose's assistant and a man of all seasons, for over a decade. When he sent Boshi to Elmhirst, he must have understood that Boshi was toying with the idea of leaving Bose. Yet he was eager to help. Geddes, Elmhirst, and Boshi's other academic contacts in America arranged for Boshi to visit various institutes and universities on the American east coast.

Elmhirst had earlier befriended Tagore and visited Shantiniketan, and was preparing for a second visit with Dorothy. Tagore and Elmhirst had planned to develop a rural branch of Shantiniketan with agriculture at its centre, in a nearby village named Surur. A plan was also afoot to start a science department in Shantiniketan. Elmhirst offered Boshi a salary of 1,000 rupees per month, with the goal of taking these plans to fruition.

Such great rise in income would tempt most young men, but not Boshi. He thought that if he took this offer, people would think that he had jumped for the sake of money. He frankly told Elmhirst that he was thinking of starting his own laboratory and this trip was a great opportunity to buy some equipment since he was in New York.

With their characteristic generosity, Dorothy and Elmhirst gave Boshi the required funds, then and there. Boshi promised, 'If I do not start a laboratory, I will either return the instruments to Shantiniketan or return the money to you.'

He purchased an ultra-microscope, a galvanometer, and a few other pieces of equipment, and set sail for India. While crossing England, he learnt that his first independent paper, communicated a year ago, had been accepted by the Royal Society for publication in its *Proceedings*. This added immensely to his confidence.

Back in India after a year, in February 1924, Boshi tried once again to remain with his professor. He approached Bose to rejoin the institute and requested the maximum scholarship permissible under the rules, which would have meant a modest rise in his income. Bose chose neither to persuade nor negotiate. Instead, he summarily rejected Boshi's request, as if he wanted to get rid of him. This kind of behaviour was most uncharacteristic of Bose, who was by nature a generous person. Boshi had no option but to resign.

In his resignation letter, Boshi pointed out that during his leave of absence, he had visited many research institutes and universities in America and England, and learned of new methods and new lines of investigation. The government sent scholars abroad and paid their expenses, for it considered such visits germane to better research. On the other hand, he had acquired such exposure at his own expense. Therefore, he deserved a raise. He added,

> With greatest pain, I find that the only alternative left to me is to tender my resignation, and this alike in the interest of the rules and regulations of the Institute and for my research work I might be capable of undertaking, after having had the privilege of sitting at the feet of my great master for twelve years.

What we have is only Boshi's side of the story. To put things in perspective, in 1917, Bose had noted in his diary that his assistant was not one to be tempted by offers of employment in foreign universities, as has been quoted earlier.

It is apparent that Boshi had turned down such offers earlier on. In May 1920, Bose had written to Boshi from England a letter of joyous satisfaction, about his selection as a Fellow of the Royal Society. What transpired between the professor and his favourite assistant-cum-student in the years after 1920, will perhaps never be known.

No matter what, Boshi Sen played an important and active contributory role for twelve long years in Bose's life. Boshi led an exemplary life of frugality, hard work, and dedication, both before and after leaving Bose and the man and his words cannot be ignored in Bose's biography.

ᔐ

Boshi inaugurated his modest laboratory in the kitchen of his house at 8 Bosepara Lane, on 4 July 1924, the twenty-second anniversary of

Swami Vivekananda's nirvana, maha-samadhi, or death. He named it Vivekananda Laboratory. There was no preparation; and yet he needed to perform an experiment to make the holy inauguration meaningful; the experiment would also be a sign of his determination. So, he measured the pH of rainwater, which was available in plenty, as the monsoon had set in. He wrote in his diary,[88]

> Swamiji Maharaj, I have dared to associate your name with this undertaking. You know what I can do and cannot do, my prayer to you, the blessed and beloved of my guru, is that I may not discredit your good name. Please destroy me before I do that. They say you are the friend of the destitute, and suffer fools gladly. Befriend me in this undertaking.... Pranams and sastanga.
>
> —Boshi.

Boshi had faith that Vivekananda would provide all that he truly needed, but not all that he might desire. This was a principle he decided to live by, that he would not accept anything he did not truly need. On that fateful day in July, he did not know how he would earn his own living.

Unsolicited donations for the laboratory came from Glen Overton, Leonard and Dorothy, Josephine MacLeod, artist Nicholas Roerich (a Russian artist friend of Boshi who had been living in America), and the Earl of Sandwich who was married to Joe's niece, Alberta. There was an additional donation from an old Indian friend who wished to remain anonymous. We know that Boshi's Indian friends of his age were all like him, leading a hand to mouth existence. There is one friend of Boshi whom we know of, who was much older and who had wealth as well as a motive to remain anonymous—Rabindranath Tagore.

The room upstairs in Boshi's house, where Sadananda had stayed, had been made into a shrine. Boshi meditated there in the morning and evening. He began work in the morning and worked through the day in his kitchen-laboratory. His experimental plants were kept in vessels in the cemented courtyard adjacent to the kitchen, not the most suitable place for plants. But there was no other option. Some scientist friends

---

[88]This diary was discovered after his death.

often volunteered a few hours of their time to help him. He was even able to keep an assistant, named S. M. Sircar, at a monthly salary of 150 rupees, who later rose to become the director of the Bose Institute. There was no room for a third person in his kitchen laboratory.

One day, Boshi received a letter from the office of Lord Lytton, the lieutenant governor of the Bengal Presidency, enquiring if it would be convenient for Mr Boshi Sen to have His Excellency visit his laboratory. Apparently, the word about his unusual laboratory had spread fast. Boshi replied expressing thanks and confirmed the visit with the rider, 'The only advice, I would like to give your Excellency, is that you should come in a small car. There is not enough space in the street in front of the house to manoeuvre a big car.'

On the appointed day, the lieutenant governor arrived. Boshi offered him a seat on the wooden stool, which he used while working with the microscope, and himself sat on a wooden box. Lytton spent an hour in discussion about his research. He offered to recommend a suitable grant for the laboratory to the Home Department.

Boshi politely said that at the moment he had all his monetary needs fulfilled; if in the future, the need arose, he would certainly write to the lieutenant governor. Later, Lytton became a good friend of Boshi, and hosted him in England during one of his visits there. Lytton referred to him as the only Indian who had treated him as a human being.

9

THE ELDERLY SCIENTIST
AND HIS DECLINING YEARS

Joe alias Josephine MacLeod grieved for two years after learning about the passing away of Swami Vivekananda and could not think of returning to an India bereft of his presence. Finally, a call came from Sarada Devi, the holy mother, and after a gap of nearly fourteen years, Joe came to India to see her. In February 1916, she was in Belur Math, which was then under the hostile gaze of the government.

After the partition of Bengal along religious lines in 1905, a very large number of Calcutta's young men joined the anti-partition movement. Eventually, the partition was annulled but the movement soon took a new direction, that of nationalism, and demanded political freedom. As mentioned earlier, Vivekananda's books were often found in the possession of these freedom fighters. A few of them were given refuge by Saradananda-swami after they decided to abjure politics altogether and take spiritual initiation.

An investigating committee appointed by the government filed a report accusing Belur Math of sedition. They ignored the fact that the brothers and sisters of the order never took part in politics. Nivedita, who had been taking part in politics, had dissociated herself from the Math and given a declaration in newspapers to that effect; she remained detached for the rest of her life. Viceroy Carmichael made a hostile speech pointing fingers at the Math.

In this situation, Joe's arrival proved to be a blessing for the Math. She contacted the American Consul General of Calcutta, Mr Patterson, the husband of a follower of the Swami, who once hosted him at his home in America. It was the same lady who had accompanied the Swami and his western companions in Kashmir also, though briefly. Joe, with her connection with the British royalty (her niece Alberta was married to the Earl of Sandwich), could easily arrange an appointment with Lord

Carmichael. Saradananda-swami and Joe went to meet with him and explained the aims and activities of the Math and Mission. In a short time, the viceroy withdrew his previous remarks.

At that time, Christine was in America; the school's charge had been left to her able assistant Sudhira. Then World War I broke out and the American government prevented her return, as her father was German. Moreover, the government in India began looking upon the school with extreme suspicion because of her heritage.

In December 1916, Joe was staying in Nivedita's school. She saved the school by hoisting a British flag over the upper storey and staying there continuously for some time, even though she found the place lonesome and bleak with no Nivedita and no Christine. Her proximity to Mr Patterson also helped and the situation cooled.

On 28 February 1917, Boshi wrote to Christine, who was still in America, 'Yesterday Mrs Geddes and Tantine [Joe] came to Dr Sircar's and went to hear Kathakata[89]. After that they came over to S's and had dinner there. Dr Bose showed them his laboratory and was so delighted— himself the most. ...After that I had to take them to the Math and came back by 12 pm.'

What Boshi actually meant by 'his laboratory' was the Bose Institute, which our scientist was so delighted to show around to his guests. In February 1917, when Joe and Mrs Geddes visited, the inside of the building and the laboratory were ready. The outside of the building and the garden were receiving the finishing touches. As stated before, the institute was inaugurated nine months later on 30 November.

Boshi wrote to Christine on 14 June 1918:

> Tantine writes that she will be in America soon.... I am, for various reasons, glad that she is going there. She has such a lot of go and will make you do quite a lot work for which Dt.[90] will jump. You know what I mean: she can help you regarding the shares [of stock] and will clear the Thorp business and you will know quite a lot of the existing conditions. By the bye, should you be with her, tell

[89]Dramatized storytelling from the Indian epics; a form of folk entertainment and education.

[90]Most probably, by 'Dt.' Boshi meant Detroit, the city where Christine and her family lived.

her about my letter to Dr Bose. You know how she is interested
in this. Bless her!

Joe went back to America a few months before the end of the war. Mrs
Bull had left a will with sizable funds for the school and Bose Institute
to the care of her brother and lawyer, Mr Thorp. After the contestation
by and subsequent death of her daughter Olea Bull, the responsibility
of executing her will had once again returned to her brother. Mr Thorp
released the annual grant for the school regularly, but not the legacy
for the Bose Institute. This is the 'Thorp business' Boshi refers to in his
letter. Joe was taking a keen interest in this matter and trying to persuade
Mr Thorp in Bose's favour; Bose was well aware of this. Thorp might
have been concerned about the inheritance of Olea's infant daughter,
and in the end, did not yield.

Six months before, in a letter to Christine on 13 December 1917, that
is, within a fortnight of the formal inauguration of the Bose Institute,
Boshi had informed her that he had received a gift from Joe, 'a draft of
Rupees One thousand from our Tantine—for my "spring board" for any
experiments in life or science that—"you would perhaps not be able to
afford" as she put it.'

In 1917, Boshi and Bose had the best of relations, the student totally
loyal and the teacher offering near-paternal care. It should be recalled
that the discord between Bose and his favourite assistant occurred in
1923, that is, six years down the line. It seems that Joe had a psychic
premonition that Boshi would want to do 'experiments in life or science'
in the future.

In 1922, Joe was again in Calcutta and staying in the guest house of
the Belur Math. Boshi wrote to Christine on 6 April, 'Tantine reached
Calcutta last Thursday...and is quite comfortable though the heat is a
bit too much. Dr Bose has invited her to Darjeeling. But she wouldn't
go there....'

Bose knew that Joe was a real well-wisher of his, and always showed
her appropriate courtesy. Joe preferred to stay in the guest house of
the monastery and visited the Boses on 12 April 1922. She sometimes
visited Bosepara Lane to see Boshi and Christine. Joe stayed on in India
for most of the next year before returning to America.

Ascent of Sap

After returning from Europe in January 1921, Bose as usual plunged into work. In addition to research and administration, he had to shoulder the responsibility of editing the *Transactions of the Bose Institute*. But now he was not alone; there were able assistants for all three types of work. He desired the transactions to be of the highest standard and sent all research papers to renowned referees before publication.

Bose had earlier discovered, by means of the electric probe, that electrical record of the spontaneous pulsation of a telegraph plant leaflet was akin to that of an animal heart. It is natural to question if there was such pulsation to be found in other plants. If the heart keeps the animal alive by circulating blood, then what function is served by the spontaneous pulsation of a plant? Bose first proved the existence of such pulsation in ordinary plants, and then tried to show that such pulsation is what causes the sap within to rise from the root to the topmost leaf of a plant. The sap means the watery fluid, containing soil nutrients, that keeps the plant alive and makes it grow.

In order to detect the pulsating layer, Bose investigated the stems of various plants with the help of his electric probe. He discovered that, in general, a layer, existing just above the phloem inside the cortex, exhibits vigorous pulsation. Fig. 9.1 shows the pulsating layer in the rose balsam plant (dopaati in Bengali). Vigorous pulsation was detected at a layer 0.3 millimetres below the skin.

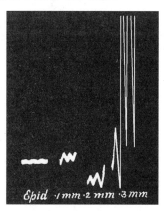

Fig. 9.1: Determination of the pulsating layer in rose balsam plant's stem.

Fig. 9.2 gives the electrical record of the pulsating layer of a mango tree, taken by Bose with the electric probe. It looks somewhat similar to that of the telegraph plant's leaflet, and also to the electrical record of the heartbeats of a frog.

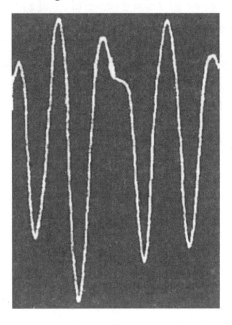

Fig. 9.2: The electrical record of the pulsating layer of a mango tree.

Even before him, some scientists had advanced the theory that sap is pumped upwards in a plant by pulsation. But they couldn't experimentally prove their point. So, this remained a theory among many other competing theories, given below:

Theory 1: The ascent of sap is either due to atmospheric air pressure or root pressure.

Theory 2: The rise of sap has nothing to do with the living cells. It automatically rises through the xylem due to capillary action, and spreads throughout the body of the plant.

Theory 3: The the mesophyll cells of the leaf lose water due to evaporation in contact with air, and thus an osmotic pressure is created.

That pressure is transmitted from cell to cell downwards to the root, causing the sap to rise through the xylem.

The first to be negated by Bose was the one involving air pressure. It is well known that air pressure can raise water to a maximum height of about 10 metres, whereas there are trees such as redwood and eucalyptus that are many metres taller. Therefore, air pressure could not be the cause of rise of the sap. Bose negated the intangible and imaginary root pressure by an experiment to be described later.

Similarly, the sap could not rise hundreds of metres due to capillary action whose capibilities are even lesser than air pressure's. Even osmotic pressure is too slow to raise watery fluid to that height, since the highest leaves would lose water due to evaporation at a rate faster than the arrival of replenishment. If osmotic pressure were to be the cause, the leaves above a certain height would dry up.

Bose not only criticized these theories, but also established his own theory using clever experiments. A branch of a chrysanthemum plant was cut or severed neatly by a sharp knife from the main stem to expose a cross section. The twig was placed in an erect position in a pot without water and left there until it shrivelled due to evaporation of water and drooped over to one side, close to death.

It was then pruned of all its leaves except one at the very top. That leaf was covered with a layer of Vaseline. The leaf was connected to the lever of a plant phytograph (see Fig. 8.1) and the bottom part of the cut branch was dipped into some water in a tube. The twig absorbed this water through the cross section where it had been cut.

The phytograph marked on its smoked plate a series of horizontal dots in the beginning. After 30 seconds, the leaf began to raise itself and the writer tip on the left end of the lever began descending, and drew a pattern as shown in Fig. 9.3. The arrow marks the point where the leaf began to rise. After a while, the whole branch became erect. The distance of the leaf (along the body of the branch) from the water level was measured and divided by 30 seconds to determine the speed of sap travel, which turned out to be 18 metres per hour (or 5 millimetres per second). Similar experiments with other plants revealed speeds up to 70 metres per hour.

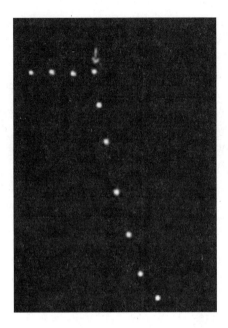

Fig. 9.3: Measurement of speed of sap travel.
Constructed by author, from a description of the experiment.

Bose proved that root pressure was not the cause of the sap's ascent, since this twig had no roots at all; also, that evaporation from the leaf and the resulting osmotic pressure were not responsible, since evaporation had been prevented by application of Vaseline. There was reason for ruling out osmotic ascent—the speed of travel due to osmosis would be much slower than 18 metres per hour. Therefore, the only option left was the pumping action due to pulsation of the living cells, present all along the body of the twig.

He did a similar experiment with a single stem of a plant with root, by pruning all its leaves but one, and applying Vaseline on that leaf. The speed of ascent of the sap turned out to be much slower. This proves that the root is more of a hindrance than help, as far as ascent of the sap is concerned. It is well known that the root absorbs nutrients and water from the soil and creates the sap. However, it does not raise the sap. The root has some pumping capacity to reach the sap up to the upper end of itself. From there on, it is the living cells that take over. Spread throughout the body of the plant, these cells pump up and distribute the sap.

Thereafter, Bose devised a method for measuring the amount of water absorbed by a cut branch, by modifying his plant phytograph (shown in Fig. 8.1). The U-tube and the link rod T in this instrument were replaced by a different arrangement, as shown in Fig. 9.4. In this figure, only the modifications are illustrated. Bose called the modified instrument automatic potograph.

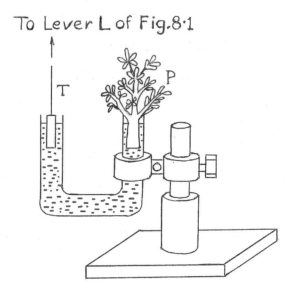

Fig. 9.4: Portion of Automatic Potograph.

A cut portion of a plant (P) is placed in one arm of a U-tube filled with water and in the other arm there is a small cylindrical glass float, which is firmly attached to a thread (T). The other end of the thread is tied to the lever L of Fig. 8.1. A thin layer of oil is added on the water surface of both arms of the U-tube to prevent evaporation; this ensures that loss of water is only due to absorption by the plant. As the cut cross section of the branch absorbs water from the U-tube, the water level gradually goes down and the glass float starts to descend, and the writer-point begins to climb and marks a series of dots as shown in Fig. 9.5.

Since the U-tube diameter is known, the volume of water sucked by the plant in a given time can be calculated from the measurement.

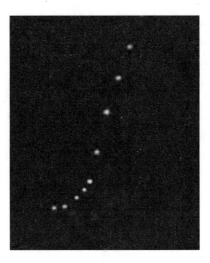

Fig. 9.5: Measurement of volume of water sucked by plant.
Constructed by author, from a description of the experiment.

Earlier, Bose had shown that the record of autonomous gyration of the telegraph plant's leaflet had a corresponding electrical pulsation at the leaflet root (see Fig. 8.2). When a depressing or exalting agent is applied, there are changes, along expected lines, in the leaflet's gyration and electrical pulsation. Now, he showed that when these agents were applied on any other plant, the automatic potograph record of its sap absorption was likewise affected. This indicates that the pulsation of its living cells was similar to that of the telegraph plant's leaflet, and the ascent of sap is somehow connected with this pulsation.

Apart from these indirect evidences, Bose had proved the existence of the pulsating cells at a certain depth under the skin for several plants (see Fig. 9.1). Thus, by different direct experiments and indirect evidences Bose justified his theory regarding the ascent of sap.

Even in the twenty-first century, there exists no consensus among scientists about the underlying mechanism of the ascent of sap. In Vienna, Hans Molisch repeated Bose's experiments and supported Bose's theory in 1928. However, there are other competing theories. The following plant physiologists concurred with Bose after conducting their own experiments: G. J. Pierce in 1934, J. H. Priestley in 1935, and W. R. C. Handley in 1939.

Bose attacked a multiplicity of problems in the field of plant physiology in the last few decades of his life and produced significant research findings. We shall but discuss only one more here.

Photosynthetic Recorder

All life processes, animal or plant, require energy and the sun is the root source of that energy. Plants acquire their energy directly from the sun, and in a sense, they are self-sufficient. Animals cannot do so and depend on plant life for their energy supply. Herbivorous animals such as elephants, camels, buffaloes, and deer feed on plants and carnivorous animals such as lions and tigers feed on herbivores.

The substance that gives plants their colour, called chlorophyll, uses sunlight to synthesize carbon dioxide (CO_2) from the air and water from the soil to form carbohydrates, while releasing equal volume of oxygen (O_2) into the atmosphere. This process is called photosynthesis. The plant stores carbohydrates in its body and draws some of it for use in its own life process, which includes absorbing nutrients from the soil. The nutrients and remaining carbohydrates are stored in the plant's body and leaves which the herbivores feed on. Thus, photosynthesis is perhaps the most important process on earth and responsible for the existence of all forms of life. Bose wanted to study and quantify this process, and invented the automatic photosynthetic recorder.

There are three effects of photosynthesis—absorption of CO_2, weight gain due to production of carbohydrates, and release of O_2. The first and second take much too long to measure, which made the task of keeping environmental conditions constant, impossible. Hence, Bose chose to measure the release of O_2.

There are two types of plants, those that draw CO_2 from the air and those who draw dissolved CO_2 from water. The latter release O_2 in the form of bubbles, which would be convenient to monitor and measure, Bose reckoned. So, he devised an instrument that worked only for aquatic plants, such as hydrilla.

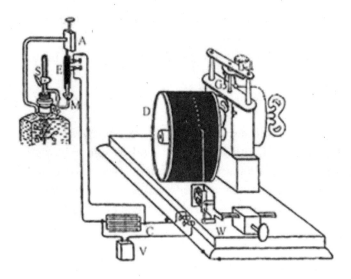

Fig. 9.6: Photosynthetic Recorder.

Fig. 9.6 shows Bose's photosynthetic recorder with its bubbler part on the top left corner. A clump of hydrilla plants is kept in a large water-filled bottle (the bottom of the bottle and its support table are not shown in the figure). A small vertical tube (S) is inserted into the airtight cork closing the bottle; there is an arrangement for opening the upper end of S to the atmosphere, when necessary. A small U-tube with one funnel-shaped mouth is connected to S. A micrometre screw (A), which is supported by a structure on the left of the bottle, lowers two vertical platinum wires (E) in a controlled fashion into the funnel-shaped mouth of the U-tube, as shown in the figure. The platinum wires have pointed tips and are insulated from each other and connected to two terminals of an electrical circuit.

Now, the inventive genius applies his magic touch by placing in the funnel a globule of mercury (M), just large enough not to pass through the bottom of the funnel. Mercury is a liquid metal and a conductor and Bose used both these properties—liquidity and conductivity—to create a two-in-one device—a valve plus circuit-breaker.

The mercury globule, initially, is not in contact with the platinum wires and blocks the exit of the funnel. A liquid globule can do this effectively, but a solid globule cannot. When O_2 is released as a by-product of photosynthesis by the hydrilla in the bottle, it collects in the bubbler (S) and the U-tube. Thus, pressure gradually builds up inside the U-tube. At some point the pressure is enough to lift the mercury globule to release O_2 into the atmosphere. The lifted globule, for a moment, makes contact with the platinum wires and completes the electrical circuit. This activates an electromagnetic writing device (W) which marks a point on the rotating drum (D), as shown in Fig. 9.6.

After releasing the pressure, the mercury globule falls back to seal the funnel exit and break the electrical circuit simultaneously. Thus, the globule acts as a valve by allowing O_2 to flow out but not allowing the surrounding air to flow into the U-tube. Then the cycle of events repeats itself again and again at regular intervals, and we get a series of dots on the drum.

The valve action of the mercury globule is so accurate that it releases the same volume of O_2 in each release. Bose calibrated the instrument to determine the released amount in a cycle. The quantity of O_2 released could thus be calculated from the number of dots on the drum in a given duration.

The simplicity and efficacy of Bose's scheme stun the mind. One is reminded of the comment made by Prince Kropotkin, after he had witnessed a demonstration by J. J. Thompson, and a week later by Bose on the same topic: 'I said to myself that this was the simplicity of the highest genius.'

Bose was the first to use a drop of mercury in this ingenous manner and many other instruments have been constructed later by using mercury and Bose's technique, all over the world. The first imitation was made by his own students in the institute, to devise an instrument called the respirometer for measuring O_2 absorption of plants at night, and humans and animals. The respirometer belonged to the class of what is now called oximeters. This early twentieth century oximeter obviously had great potential for medical application and was the first oximeter in the world.[91]

----

[91]Author's remark: It is ironic that India now (in 2021) imports almost all of its oximeters from a neighbouring Asian country. Bose and his institute had created a momentum for

Next, Bose used his photosynthetic recorder to determine the effect of light intensity on photosynthesis. Since the intensity of the sun would not remain constant over time, he used a pointolight lamp that maintained its intensity over a fair duration. Additionally, its intensity could be varied by changing the applied voltage. Fig. 9.7 shows a strip from the recording drum, where the intensity of light was varied from 7.5 hectolux (= 7.5 x 100 lux) to 15 hectolux.

Fig. 9.7: Rate of photosynthesis increases with increasing light intensity.

It was observed that the rate of photosynthesis remained constant if the light intensity was kept constant. The rate increased with increasing intensity over a fair range. Beyond a certain point, which in this case was above 1500 lux, the rate began to diminish with rising intensity. This indicates that the plant begins to suffer due to excessive intensity of light.

Bose discovered a seasonal effect too. The rate of photosynthesis is considerably higher in the spring season of Bengal than in the winter, for the same intensity of light, while the room temperature is kept constant. In spring, photosynthesis starts at as low an intensity as 100 lux; whereas in winter it might take 500 lux or more to get started. He conducted all his experiments with hydrilla from the same pond to make sure that the same genetic strain was used throughout.

Noticing the sensitivity of the plant to excessive light, and the subdued rate of photosynthesis in the winter, Bose concluded that photosynthesis was not merely a chemical reaction of inert matter, but had much to do with the plant's biological process. Hence, it was biochemical in nature.

---

invention and innovation among Indian researchers. An aversion to risk and industrial research, on the part of Indian businessmen and industrialists, curbed that momentum instead of enhancing it. As a result, India now imports most of its medical equipment.

That photosynthesis could depend on the colour of light was an obvious possibility. So, Bose split sunlight into its spectrum using a prism of carbon disulphide, and subjected the hydrilla plant to each component colour, one by one. As a first guess, he had thought that invisible radiation would have no effect; however, in the infrared, which is an invisible radiation, the plant revealed a slight increase in photosynthetic activity, contrary to expectation. In red light, which is next to infrared in the spectrum, there was a sharp and huge increase in the rate of photosynthesis. Thereafter, in the subsequent colours the rate progressively decreased and became nil at the end of the spectrum—violet. He assigned a value of 100 to the rate in red light, and proportionately scaled the other colours as follows:

Red	Orange	Yellow	Green	Blue	Indigo	Violet
100	42	18	12	3	–	0

Bose has not given the value of indigo, presumably because it was indistinguishable from violet in his measurements.

It is well known that each colour of the solar spectrum corresponds to a particular frequency of electromagnetic oscillation. The frequency increases from the red (460 THz) to the violet (750 THz), where T stands for Tera meaning 10^{12}. The infrared has a frequency lower than the red. Bose wondered: does photosynthesis depend on the frequency or the energy content of a particular colour? He resolved this question by measuring the radiant energy of light of different colours of the solar spectrum by a novel method with the help of his magnetic crescograph.

Instead of measuring the growth of a plant, he measured the expansion in length of a thin metal rod. The plant in Fig. 8.11 was replaced by a rod, painted matt black, so that all radiations were fully absorbed by it, irrespective of colour. The rod was subjected to the light of a particular colour. The radiant energy of the light led to the heating of the rod and it expanded in length, which was recorded by the crescograph. The rate of expansion was a measure of the radiant energy of that colour.

He found that the sun's infrared contains much more energy than red, but photosynthesis is much more rapid in red than in infrared, which led him to conclude that frequency was more important than radiant energy for photosynthesis. For the subsequent colours in the solar spectrum, the energy kept decreasing and so did the rate of photosynthesis, while the frequency increased. Hence, no conclusion could be drawn from this part of the spectrum.

Bose then turned his attention to the concentration of CO_2 and its effect on photosynthesis. Fortunately, as his sample plant was aquatic hydrilla, it was easy for him to vary the concentration of dissolved CO_2 in water. Bose standardized concentration of the gas in units of milligram (mg) per 100 cc of water. He began with a very low concentration of 3 milligrams and moved to a very high concentration of 30 milligrams. His measurements were carried out during the spring and charted as in Fig. 9.8.

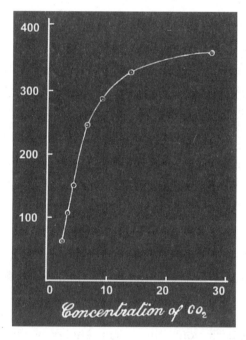

Fig. 9.8: Effect of concentration of CO_2 on photosynthesis during spring.

It seems that he counted the number of dots in a given time, say an hour or so, as a measure of the rate of photosynthesis, and plotted them on the vertical axis. The rate initially increased proportionately with the concentration, depicting a straight line between 3 and 8 milligrams.

Above 8 milligrams of concentration, the curve starts to level out, as shown in the figure. It means that the rate of photosynthesis still increases but progressively becomes slower. If the concentration exceeds 30 milligrams, the gas reveals a retarding effect (not captured in Fig. 9.8) and acts as a poison. On the flipside, in the winter the photosynthesis process started above 2.5 milligrams of concentration, whereas in spring it occured at a much lower value of 1 milligrams, hence solidifying Bose's theory that seasonal changes affected all plant growth.

Sixth Scientific Mission to Europe

Bose's next book, *Physiology of the Ascent of Sap*, was published in 1923. Two years before this, his special temporary appointment had ended, and he was no longer in the service of the government. Now that the Bose Institute was firmly established with better finances, Bose was able to use his own personal income to finance another trip to Europe. He reached Europe on his own towards the end of 1923. This time too, he carried newly invented instruments such as automatic potograph and photosynthetic recorder. The latter was a star attraction in his lectures, much like the crescograph during his previous trip.

Bose demonstrated the photosynthetic recorder in a lecture arranged by the London University. Dr Frederick G. Donnan, professor of physical chemistry, expressed his appreciation for this invention. Professor Blackman and his colleagues, who specialized in photosynthesis research, were impressed by the accuracy and simplicity of the instrument. Bose was invited to speak at the University of Leeds, Imperial College London, the Royal Society of Medicine, and many other centres of science.

In February 1924, the secretary of India at that time, Lord Olivier, invited Bose to deliver a lecture in a meeting at the India Office, that was attended and spoken at by Prime Minister Ramsay MacDonald. Lord Hardinge and litterateur Bernard Shaw were also in the audience.

Soon after World War I, the League of Nations had been established. The India Office wrote to Bose that an Indian representative would be appointed in the Intellectual Cooperation Committee of the League of Nations, and asked if he would consent to take that post. He readily agreed.

Bose was invited by the Sorbonne University in Paris, where his subject of speech was the ascent of sap in plants. At this time his books, *Comparative Electroophysiology* and a few others, were translated into French and German.

In March 1924, Bose was invited to a science congress arranged by the League of Nations in Brussels, but could not attend due to lack of time, as he had to return to India in April.

An Inspiring Figure

Bose now decided to compile all his recent research, scattered in various journals and transactions, into books. The book, *The Physiology of Photosynthesis*, was published by Longmans, Green, and Co. in 1924.

Bose delved into more detailed research of the biological process of plants and how it is related to its nervous system. In 1926, Longmans published his *The Nervous Mechanism in Plants*. In the following year, his *Collected Papers* was brought out by them. Bose dedicated *The Nervous Mechanism in Plants* to Rabindranath Tagore, and sent him a copy. The poet wrote to the scientist on 28 December 1926,

> I felt great joy when this book arrived as a messenger carrying words of friendship. I keep receiving the news of your wonderful deeds continually. The glory of those deeds has now crossed all barriers to spread to the furthest corner of the world. What delight and pride do I feel cannot be expressed in words!

Alongside book writing and research, Bose kept up his nation-building work. In December 1924, Bose was invited as the chief guest at the convocation ceremony of the University of the Punjab in Lahore. This was his second visit to the university. Earlier during his first trip in February 1913, he had delivered a series of lectures in the university hall. Then he had said, in the opening remarks of his first lecture,

> Jivaka, who later became the physician of the Buddha, came all the way from Bengal to the University of Taxila[92] in quest of knowledge.

---

[92]The ruins of the University of Taxila are not very far from Lahore. Taxila was an ancient settlement on the bank of River Indus in the Gandhara region in the Indian subcontinent. The first university in the world was located here and students from many

Twenty-five centuries have gone by and now before you stands another pilgrim who has journeyed the same distance to bring, as an offering, what he has gathered in the domain of knowledge.

The university hall was overflowing with enthusiastic listeners, mostly students. It is quite likely that among them there was a bright young student, named Shanti Swaroop Bhatnagar, who was then studying science in the intermediate class, at the Dayal Singh College of the same university.

Within a few years, Shanti Swaroop earned a scholarship for his doctoral studies under Professor Frederick Donnan in London. He acquired the degree in just two years, served a stint as a professor at the Benaras Hindu University and was back in Lahore as a professor of physical chemistry in the University of the Punjab. This was a few months before Bose's second visit to Lahore. It can be assumed that Dr Shanti Swaroop Bhatnagar, being a professor, was present in the audience during Bose's convocation address in 1924. Bose spoke at length about the revival of the ancient tradition of learning for enriching national life. Again, he referred to the ancient University of Taxila and said in his concluding remarks,

It was a woman[93] in the Vedic times, who when asked to take her choice of the wealth that would be hers for the asking, inquired whether that would win for her deathlessness. Many a nation has arisen in the past and won the empire of the world. A few buried fragments are all that remains as memorials.... Not in matter but in thought, not in possessions but in ideals, are to be found the seed of immortality. It is not through material acquisition but through active service and generous diffusion of ideas and ideals that the true empire of humanity will be established.

At that time, it was well known in university circles that Bose never patented his inventions, because he abhorred making personal gain out

parts of Asia came here for higher learning. It functioned from the tenth century BCE to the fifth century CE.

[93]A reference to Maitreyi, an erudite woman of the Vedic age, mentioned in Brihadaranyaka Upanishad.

of his scholarship. Bose's personality and speech might have left an impression on young Bhatnagar.

Bhatnagar had likeness to Bose in many ways—he was devoted to science and yet had an abiding love for literature, right from his high school days. As an undergraduate, he wrote a one-act drama and many poems in Urdu; his drama won a prize in a college competition. While serving as a professor in Benaras Hindu University, he wrote a song in Hindi, which was adopted as the kulgeet (song of the university) and is sung there on auspicious occasions even today.

Bhatnagar's main contribution to fundamental research was in the field of magnetochemistry and colloidal chemistry. Many titles and decorations were conferred upon him, including the coveted Fellowship of the Royal Society (FRS). His creative instinct was equally active even after he turned his attention to industrial and applied research. He solved a strange problem faced by Messrs Steel Brothers & Co., London, in drilling operations for petroleum, so successfully that the company put a huge fund of 1.5 million rupees at his disposal through the university. This was used to establish the department of petroleum research under his supervision.

Bhatnagar steadfastly spurned any offer of personal benefit arising out of his research activities and always looked to enhance the facilities at his university. Renowned physicist Dr Meghnad Saha, FRS, who once was a student of Bose in the Presidency College, was an admirer of Bhatnagar. In this context, Saha wrote to Bhatnagar in 1934, saying that Bhatnagar's selflessness has raised his esteem in the public eye.

Those were the days of an India under foreign rule, when scientists, poets, businessmen, lawyers, politicians, and people in many other walks of life made sacrifices, some big, some small, for uplifting the nation. It is exactly for this reason that Bose rarely missed any opportunity to address the younger generation. He considered it his sacred duty to kindle a national spirit and an interest in science and research in the students of various colleges and universities.

When an invitation came from Patna University in 1925, Bose took time off his busy schedule and travelled there to address their convocation ceremony. His speech on such occasions usually included a short account of his research and the hurdles that he had to cross, followed by a call to revive the traditions of Taxila and Nalanda.[94]

At this time Bose was offered the position of the vice chancellor of the Calcutta University. He politely turned it down with thanks. He knew that vice chancellorship meant money and prestige but would be a distraction from his avowed goal of pursuing research and putting India on the scientific map of the world.

Seventh Trip to Europe

In all the years after its inception, the scope of research at the Bose Institute had been expanding, and a greater number of personnel were recruited. More funding was now necessary for expanding space and facilities. Bose appealed to the government for more grant-in-aid and to the public for donations. The government did not increase the grant amount but extended it for five more years until 1931.

However, there were generous contributions from Rao Sahib Kumar K. P. Singh, Messrs Birla brothers of Calcutta, and Shri Onkar Jalan of Patna. Maharaja Pratap Singh of Kashmir, who had visited the Bose Institute recently, promised a huge sum. Unfortunately, he passed away before fulfilling his promise.

In April 1926, Bose was invited to participate in the deliberations of the Intellectual Cooperation Committee, and the cost of his travel to Europe and incidental expenses related to the event were borne by the League of Nations. Therefore, it was not primarily a scientific mission or trip. However, Bose stayed on in London at his own expense and visited and lectured at a few universities and scientific societies. He had a meeting with the British Prime Minister Stanley Baldwin and urged him to pay greater attention to the revival of scholastic tradition in India.

A reception was arranged by the British Indian Union in Bose's honour. A demand that began here culminated in a memorandum to the viceroy of India, urging that generous aid be provided to the

---

[94]The ruins of the ancient Nalanda university and Buddhist monastic centre is located in Bihar. Nalanda's traditional history dates to the time of the Buddha (sixth to fifth centuries BCE). The university and monastery were destroyed by the first wave of Muslim Pathan invaders in the thirteenth century CE.

Bose Institute. The signatories included a large number of eminent scientists and editors of magazines and newspapers, such as Sir Charles Sherrington (president of the Royal Society), Lord Rayleigh, Sir Oliver Lodge, Julian Huxley (professor of zoology in King's College), Sir R. A. Gregory (editor of *Nature* magazine), Lord Burnham (editor of *Daily Telegraph*), and J. A. Spender (editor of *West Minster Gazette*).

King Leopold of Belgium and his queen had visited the Bose Institute while touring India in the previous year. He now took this opportunity to invite the Boses to Brussels to speak at the Foundation Universitaire. This was followed by a royal reception held at his palace in Bose's honour, where the scientist was made a member of the Order of Leopold.

After the meeting of the Intellectual Cooperation Committee at Geneva, Bose was invited to lecture at the university there. Among the scientists who attended his lecture were Albert Einstein and Hendrik A. Lorentz, the former famous for his theory of relativity and the latter for a mathematical transformation called lorentz transformation. Both of them paid generous tribute to Bose for his contribution to physics as well as physiology and botany.

The Boses returned to India in October 1926. The main purpose of enhancing the profile of his institute and attracting greater funding was well served by this tour.

Joe Gives a Break to Boshi

For the first few years after leaving the Bose Institute, Boshi continued the research that he had been doing with his mentor, and kept up a steady rate of publications. He was studying whole tissues of the mimosa and the telegraph plant; and determining the changes of permeability induced in the protoplasmic membrane by electrical and mechanical stimulation. Years later, he turned his attention to the individual cells of these plants and many others.

The beginning of April 1926 saw Boshi spending much of his time at Belur Math. His American acquaintance Josephine MacLeod had arrived as well and was staying in the Math's guest house. Around this time, an American artist couple, friends of Joe, Earl and Achsah Brewster, arrived. They braved the heat of the fast-receding Indian spring, as did the ailing Christine who was being looked after by Boshi. But the heat of the summer proved too much. Joe proposed that all of them should go to the Himalayas with Boshi.

Boshi knew only two towns in the mountains—Darjeeling and Almora. He preferred the latter because of its proximity to the Mayavati ashram. Joe rented a bungalow in Almora chosen by Boshi, named Kundan House, which had a large garden within its compound. Joe, the Brewsters, Christine, and Boshi, all went there to spend the summer.

Kundan House, Almora

Next, Boshi shifted his laboratory to the Kundan House. It now occupied the drawing room of the house, an improvement in comparison to the kitchen. There were enough rooms to accommodate all five of them comfortably. Besides, there was enough land at Boshi's disposal for growing plants, creepers, and trees, and the botanist in him was very pleased. The party and the laboratory returned to Kolkata in two months when the rains arrived.

The following year too, Joe, Boshi, and Christine spent the summer in the Kundan House; the laboratory had to be shifted back and forth. The rental of the Kundan House and the cost of the journeys were on Joe's account. This was a real break for Boshi because of the availability of the large garden there and greater space for his laboratory. For several years thereafter, Boshi and Christine kept going back and forth between Almora and Calcutta.

Gertrude Visits Bose and Meets Boshi

Gertrude travelled to Calcutta from village Pachperwa in March 1927 to withdraw some money, transferred into a bank in the city from America. She also wished to contact potential contributors to the *Asia* magazine. She remembered that Bose had invited her years ago to visit his laboratory, while they were in Darjeeling. When she contacted Bose, the latter offered to show her his laboratory and also invited her to have lunch with him and his wife.

Bose's drawing room had a Mahabharata frieze all around, painted by Nandalal Basu, and Gertrude had the feeling that she was being talked to by a religious savant, not a famous scientist. Shortly, Abala joined them and they had a sumptuous vegetarian meal. Then she was taken on a guided tour of the laboratory. She wrote in the *Asia* magazine,

> [Bose] took me all about his wonderful laboratory and for three hours showed me all his instruments and how they worked. Of course, I knew about how he measures the pulse of plants, but to see the glass pen write the life-story with little dots on a smoked plate gave me a thrill such as I have not often experienced.... Recently, he has applied some of his plant experiments to animal life; that is, he has fastened his hair-like threads attached to the glass pens to the heart of a frog and of a fish. I saw his most recent experiments in progress, and he says that as a matter of fact, I am the first person to see them.... The real experiment consists in finding reviving drugs made from plants.... He thought he would try them on animal organisms. The graph of a fish's heart went up and down, up and down, like a typhoid fever chart, and then less up and less down, and less and less, until the pencil was making simply a straight line on the plate. The fish was all but dead. He injected one of his preparations into it, and after five minutes the pen gave a mighty jump and began tapping the old jagged seesaw lines again. The same thing happened with the Froggie. Since death is, in bald

fact, stopping of the heart, you can see the possibilities opening up with his new knowledge of stimulants at critical moments.

...[T]he whole atmosphere of the institute is one of the religious feeling. At the same time a spirit of great beauty pervades the place. ...He soon hopes to have provision for foreign students, and he even invited me to stay and become a worker at the institute.

Gertrude felt a momentary temptation to accept Bose's invitation, but decided otherwise. While chatting with her, Bose made a sorrowful remark that there was no loyalty; that you trained people and afterwards they left you, but mentioned no specific names. This puzzled her slightly.

During her remaining days in Calcutta, she was busy finding interesting topics and potential contributors for the *Asia* magazine. She contacted her acquaintances and the American Consul General, Alexander Wedell, was one of them. He suggested she visit the Belur Math; Gertrude immediately expressed her eagerness for such a visit. Wedell promised to take her there and added that he knew a young Indian, named Boshi Sen, who would be an excellent escort for their visit. Gertrude had heard that name, and said 'Boshi Sen! I met Mr Sen in New York in 1923.' Wedell phoned Boshi and he readily agreed to escort the two on the next Sunday. Boshi had, for long, wished to meet the author of some extraordinary articles, which told the true story of village life in India, that had been published in *Asia*.

On reaching her hotel, Gertrude received a phone call from Boshi. 'I would be happy to take you and Mr Wedell to Belur on Sunday. But for tomorrow, I would like to invite you for lunch at my residence at 8, Bosepara Lane.' Gertrude accepted the invitation and Boshi continued, 'But you will never be able to find the place in this rabbit-warren of lanes in North Calcutta; so, I will call for you at 12 o'clock tomorrow.'

The next day she went to the publishing firm of Thacker, Spink, and Company for consultation about potential authors for *Asia*. In her commitment to duty, she completely lost touch with time and forgot about her appointment with Boshi. When she returned to the hotel two hours late, she found Boshi still waiting for her. Even before she could utter a word of apology, Boshi exclaimed, 'Oh! I am so relieved, I thought something must surely have happened to you.' There was no trace of annoyance in his voice, nor did he care for an apology; his behaviour left a mark on Gertrude's mind.

On the way to his house, Boshi told her that an American disciple of Swami Vivekananda, Sister Christine, lived with him and, 'She has given her life for India and the least India can do for her is to take care of her now.' Gertrude, who had read quite a lot about Swami Vivekananda, understood his passionate statement.

They went to his house and Christine welcomed her cordially. Gertrude saw his kitchen laboratory and the shrine in the room where Boshi's guru, Sadananda-swami, had lived. She knew nothing about Sadananda and was now curious, but held back for the time being. Gertrude learnt that Boshi had been Bose's student and assistant for twelve long years but had now left him. She connected the dots and interpreted Bose's earlier sad remark to have been about Boshi.

After their meal, when it came time to part, both Christine and Boshi invited her to come to the Kundan House in Almora in a few months' time, when the fierce summer would set in and scorch everything in the plains.

They went to the Belur Math on Sunday as planned. She saw all the temples, including the one of Swami Vivekananda. She recalled that in 1900, when she had been ten years old and was in Paris with her parents, the venerable Swami had lectured there, though, unfortunately, she remembered very little of the precious experience. After this, Gertrude went back to Pachperwa village and settled back into her rural life.

In the village, she began spending more and more time attending to the medical concerns of the residents with what limited knowledge she had. She had taken a year's leave from *Asia* to write a book on India, which she would title *Voiceless India*. However, she was unable to find the time to sit down and put pen to paper. She braved the summer heat and stayed in the village and tried to mix authorship with medicine, but in vain. In the meanwhile, letters at regular intervals arrived from Boshi, urging her to come over to Almora. A letter came also from Christine. Finally, by the end of August she decided to go to the mountains, although by that time the heat had receded a bit due to the onset of monsoon.

Boshi and Christine made every effort to make her comfortable.

Gertrude now started to write her book, while Boshi remained glued to his microscope for most of the day. Christine was quite sick, could not do or walk much and remained mostly in her room.

In the beginning, Gertrude and Boshi would go out for a walk at sundown. Christine, who was of the opinion that Boshi was cut out to be a monk, resented this, thinking that Boshi was perhaps getting distracted from his path in life. Sensing this, Boshi and Gertrude arranged for a palanquin for her, and all three began going out together. At nightfall, all of them would get together in the guest room and read from Swami Vivekananda's works. On one such evening, Gertrude suddenly cried out, 'Why, there is Swamiji!' She had a vision of the Swami, standing with his back towards them.

Presently, they went to the dining room for their evening meal. When they returned to the guest room, she perceived that the Swami was still there. After this incident, Christine realized that Gertrude too was spiritually inclined and not an ordinary soul. Her acceptance of Gertrude increased from there on.

Gertrude went back to the village in October and then returned to America in April next year, in 1928. Christine, too, returned to America in 1928 due to ill health, and admitted herself into a nursing home in New York, which was run by a friend. She was too sick to travel alone and Boshi accompanied her; besides, he needed to work in a laboratory in London for about six months to complete a research project. Leonard Elmhirst financed their trips. After London, Boshi could go to New York and work in a laboratory there for two years, thanks to his old friend Glen Overton. Boshi visited both Gertrude and Christine every evening while in New York. Christine died two years later, in 1930.

Boshi shared with Gertrude the stories of his troubled times; the agony of running away from his mother as a child; the harsh chidings, sprinkled with tenderness, that he received from his guru Sadananda-swami; the anguish of parting with his mentor, J. C. Bose. He told her about his mixed feelings of exhilaration and forebodings of an uncertain future, when he started his kitchen laboratory; also, about the pact he had made with Swami Vivekananda about how he would conduct himself while doing research.

Boshi returned to Calcutta in late 1930. Gertrude's book *Voiceless*

India, for which Tagore wrote the foreword, was published in the same year and created a sensation. Boshi and Gertrude got married in 1932 in a civil ceremony at the American consulate in Calcutta. The wedding was later solemnized as per Hindu rituals. They shifted between Bosepara Lane and the Kundan House, once a year, for the next three years. Calcutta's main attraction for both was its proximity to the Belur monastery. But finally, in 1935, the pull of Almora proved stronger for the botanist owing to its garden space, and the Vivekananda Laboratory was permanently relocated there.

Reconciliation

Once Tagore stayed with Boshi and Gertrude in Almora for a week. Tagore's friend J. C. Bose must have been aware of Tagore's visit to Boshi. Bose had been observing with great pride the rising reputation of his former student. In fact, their common friend, Leonard Elmhirst started thinking of Boshi as the true heir-apparent of Bose. While trying to raise funds for Boshi, Elmhirst wrote to a potential sponsor, Asia Foundation,

> Hearing about Mr Sen's work from some of our most competent science men here, backed by your own comments and opinions gathered by you from Dr Harris and Dr Chambers, both Mrs Elmhirst and I would like his application to go forward to the committee with a strong recommendation from us. The reasons are these: If anything happened to Sir J. C. Bose, there is no Indian scientist that I know of who has anything like the international connection that Mr Sen has. Grants by the committee have enabled Mr Sen to preserve his own integrity and independence, where otherwise, the valuable combination of his personality and his training might have been lost in commercial or purely academic work.

Bose was then in his seventies and Elmhirst, the agriculture specialist, was worried about the void that would be left in Indian science 'if anything happened to Sir J. C. Bose'. Julian Huxley, E. D. Adrian, and Robert Chambers, all renowned biologists of the time, thought highly of Boshi's work and tried to arrange funding for the Vivekananda Laboratory.

Boshi's biographer, Mehra has written that 'Happily, friendly relations were re-established with Bose himself, and maintained as long as Bose lived', but has not provided any concrete dates for this reconciliation. Letters written by Boshi, except one, are not available; most probably, the biographer had access only to the papers in the possession of Boshi and Gertrude. These letters will be quoted here exactly as they are available in the biography without any abridgement and in the same order.

Bose wrote in one letter, 'Having not heard from you for a long time, I was worried.'

The sentence bears the mark of generosity, so characteristic of Bose. In another letter, Bose wrote,

> I dreamt yesterday that Vines had organized a great reception for us at Oxford, where there was an enthusiastic crowd to welcome us, the essential mechanisms of life processes being now better understood. Vines was in great form, and was asking Boshi what additional things would he want for a demonstration.

Expressing great satisfaction about the progress of the Vivekananda Laboratory, Bose wrote, 'This has been due to the whole-hearted devotion with which you followed advance research.'

The Vivekananda Laboratory started attracting international attention from 1930 onwards. Hence, it seems that the Boshi–Bose correspondence started around then. In another letter, Bose wrote, 'Great things follow from small beginnings, provided there is a steadfast purpose behind.'

A more encouraging and complimentary note can be heard in a subsequent letter, 'Is there anything that could give me greater happiness than the fact that my trust in some of my disciples has been fully justified and that the light that has been enkindled will continue to burn with undiminished brilliance.'

Boshi's humble and respectful reply to this letter is available. Its source is not mentioned by Girish N. Mehra, and therefore, we may assume that Boshi had kept a copy:

Beloved Master, my little contribution to physiology is from the sparks which emanate from you. Those sparks are enough to keep me busy for the rest of my life.... So long as life endures, wherever I might be or whatever fate may bring, you will have at least one disciple. I ask for your blessings.

Our joy at this reconciliation is slightly eclipsed by the fact that there is no evidence that they ever met after parting ways.

Eighth Trip to Europe

In 1927, Bose's book *Plant Autographs and their Revelations* was published in London. The meeting of the Intellectual Cooperation Committee that year was scheduled for July. Bose set sail for Europe mainly to attend this meeting. However, he reached in April in order to renew contact with old friends.

The Boses had an invitation from the French philosopher-author Romain Rolland, a Nobel laureate. Rolland was well read in Vedanta philosophy and was an admirer of Swami Vivekananda, having written a book on him. The Boses reached Marseilles in May. Bose lectured at two universities in southern France and then they proceeded to Paris to spend some time with Rolland. The latter was aware of Bose's love for literature and Indian history, and Bose knew about Rolland's interest in Indian history and philosophy. Their friendship grew from there on. Later, Rolland presented Bose with his latest novel *Jean-Christophe*.

Bose's next stop was England, where he learnt that Aldous Huxley had reviewed his latest book *Plant Autographs* in glowing terms, in the *Spectator*. Aldous Huxley, when he was a student at Oxford, had visited the Bose Institute in Calcutta and recorded his experience in a book named *Jesting Pilate*. In appreciation of Bose's love for literature, Bernard Shaw presented him a set of his own books with a complimentary note, 'From the least to the greatest living biologist, from G. Bernard Shaw to Sir J. C. Bose'.

Bose attended the meeting of the Intellectual Cooperation Committee in July at Geneva. After this, he suffered a severe physical breakdown and had to rest for a while in Territet near Lake Geneva, before he was fit enough to return to India.

At this time, he started using Ayurvedic pharmacology in his biological research. Indian traditional doctors for centuries had been using a preparation, called suchikabharana, made from snake poison, for stimulating the human heart. Bose tried it on plants and found it was effective in stimulating the pulsating layer inside the cortex. In fact, he could even use this to revive a pulsation that was very faint and about to die due to its prior exposure to a depressing agent. This was another proof that plant physiology had much in common with animal physiology.

Bose thought that there were undiscovered gems like this in Indian traditional medicine, and instituted an award for the best research paper on Indian herbal medicine at the University of Madras. His friend Brojendra Nath Seal, then vice chancellor of the Mysore University, became a member of the committee that adjudged the competition.

Bose had been consolidating his research findings in the form of books for quite some time, and in early 1928, his next book *Motor Mechanism of Plant* was published. A famous science reviewer Robert Lind wrote a detailed review of this book in the *London Daily News*. It contained the following significant lines:

> Twenty years ago, the scientists of the world were not fully sanguine about the value of research of J. C. Bose. But now they are convinced that none of his discoveries are based purely on imagination. His delicate instruments have given us sensible evidence that leaves no scope for any doubt whatsoever.

Ninth Trip to Europe

Bose was always looking for greater sources of funding for the Bose Institute. Hence, he was keen to visit Europe—he had perceived a connection between these visits and international attention, which led to better funding for his institute. The annual meetings of the Intellectual Cooperation Committee presented him with an opportunity for such visits. They were attractive because the basic travel costs were borne by the League of Nations. For his additional trips, he would pay from his own resources. He went to Europe again in May 1928, his main purpose being to attend the annual meeting of the aforementioned committee for the third time. This time, too, he reached a few months ahead of the meeting.

Bose was invited to deliver a lecture at the University of Vienna, where his friendship with the rector Hans Molisch deepened further, culminating in an invitation for the latter to visit the Bose Institute and pursue joint research. Molisch later honoured the invitation. They both believed that their friendship was a symbol of the union of the West and the East. To give it an external expression, the two elderly scientists together planted the saplings of a pair of coconut plants joined at the roots, in the garden of the Bose Institute. Molisch published a comprehensive account of his stay and his research activities at the institute in *Nature* magazine, dated 3 April 1930.

From Vienna, Bose travelled to Munich where a reception for him had been arranged by the faculty of science of the Munich University. Dr Goebble, professor of Botany and director of the botanical garden, presided over the reception and said,

> The contribution of India in religion, philosophy, poetry and art is well known. Now, courtesy Prof. Bose, India is contributing to life science, as well.... When I went to Asia in 1924, I had every wish to visit the Bose Institute, but there were restrictions on people of German origin entering India.

The session of the Intellectual Cooperation Committee was held in Geneva in July. Thereafter, Bose spoke at the Geneva School of International Studies. The topic of his lecture was 'The Plant as a Sentient Being'. The minister of agriculture of Egypt, Nakhla Pasha, was in Geneva at that time and invited Bose to visit his country on his way back to India.

King Fuad I received the Boses in the Montaza palace in Alexandria. Bose addressed the Royal Geographical Society of Egypt in Cairo, and spoke about the contact, in the Ashokan era, between the two ancient civilizations of the Nile and the Ganges. His extensive knowledge about this chapter of history surprised the listeners. The Boses returned to India in September 1928.

The Bose Institute was branching out into newer fields and an overall expansion of the establishment was imperative, thought Bose. In May 1928, while in England, Bose had appealed to the Indian high commissioner for a pension of 7,500 rupees per annum. He had written, 'At the time of retirement from the Presidency College, I was too busy pursuing research to pay attention to my pension. The Institute needs to be expanded immediately; the pension would go a long way for mitigating the attendant expenses.'

The government took a long time to consider his request but his pension was not granted. On 30 November 1928, Bose's seventieth birth anniversary was celebrated with great fanfare at the institute. Tagore could not attend due to ill health, although he was the main initiator of the celebration. His poem titled 'Jagadish Chandra', written especially for this occasion, was read out by Dr Kalidas Nag.

In response to the felicitation, Bose said in Bengali,

I have struggled for the last 40 years to expand the horizon of knowledge, with the sole purpose of establishing India in the scientific comity of the world....

I was never alone in this struggle. We [Tagore and I] were both young and unknown. In the days when I was troubled by endless hurdles and self-doubt, my all-time friend Rabindranath inspired and encouraged me by his poetry and helped in other ways.

At this time, French philosopher Romain Rolland wrote in a letter to Bose that though people more competent than himself could better appreciate Bose's genius, he still wished to felicitate the truth-seeking hermit who had discovered life in trees and stones.

Sir Richard Gregory, the editor of *Nature*, sent a message: '[Bose] has found that the physiological mechanism of plant is essentially the same as that of the animal, and he has been able to lift the veil which had previously enshrouded the analogous workings of plant and animal life.'

Since his return from Europe, Bose had busied himself in writing his next book *Growth and Tropic Movement of Plants*, which was brought out a few months later, in 1929. The book was widely acclaimed and prompted the government to promise to release greater funding for the institute.

Tenth Trip to Europe

The Intellectual Cooperation Committee was to again meet in Geneva in July 1929, and, as usual, Bose was an invited delegate. As was customary for him, he reached London a little ahead of July. William Wedgwood Benn, the secretary of state for India, had invited him to lecture at the India House on 9 July. He demonstrated various experiments on the faintest of plant responses. He then attended the meeting in Geneva as scheduled, whence his term as a member came to an end. Thus, the tenth trip was more or less a routine affair.

His books had become quite popular in Europe and he wrote about this to his deputy Nag, on 31 July, 'The Longmans [publisher] have informed me about the great demand for my books, in particular of *Motor Mechanisms*. Gauthier Villars are publishing the French translation of *Plant Autographs*. ...Another edition of the same book in German would be published in the next month.'

Bose had an invitation to visit South Africa on his way to India. However, he fell ill due to exhaustion, and rested for a few weeks before sailing back home in September.

The Elderly Scientist Who Also Administered

The tenth trip was Bose's last visit to Europe. Two months later, around the time of his seventy-first birthday, Bose was conferred with the honorary membership of the Finnish Society of Sciences and Letters. Frederik Elfving, emeritus professor, University of Helsinki, wrote in the covering letter, dated 23 November 1929,

> Sir Jagadis Chandra Bose
> Emeritus Professor, Calcutta
>
> Dear Sir,
> I have the great pleasure of sending you the diploma as Honorary Member of our Society.... I was the first to prove that in transpiration the water is moving in the interior of the vessels, not in the wall. I considered that the propulsion of sap could be mechanically explained, but your experiments have completely converted me.

Your views of the fundamental unity of life reactions in plants and animals, and also of the agreement between the Living and Non-Living will certainly have an immense influence on the evolution of Biology. I am glad to have lived to see the commencement of this new era and hope that you would give us more sublime thoughts and marvelous apparatus.

Yours Sincerely
Frederick Elfving.

Finland then was a sparsely populated country, dependent mostly on agriculture and animal farming, wedged between two powerful neighbours, the Soviet Union and Sweden. Bose never visited Finland and had no personal acquaintance with the botanists of that country. Yet such a true appraisal of his life's work was captured in a few sentences by a Finnish scientist. Bose acknowledged the honour with immense gratitude.

Bose now focused his attention on inculcating an interdisciplinary spirit among his junior researchers. He believed that one branch of science fuses with another seamlessly and there was no hard and fast boundary. His mantra was 'unity in diversity', the mantra that was handed down by the ancient Indian sages, from generation to generation. In his attitude and outlook, he was so far ahead of his time that he was often resented by senior physiologists of Europe.

In the next few years, Bose received many felicitations, awards, and invitations to meetings and convocations. He travelled to different parts of the country as long as his waning health permitted. At other times, he helped his juniors in solving the research puzzles they often faced.

On 14 April 1931, the Calcutta municipal corporation felicitated Bose as an eminent citizen of the town. There was a huge meeting in the townhall on this occasion. The mayor, Subhash Chandra Bose[95], delivered the felicitation address; the main theme of it was gratitude for putting Calcutta on the scientific map of the world and presenting her with a great institution.

In reply Bose said,

---

[95]Later, Subhash Chandra Bose became one of the tallest political leaders of India.

This city has been the place of my work and struggles for more than 40 years. At the beginning, many years had to be patiently devoted for the removal of the paralysing influence of the prevailing prejudice that the Indian mind by its very constitution was incapable of advancing exact knowledge. That prejudice has now been removed, and India, by her intellectual achievements in many fields, has succeeded in winning an honoured place in the federation of nations. The valuable work conducted by Sir Chandrasekhara[96] in the field of physical science has everywhere been received with high appreciation.

On 28 March 1931, Bose was awarded the Shri Sayajirao Gaekwad Prize and Annuity. The prize had been instituted six years before for achievement in literature, science, and art. Bose travelled to Baroda to receive the prize and speak at the attendant ceremony, which was presided over by the Maharaja Sayajirao Gaekwad III himself.

From 1931 onward, quite a few scientists and science-writers in the West visited the Bose institute. Magnus Hirschfeld[97], a German physician and sexologist, was then visiting Calcutta as an acquaintance of Girindra Sekhar Basu, the founder and president of the Indian Psychoanalytic Society. The latter had authored a seminal book, *The Psychological Outlook of Hindu Philosophy*, in 1930, and Hirschfeld was keen to learn about the attitude of Hindus towards sex. He had heard about J. C. Bose and the psychological aspect of his research, and he decided to visit the Bose Institute and see its laboratories to find out more. About the same time, an eminent educationist from America and the director of arts and sciences, Brooklyn Institute, George Ward, visited the Bose Institute. In early 1933, Sir Richard Gregory, the editor of *Nature* magazine, paid a prolonged visit to look at all of Bose's inventions and the laboratory.

This was also the period when the Great Depression had its hold on the economy. The government had to curtail its expenditure on all fronts and so, instead of fulfilling its promise for increased support, it

---

[96]'Sir Chandrasekhara' was a reference to Sir C. V. Raman who had been working in Calcutta for more than two decades and had won the Nobel Prize in the previous year.
[97]Dr Magnus Hirschfield, a vocal sexual rights activist, was of Jewish descent and left Germany when he felt insecure in the country. He arrived in America in November 1930.

further reduced the existing allocation. The Bose, Institute suffered a massive loss of 47 per cent of its annual grant. Bose summoned all his administrative skills to direct the institute in meeting this crisis and, at the same time, keep up with the research projects at hand.

An Enigmatic Silence

The institute, being very beautiful and architecturally sound, attracted lay visitors in good numbers. Visitors who saw Nandalal's painting of Sister Nivedita, wondered why there was no inscription or indication as to her identity. Was she only a decorative symbol or much more?

Both the Boses cherished the memory of Sister Nivedita, but strangely, throughout Jagadish's life, he maintained a deafening silence in his public utterances and writings about Nivedita. Abala wrote a condolence message in *Modern Review*, after Nivedita's death, 'How manifold were the blessings she conferred on all who came in contact with her, and in how many directions she has effectively served our motherland, it is too early yet to speak.' It is difficult to understand why she felt it was 'too early yet to speak'. An early record may be incomplete, but it is better than no record.

The manuscript of one of Bose's books, *Plant Response,* is in Nivedita's handwriting. We have seen earlier that her science background, backed by her sharp intellect, made her a formidable science reviewer. She spent time with Bose to understand his research, gathered his main points and wrote them down as a scientist would. We can only wonder how much time she saved for Bose in writing this book. Siladitya Jana, an expert in style analysis, has studied the writings of Bose and says[98],

> Three important style markers—function words, punctuation marks, and usage words are used to trace the changes in Bose's writing style, if any. The results show that during the association between Bose and Nivedita, Bose's style of writing changed considerably in comparison to the earlier period when they did not know each

---

[98]The primary source for this is a paper published by Siladitya Jana in the June 2014 edition of the *Journal for the Association for Information Science and Technology.*

other. It shows that Nivedita helped Bose preparing his journal
articles and books. ...Bose slowly moved back to his original style
of writing after Nivedita's death, but his later works still carried
Nivedita's influence.

Nivedita, as long as she lived, was intimately connected with the life of
the Boses, in sorrow and joy, in illness and health. She encouraged Bose
when he felt depressed, and wrote him inspiring letters when she was
away. She wrote in magazines to attract people's attention to his work.
She tried to protect Bose by her beneficent presence in every possible
way and asked Sara to do the same.

Bose was indebted to Nivedita in another way. She was the one
who first realized the significance of the symbol of the vajra for India's
nascent nationalist movement when she spotted an engraving of it in
Bodh Gaya. The symbol can now be found on the doors, cornices, etc.
of the Bose Institute. The crossed vajra was adopted by Bose as the logo
of the Institute and is displayed at the entrance as well as at the top of
the building. However, Nivedita remained anonymous throughout the
ceremonial inauguration of the Institute.

Only acknowledgement to Nivedita came from Rabindranath
Tagore, when he was addressing a group of students in Shantiniketan:
'In the days of his struggles, Jagadish gained an invaluable energizer
and helper in Sister Nivedita, and in any record of his life's work, her
name must be given a place of honour.' Even this acknowledgement
came only after Bose's death.

Unknown to Rabindranath, there was another person who had to be
given a place of honour in any work on Bose's life—Mrs Sara Chapman
Bull. Her silent benefaction supported the publication of all of Bose's
early books, apart from helping him in numerous other ways. At that
juncture, Bose was being prevented from publishing his research findings
in the journals. Books were the only option left to him, but he had no
money to publish them. If Sara had not stepped in to rescue him, his
research career might have been nipped in the bud.

Sara arranged and paid for Bose's lifesaving operation in London
in December 1900, and also took part in nursing him back to health
after the operation. The Boses were often invited to stay with her in

beautiful locations, such as Brittany and Bergen, which was a source of much succour. The costs of these trips were always borne by her.

When she got a chance, she worked on his manuscripts as well. She took Bose to America to file applications for two patents jointly with herself. These patents were instrumental in giving priority to Bose in the invention of the solid-state diode detector. Sara donated huge sums of money to Bose to fulfil his dream of opening his own institute, and even left a fair legacy for it in death.

She encouraged Nivedita to help Bose in his scientific endeavours, and considered Jagadish as her own son. But Bose maintained an enigmatic silence about both Nivedita and Sara.

We have traced in previous chapters how Bose had been following a policy of not leaving a written record of his relationship with Sara and Nivedita. In his letters to Tagore, once or twice he takes the name of Nivedita, but never in his personal context. In contrast, both Sara and Nivedita named Bose freely and often referred to Bose's work as 'our work' in their letters.

In March 1906, Bose sent the manuscript of his book *Plant Response* to Sara. He dedicated the book to 'The Mother', without mentioning Sara's name, and told Sara it was dedicated to her in the accompanying letter. The fact remains that Sara's name did not appear in print—how would any reader of the book know who 'The Mother' was?

Bose's speech at the inauguration of the Bose Institute included, 'In all my struggling efforts, I have not been altogether solitary. While the world doubted, there have been a few, now in the city of silence, who never wavered in their trust.' A few in the audience understood it as a tribute to Nivedita, since she lived in Calcutta and it was public knowledge that the Boses and Nivedita were friends. But they knew nothing about Sara, who mostly stayed behind the scenes, and must have been perplexed about why Bose had referred to the deceased in the plural.

Bose's letter of 27 October 1916 to Nivedita's sister, Mrs May Wilson, is full of adoration for Nivedita. In it, Bose conveys that the bas-relief beside the lotus pool at the institute's entrance, is that of Nivedita. But even in such a private communication, he is careful not to take Nivedita's name. When he buried a boxful of Nivedita's ashes, under the bas-relief, strict secrecy was observed. This information came to light almost after a century, in 2007, through Boshi Sen's statement. The letter to Mrs Wilson was found more recently, and it further corroborated Boshi's statement. Thus, we come to know about Bose's secret adoration of Nivedita and her ashes, as late as in the twenty-first century. Bose appears to be torn between loyal adoration on one hand, and a policy of non-acknowledgement on the other.

But why did Bose choose to follow such a policy? We ask again and again, and get no answer. It is truly an enigma.

In his letter to Nivedita's sister Mrs Wilson, he attributes his behaviour to his natural shyness and reticence and lack of ability to make friends. We do not perceive this reticence when in his very first meeting with Gertrude Emerson (in Darjeeling), Bose invited her to visit his institute in Calcutta. We know from the autobiography of Paramahansa Yogananda that when he first visited Bose at his residence, he was a complete stranger. Yet Bose received him cordially, spent some time in conversation, and invited him to visit his laboratory a few days later. The impression we get is that Bose was not overly accessible to people, but he was not naturally reticent either. In this respect, he was like most academics of his age.

Bose acknowledged receiving help from his old teachers in Cambridge, Lord Rayleigh and Professor Vines, in no uncertain terms. In the case of his all-weather friend Rabindranath Tagore, he never shied away from making his gratitude and adoration known in public. This reinforces our impression that Bose had been following a policy of silence with regard to Nivedita and Sara, for some other reason.

We observe that Bose, a strict Brahmo with an aversion to idolatry, had an ambivalent attitude towards the people of the Vivekananda circle and the institutions founded by them. He never visited the Belur Math, but stayed at the Mayavati monastery, more than once. His friend Tagore, too, was a Brahmo and never set foot in Belur Math. The difference between Belur and Mayavati, both set up by the Swami, was that in the former idol worship was a daily practice, whereas in the latter idolatry was strictly prohibited. Bose was extremely loyal to his father, who was strict in his Brahmo faith. This strictness was inherited by Bose.

Bose admired Mrs Sara Bull, adored Sister Nivedita, and was

extremely friendly towards Josephine MacLeod. However, there was something else at the back of his mind that prevented him from acknowledging their contribution to his life and its scientific mission.

It is possible to speculate that it was the practice of idol worship by the people of the Vivekananda circle that stayed his hand; that Bose was harrowed by two opposing pulls—his Brahmo faith and his adoration for Nivedita and Sara. The former prevailed.

This speculative interpretation of Bose's behaviour may also explain another aspect of his life—his estrangement from Boshi Sen. According to Boshi, Bose's attitude towards him took a sharp turn in the middle of 1922; he had no clue as to what caused it. It is true that we do not have Bose's version of the chain of events. However, there are many elements in Boshi's narrative that are verifiable, such as his low salary. Boshi's low salary might have been justified on the grounds that Boshi had no higher qualification other than a bachelor's degree. However, Boshi's allegation that Bose appointed a relative to an administrative post carrying a much higher salary cannot be overlooked.

What Boshi had in common with Sara and Nivedita was that he practiced idol worship. It is possible to speculate that, at some point, the presence of such a person in his laboratory became unacceptable to Bose.

Sara and Nivedita were saints. They were least concerned with fame and acknowledgement, either from Bose or anyone else among their many beneficiaries. But Boshi, though spiritually inclined, did care for his share of the credit in published research and was concerned about the salary he deserved. So, he parted ways with Bose.

Bose was, however, essentially a kind and fair-minded person, generous to the core. His treatment of Boshi and non-acknowledgement of Nivedita—Sara were most uncharacteristic of him and must have been tormenting his conscience. Perhaps, that is why he eventually reconciled with Boshi and why he had Nivedita's ashes buried under the bas-relief of hers.

Bose had no way of making up for his non-acknowledgement of Sara, except that remark about a few who had kept faith in him and were now 'in the city of silence'. His position was truly an unenviable one, being torn between opposing principles—loyalty to true friends and the call of his Brahmo faith.

The Flickering Flame

Since 1930, Bose had been falling ill more frequently and spending recesses at relatively cold Darjeeling was no longer advisable. He started to stay in Giridih during the winters for rest and recuperation. In 1931, when Calcutta was celebrating his friend Rabindranath Tagore's seventieth birthday, Bose was too weak to attend and was convalescing in Giridih. A souvenir titled, *Golden Book of Tagore*, was published, in which Bose contributed a long essay in Bengali, titled 'Jayanti Utsarga' ('Anniversary Offering'). It was all about his long association with the lyricist, his literary soulmate. A translation of an evocative line from it is as follows: 'Once, when I was trying to engage with the diverse cross-currents of life, and advancing ever so slowly, in that tireless struggle year after year, [Rabindranath] kept me company offering unflinching solidarity.'

Bose's life was now restricted under the strictest supervision of his dear wife, Abala, according to the instructions of his dear friend and eminent physician, Dr Nilratan Sircar.

In the winter of 1937, the Boses were in Giridih. He took work to his holiday abode and was busy editing the *Transactions of the Bose Institute*. Only a week was left for the celebration of the institute's foundation day, which was also his seventy-ninth birthday. Sir Jagadish was bathing in the morning, as was usual, while Lady Abala was holding a discussion with the administrators of the institute for holding a proper celebration.

When after a reasonable time Jagadish did not exit the bath, Abala had the door opened. Bose had quietly breathed his last in the bathroom; the doctor on call pronounced him dead. It was 23 November, 8.30 a.m. The cause of his death was cardiac arrest. The lamp had been flickering for some time, now it had been put out.

The news of his death spread fast and a day of mourning was declared. The academic and public institutions of Calcutta were immediately closed. Sir John Anderson, the lieutenant governor of Bengal, sent a message of condolence to Lady Bose. The citizens of Giridih offered their last homage, and then Bose's mortal remains were brought to Calcutta.

His body was first placed at his residence, where family prayers were offered, and then brought to the Bose Institute, where it lay in state for some time for friends and admirers to pay homage. His remains, literally buried under flowers and florid wreaths, were brought in a procession to the house of the Sadharan Brahmo Samaj, where a short prayer service, amid chants of Vedic mantras, was held.

Thereafter the funeral procession continued its journey and an immense crowd joined it to offer final tribute to their science hero and national icon. The lifeless body of the departed soul was carried to the Corporation Crematorium and consigned to the flames. Later Bose's ashes were collected in an urn and buried in the courtyard of the Bose Institute, and a small samadhi structure erected over it.

Obituary and Legacy

Many condolence messages poured in from friends in India and abroad. Numerous obituaries were written in the newspapers of Calcutta and London. The obituaries written by Rabindranath Tagore and a renowned physicist Meghnad Saha, FRS, are significant.

Tagore wrote a fairly long obituary, the first half of which is a recollection of their early relationship. In the latter half, he wrote,

> Afterwards he shifted his enquiries from the field of physics to the biological realm of plants. With the marvellously sensitive instruments which he invented he magnified the inaudible whisperings of vegetable life, which seems to him somewhat similar in language to the message of our own nerves. My mind was overcome with joy at the idea of the unity of the heartbeats of the universe, and I felt sure that the pulsating light which palpitates in the stars has its electric kinship in the life that throbs in my own veins....
>
> With what little lay in my power. I helped him in his adventure but, fortunately, since then no more help was needed either in companionship or in other ways from a man like me who was too heavily burdened with his own responsibilities. His fame spread rapidly and material contributions from all sides showered upon his schemes, which centralized at last in the Bose Institute....
>
> This tribute of mine to the memory of Jagadis will appear

inadequately feeble, especially in contrast to the repeated
magnification of his name in my writings both in prose and verse
at the time when his fame was not luminously apparent above
the horizon and when, I am sure, my fellowship and unfaltering
faith in his genius did hearten and help him. But my struggling
health, which has lately been wrenched back from the grip of
death, is incompetent for most of my important tasks and also
the singing hope that began its first soaring in immensity and has
now completed its journey in its terminus.

In this obituary, Tagore sublimated his grief by discovering poetry in
science and a scientist's journey to its ultimate destination. In contrast,
the obituary penned by Saha, FRS, once a student of Bose in Presidency
College, is quite matter-of-fact. It was a long essay, which revisited
Bose's achievements, and pointed out where he had not been duly
acknowledged. We shall quote only the concluding portion:

> To sum up Bose's contribution to physiology; he tried to show
> that all the characteristics of response exhibited by animal tissues
> are equally exhibited by plant tissues; he has invented a unique
> series of automatic recorders of great precision and extreme
> sensitivity; he has secured the automatic records of all forms of
> plant movements....
>
> He has left behind nineteen volumes which form a record of
> the work carried out and directed by him over a period of nearly
> 37 years.
>
> In the compilation of this obituary, the writer has received
> invaluable help from Dr D. M. Bose, successor of Sir Jagadish C.
> Bose as director of the Bose Research Institute, and of Mr Boshi
> Sen, one of the former pupils of Sir Jagadish C. Bose, and at present
> director of the Vivekananda Research Laboratory, Almora.

In writing this obituary, Saha chose to consult with the two most
accomplished and internationally acclaimed scientists who had
been trained by Sir Jagadish Bose. One of them was Bose's nephew,
Dr Debendra Mohan Bose, a highly qualified physicist, who had been
educated at Cambridge, London and Humboldt University, Berlin. In

contrast, the other, Boshi Sen[99], did not even have a master's degree. Saha, however, thought Boshi to be the botanical heir of Bose and sought his help in writing the obituary, although there were many other botanists working in the Bose Institute at the time.

Dr Debendra M. Bose, when appointed the director of the Bose Institute, had to leave his professorship at the Calcutta University to take charge. Out of his accumulated savings of 17 lakh rupees at the time of his death, Sir Jagadish left a legacy of 13 lakh rupees for the institute. This helped Debendra to expand the activities of the institute and open a new department of microbiology.

Sir Jagadish bequeathed the rest as follows; Lady Abala executed the distribution: 1 lakh rupees was placed at the disposal of Bose's trusted former student Dr Rajendra Prasad[100] for promoting 'Bengali–Bihari amity'; 1 lakh was donated to the University of Calcutta, and 50,000 rupees to Presidency College. The rest was disbursed among various charities. Even in death, Bose was concerned about creating unity among his countrymen and advancing research and education.

During his lifetime, Bose had created a trust whose annual income was about 40,000 rupees. Lady Abala received an allowance from this for as long as she lived. Thereafter, the money was distributed among charities according to her wishes.

There is one part of Bose's legacy that has escaped the notice of his biographers, but not of Sister Nivedita's biographer, Pravrajika Atmaprana. Bose left behind 1 lakh rupees for a memorial of Sister Nivedita; Abala was the custodian of this money. Later, she founded an educational institution called Vidyasagar Bani Bhavan, where she built the Nivedita Memorial Hall with this money. Thus, Bose's silent adoration of Sister Nivedita found fulfilment.

Bose left behind a more precious legacy, of a different kind from monetary bequest—a great research institution with a band of inspired

---

[99]Boshi Sen turned his attention to applied agricultural research after the Great Bengal Famine of 1943. He was a pioneer of the Green Revolution that made India self-sufficient in food production. He was awarded the Padma Bhushan, in 1957, for developing hybrid high-yielding maize and onion.

[100]He would later become the first president of independent India.

scientists and the spirit of relentless struggle for a noble cause. Bose, together with his younger colleague Prafulla Chandra Ray of Presidency College, pioneered a tradition of scholarship and scientific research. He instilled self-confidence in his people by dispelling a false racist notion, that had been foisted deliberately to paralyse the scientific intellect of Indians.

During his long teaching career, Bose inspired many students who later became illustrious professors in various universities and colleges in India. They are part of Bose's academic legacy. Several of them became renowned for doing outstanding research. To name a few:

Satyendra Nath Bose, FRS, Padma Bibhushan, known for his contribution to a theory which came to be called Bose–Einstein statistics; a class of elementary particles is named Boson after him.

Meghnad Saha, FRS, astrophysicist, formulated the Saha ionization equation, which is used to describe physical and chemical conditions in stars; invented an instrument for measuring the weight and pressure of solar rays; founded the Saha Institute of Nuclear Physics in Calcutta.

Debendra Mohan Bose, the second director of the Bose Institute, a famous physicist who worked, with a junior colleague at the Bose Institute named Bibha Chowdhuri, to develop a novel photographic method for recording traces of cosmic rays.

Sir Jnan Chandra Ghosh, Padma Bhushan, electrochemist, famous for his theory of strong electrolytes and consequent Ghosh's law; director of Indian Institute of Science Bangalore, director of Indian Institute of Technology Kharagpur, vice chancellor of Calcutta University, in that order.

Sir Jagadish is no more but his academic legacy continues.

A Scientific Appraisal

In the first phase of his research career, Bose worked in the field of physics, but this lasted for only about six years. In 1900–1901, he made a sharp transition from physics to physiology, especially plant physiology. He stayed with plant physiology for the rest of his life, for nearly thirty-seven years. Hence, we begin our appraisal with the extensive physiological phase of his research career.

When he began to make his presence felt in physiology, he became a victim of plagiarism, jealousy, and pique. It took him nearly a decade to overcome the hurdles before him and win recognition, eventually leading to his election as a Fellow of the Royal Society.

The physiologists before him had been following an erroneous sign convention in electrophysiological work. Bose pointed out this fundamental mistake and compelled them to correct the vast body of literature that had grown so far.

Bose lifted the method of investigation into plant life to a new level by inventing procedures and instruments, known for their simplicity, directness, and ingenuity. His instruments, in general, were automated. Thus, any chance of error due to human intervention was eliminated. The resonant recorder, the two crescographs, and the photosynthetic recorder were especially highly appreciated.

The magnetic crescograph was, initially, received with great incredulity, though this did eventually change to awestruck admiration. Previously, physiologists were content with a plant growth magnification of twenty, delivered by an instrument called auxanometer. In the starkest possible contrast, the magnetic crescograph produced a magnification of ten million.

Bose discovered a nervous system in plants similar to that of animals. Modern researchers consider him a pioneer in the field of plant neurobiology. He was the first to devise an automatic recorder of photosynthesis in plants. All these were wonderful achievements and earned him unreserved applause from physiologists worldwide.

Interest in Bose's work regarding photosynthesis has been renewed among researchers of the twenty-first century. In this context, Raghavendra[101] and Govindjee[102] say,

> Bose made a phenomenal discovery that a unique type of carbon fixation pathway operated in Hydrilla. The plants of Hydrilla during summer time were more efficient in utilizing CO_2 (carbon dioxide)

[101]A. S. Raghavendra is a professor in the department of plant sciences, School of Life Sciences, University of Hyderabad.
[102]G. Govindjee is a professor emeritus of biochemistry, biophysics, and plant biology at the University of Illinois in the USA.

and light. The summer-type plants used malate as a source of CO_2....
These findings of Bose appeared anomalous at his time, but are
now known to illustrate an instance of nonKranz single cell type
C4-mechanism. In view of his major research contributions, we
consider J. C. Bose as a pioneer of photosynthesis research not
only in India but also in the world.

Bose died a contented man, knowing that he had succeeded in putting
India onto the scientific map of the world. In the process, he earned the
highest honour of the time for his work, the Fellowship of the Royal
Society, the Nobel Prize being out of reach for plant physiologists. Alfred
Nobel, who instituted the Nobel Prizes, had set a certain policy; there
is a prize for Physiology and Medicine; however, as per Nobel's policy,
this is really for human physiology related to medical science. No plant
physiologist has ever been given the Nobel award.[103]

Now to the physics phase of Bose's work. We have compared his
work, between 1895 and 1900, with that of Wilhelm Röntgen and shown
how much of Guglielmo Marconi's success depended on Bose's research.
Both Röntgen and Marconi are Nobel laureates, whereas Bose was
never even nominated for the prize. Moreover, Marconi was nominated
repeatedly, even after having won it once. One cannot be faulted for
suspecting an overarching Eurocentric bias.

Bose happened to have started his research in a certain transition
phase of history, when one era was giving way to another. Maxwell had
died after presenting his theory of electromagnetism to the world, but
this was not found convincing by a sizable section of physicists. The
four equations of Maxwell had not been formulated yet, as we know
them today; only a handful of Maxwellians were trying to decipher the
meaning of the abstruse theory, contained in the voluminous pages of
Maxwell's book.

Maxwell had predicted the existence of electromagnetic waves,

---

[103]The example of Dr Norman Borlaug, the famous plant pathologist and agronomist,
is a case in point. He developed a high-yielding, pest-resistant variety of wheat, and
worked and travelled tirelessly to popularize it in Latin America and Asia to usher in
the Green Revolution. He was awarded the Nobel Prize for Peace, in the absence of a
similar prize in botany/agronomy.

of much larger wavelength than light's, which would obey the optical laws. These waves eventually came to be called radio waves. Bose was the most successful among a small group of physicists who gathered quantitative evidence to support Maxwell's predictions. Bose was the first to show that radio waves could be polarized by certain naturally occurring crystals, just like light waves. His research led to an accurate estimation of the speed of radio waves, which turned out to be exactly equal to that of light.

Bose's remarkable ingenuity in his work with electromagnetic waves made him stand out in the group. He completed Hertz's unfinished work by obtaining quantitative evidence, but the sole credit for all this work has been given to Hertz alone.

It is a tragic irony that the main purpose of Bose's research is forgotten today, and he is now only known as one of the few who began work on millimetre waves. There is no commemoration for Bose in the form of a method or unit named after him, as is conventional in physics. And so he remains an unsung physicist, only to be remembered for his botanical work.

EPILOGUE

Time and again when I contemplate the landmark events in J. C. Bose's life, I try to glean the primary principles that our scientist lived by—to have a passion for one's chosen subject, to have a goal in life beyond one's narrow selfish interests, to strive higher, higher, and higher, and to probe deeper, deeper, and still deeper. His passion was science. His goal was to establish his motherland India in the scientific comity of the world and instil confidence in his downtrodden people. He wished to revive the lost tradition of scientific pursuit as in the ancient universities of Takshila[104] and Nalanda.

Bose was a combination of passion, dauntless determination, and the genius of an inventor. He was indifferent to power and pelf. During his tenure in Presidency College, he did not care to find out that a raise in his salary was due; it was discovered fortuitously and he received a windfall of arrears, which he invested promptly towards building his science institute.

He turned down the offer of promotion to the position of director of public instruction, although it carried a much higher salary besides power and prestige. He did so only because it would have taken him away from his precious research. Even in an advanced age, well beyond superannuation, he refused the vice chancellorship of Calcutta University, and exactly for the same reason.

Bose constructed his research institute after retirement from the Presidency College and though he became its director, he left the greater part of the institute's administration to Nagendra Chandra Nag. Bose's creative instinct was still active and he made major contributions to plant growth and photosynthesis research thereafter. In the process, he invented the high magnification crescograph, magnetic crescograph and the photosynthetic recorder. To the last day of his life, he remained busy editing the *Transactions of the Bose Institute*.

---

[104]Now called Taxila, located in Pakistan.

That Bose turned down lucrative, prestigious but purely administrative posts and chose to stay with research is admired by the knowledgeable in India. However, very few of the renowned researchers among Bose's countrymen follow his example nowadays; most hanker after the purely administrative post of a dean, director, or vice chancellor. As a result, India loses a brilliant researcher when they are fully mature and when their experience and active guidance would be most valuable to their juniors; over the years the society of lay people at large has learnt to accord greater respect to an academic bureaucrat rather than a devoted and brilliant researcher.

The policies of the Indian government also do not do much to encourage scholarship among researchers after they reach middle age. In many countries in Europe and America, there is a bifurcation of the academic cadre at around age fifty, when the professors are required to choose between a life of continued research and teaching, or, of academic administration. Traditionally, relatively mediocre researchers choose administration, whereas the brilliant ones stay with academics, the salaries for both choices being comparable. There is no such bifurcation in India. Bose's trailblazing example has not been followed generally, and hence, there is no such tradition here as in the West.

Bose, during his days in the field of physics, invented many instruments; likewise, while researching plant physiology, he invented many more. His magnetic crescograph is a most ingenious and astonishing invention. Apart from instruments, he invented numerous new procedures and techniques. He was a living example of a great scientist for his students and assistants to emulate.

Bose's photosynthetic recorder is another remarkable invention for its ingenuity. Its core principle was adapted by his own students in the Bose Institute, to devise an instrument called respirometer for measuring oxygen absorption by humans and animals. This is but only one example. Bose and his institute created a fair momentum for invention and innovation among Indian researchers.

Returning to the fallout of Bose's physics research, I was delighted when my boyhood rumours about Bose and Marconi proved to be true. I derived even greater joy in presenting the facts, and exposing this turn-of-the-century scandal, while writing this biography.

While researching material for this life story, I came to know how two western women, Sister Nivedita and Mrs Sara Chapman Bull, both disciples of Swami Vivekananda, became friends with Bose at their own initiative and selflessly rendered all possible help to him, for over a decade. Bose did not accept the Swami as a rishi because the latter practiced idol worship. Yet Nivedita and Sara helped Bose, because he worked, through science, for their guru's beloved motherland, their adopted motherland. I was wonderstruck at how the Swami's inspiration worked in so many ways!

I feel satisfied that I have not compromised with truth, and yet tried to be scrupulously fair to all the characters in this saga.

APPENDIX

1

THREE PATENTS OF BOSE HELD JOINTLY
WITH SARA C. BULL

N° 15,467   A.D. 1901

Date of Application, 30th July, 1901
Complete Specification Left, 31st May, 1902—Accepted, 30th July, 1902

PROVISIONAL SPECIFICATION.

"Improvements in and connected with Wireless Telegraphy and other Signalling."

We, JAGADIS CHUNDER BOSE, Professor at the Presidency College, Calcutta, India, and SARA CHAPMAN BULL, of 168, Brattle Street, Cambridge, Massachusetts, United States of America, Widow, do hereby declare the nature of this invention to be as follows:—

5   This invention relates to telegraphy, and has for its object to improve the sensitiveness and quickness of response of detectors (and so-called coherers) for receiving wireless or other signals.

According to the theory on which this invention is based, the changes produced on or in the sensitive substance of the detector by Hertzian waves or
10 other radiations or electrical disturbances is molecular distortion. It is necessary to remove this distortion for the reception of fresh signals. This distortion may be removed quickly by subjecting the tube or medium containing or carrying the sensitive substance such as iron or other filings to either a one directioned or to an oscillatory twist; in order that thi...

Bose's British patent No. 15467, Source: GB 190115467A I, IEEE, Milestones.ethw.org.

N⁰ 18,430   A.D. 1901

Date of Application, 14th Sept., 1901

Complete Specification Left, 16th June, 1902—Accepted, 7th Aug., 1902

PROVISIONAL SPECIFICATION.

"Improved Means or Apparatus for Detecting or Indicating Light Waves, Hertzian Waves and other Radiations"

We, JAGADIS CHUNDER BOSE, Professor at the Presidency College, Calcutta, India, and SARA CHAPMAN BULL, of 168 Brattle Street, Cambridge, Massachusetts, United States of America, Widow, do hereby declare the nature of this invention to be as follows:—

This invention has reference to means or apparatus for detecting or indicating light waves, Hertzian waves and other radiations.

The apparatus to which the present invention relates, when arranged for use with light waves, may be regarded as an artificial retina. By suitably modifying the arrangements, however, as hereinafter described, it may be used as a relayer or detector of Hertzian waves for the purpose of wireless or other telegraphy, or for the reception of other radiations.

In the apparatus to which the present invention relates, a sensitive substance is employed which has a varying electrical resistance under the action of varying intensity of light waves, Hertzian waves and other radiations.

Bose's British Patent No. 18430, Source: Bandyopadhyay et al. (2008).

No. 755,840.   Patented March 29, 1904.

UNITED STATES PATENT OFFICE.

JAGADIS CHUNDER BOSE, OF CALCUTTA, INDIA, ASSIGNOR OF ONE-HALF TO SARA CHAPMAN BULL, OF CAMBRIDGE, MASSACHUSETTS.

DETECTOR FOR ELECTRICAL DISTURBANCES.

SPECIFICATION forming part of Letters Patent No. 755,840, dated March 29, 1904.

Application filed September 30, 1901. Serial No. 77,028. (No model.)

To all whom it may concern:

Be it known that I, JAGADIS CHUNDER BOSE, a subject of the King of Great Britain and Emperor of India, and a resident of Calcutta, India, have invented certain new and useful Improvements in or Relating to Detectors for Electrical Disturbances or other Radiations and in Electrical Resistances, of which the following is a specification.

effect of facilitating the action of the twist upon the sensitive substance and of insuring quick recovery, or with the same object of increasing the sensitiveness and quickness of self-recovery of the sensitive substance I may subject the mass forming the receiver to certain forces, physical surroundings, and conditions suitably adjusted and applied, whereby said mass becomes more responsive to electric

US Patent No. 755840 of Bose, Source: Wikimedia Commons.

2

WHAT DUNLAP FALSELY ASCRIBED TO BOSE

Dunlap quoted extensively from *McClure's Magazine*. However, he falsified certain parts of the quotations in order to ascribe to Bose certain statements about Marconi, which Bose never made. Pages 35 and 36 of Dunlap's book, *Marconi: The Man and His Wireless*, 1937, give these quotations. Statements ascribed to Bose begin at the last paragraph of page 35. These two pages are appended here.

SECRETS OF MARCONI'S SUCCESS   35

"Marconi's success may be summed up in patience and infinite persistence plus a great deal of natural ability," said one of his early associates. "I have seen him work thirty hours at a stretch. He hates routine business, and while he has a business sense he lacks administrative and organizing ability. He is no mixer; out of 700 on the Marconi staff probably not more than a half dozen knew him well enough to speak to him. He never cared for sports.

"I knew his brother Alfonso. He had none of Guglielmo's characteristics. He was a pleasant, amiable chap; a good-natured man, but you would never suspect they were brothers physically or mentally. Alfonso, however, was for years a director of all the principal companies of the Marconi organization. He was distinctly Italian; and so was Guglielmo, who possessed, moreover, a sharp inborn knowledge of the world.

"It was natural that an inventor of Marconi's personality and ability should attract the cream of the engineering crop. He had a fine collection of experts. George S. Kemp, an ex-Navy man, was his first assistant and remained with him until his death in 1933. Andrew Gray was Marconi's first chief engineer. R. N. Vyvyan, also on the engineering staff, was a graduate of a big university, perhaps it was Oxford or Cambridge; he was a society man with wide acquaintances in government circles. He jollied the officials when documents were delayed. We called him the red-tape breaker."

Marconi, himself, was credited with "opening new doors in the electric wing of the temple of truth." Dr. Jagadis Chunder Bose, the Hindoo, Professor of Physics in the Presidency College at Calcutta, and distinguished student of electrical radiation, foresaw, "all the special sciences marching abreast along the old Roman road of science which leads no one knows whither." And he espied an obstacle—a great high wall blocking the way in all directions. Upon the wall,

36 MARCONI: THE MAN AND HIS WIRELESS

as upon the wall in the palace of Babylon, he perceived "a strange and as yet unintelligible inscription—the mysterious word 'ether'.[a]

"What new and great discoveries lie beyond this wall no one knows," said Dr. Bose; "but more than one high authority believes that these discoveries will startle the twentieth century more greatly than the nineteenth has been startled. To suggest in the crudest possible fashion, how the ether is at present regarded by scientists, imagine that the whole universe, to the uttermost stars is a solid mass of colorless jelly; that in this jelly the stars, solar systems and spaceworlds are embedded like cherries in a mould of fruit jelly. . . . In short, this jelly or ether is a universal substance so thin that it permeates everything in space on earth. Only by its quivering, only by the waves in it, which light rays and electric rays excite, are these rays enabled to travel and produce their various results.

"Strange to say, considering the number of brilliant electricians today, and the enormous amount of interest in electrical phenomena, it has been left to a young Italian scientist, Guglielmo Marconi, to frame the largest conception of what might be done with electric waves and to invent instruments for doing it."

> One ship drives east, and another west,
>   With the self-same winds that blow;
> 'Tis the set of the sails, and not the gales,
>   Which decide the way we go.
>
> Like the winds of the sea are the ways of fate,
>   As we voyage along through life;
> 'Tis the will of the soul that decides its goal
>   And not the calm or the strife.

3

BOSE'S LETTERS TO JOSEPHINE MACLEOD
AND THEIR TRANSCRIPTS

The following letters are not readable in a few places due to fading ink and wear. Also, a few pages were lost. Fortunately, transcripts for all had been prepared by the Ramakrishna-Vivekananda Center, New York, and are reproduced here with their kind permission.

Bose's letter (dated 7 July 1902) to Josephine MacLeod after the passing away of Swami Vivekanand on 4 July 1902.

(To Miss MacLeod)

1 Birch Grove, W.

7th July 1902

My dear friend,

I cannot tell you how grieved I am to send you the enclosed copy of a telegram which came for Mrs. Bull.

India has lost her great son. But his has been a heroic life, and he carried the banner of glory.

Yours sincerely,

J.C. Bose

Transcript of Bose's letter to Josephine MacLeod, dated 7 July 1902, given above.

(To Miss MacLeod)

Darjiling
10th Oct., 1911

My dear friend,

What can I say? Nivedita is in extreme danger. The illness has taken a very bad turn, and in spite of Dr. Nil Ratan Sircar and the best medical aid, the case is getting worse every day.

Pray for us.

Yours

J.C. Bose

Transcript of Bose's letter to Josephine MacLeod, dated 10 October 1911, after Nivedita fell ill. The original letter was lost.

18th Oct 1911

My dear friend

We could not keep her. The light has gone out of our light.

She was conscious to the last, and spoke of the continuation of her works. There is a great deal that she has left, which we have to complete. May we be true to the utmost.

First page of Bose's letter to Josephine MacLeod, written after Nivedita's death, dated 18 October 1911.

No need of talking about personal loss. God has been Kind too Kind too us to have given us a glimpse of the divine.

J C Bose

Second page of Bose's letter to Josephine MacLeod, after Nivedita's death.

18th Oct., 1911

My dear friend,

We could not keep her. The light has gone out of our life.

She was conscious to the last, and spoke of the continuation of her work. There is a great deal that she has left, which we have to complete. May we be true to the utmost. No need of talking about personal loss. God has been kind, too kind to us to have given us a glimpse of the divine.

Yours

J.C. Bose

Transcript of Bose's letter to Josephine MacLeod,
dated 18 October 1911, given above.

written to Miss MacLeod.

93 Upper Circular Road.
Calcutta. Oct 26ᵗʰ/11.

My dear friend.

A cry of anguish has gone through out the land, which loved and worshipped her.

A light has gone out of our lives. She it was, who maintained for us high resolve. Here lie many works unfinished - some she wished me to do, others she wanted to carry out herself.

There are many literary pieces, which have rare value. Then she spoke constantly of the woman's education. Mr. Thorp had written her a very cheering letter, and she was happy to think that woman's educational movement here would go on even in her absence.

It all seems a blank. Days as they pass appear more dreary.

How can we make her life and memory great? Tell me what could be done. Much can be done by collecting her literary pieces & publish them.

She wanted two other things — the publication of my book & the establishment of the laboratory. All was nearly ready, but now the only one who stood by us all the time is not with us. Yours— J. C. Bose.

Bose's letter to Josephine MacLeod, dated 26 October 1911.

(To Miss MacLeod)

93, Upper Circular Road
Calcutta

26th October, 1911

My dear friend,

A cry of anguish has gone throughout the land, which loved and worshipped her. A light has gone out of our own lives. She it was who maintained for us high resolve. Here lie many works unfinished, some she wished me to do, others she wanted to carry out herslef. There are many literary pieces, which have rare value.

Then she spoke constantly of the woman's education. Mr. Thorp had written her a very cheering letter, and she was happy to think that the woman's educational movement here would go on even in her absence.

It seems all a blank. Days as they pass appear more dreary.

How can we make her life and memory great? Tell me what could be done. Much can be done by collecting her literary pieces and publishing them.

She wanted two other things - the publication of my book and the establishment of the Laboratory. All was nearly ready, but now the only one who stood by all the time is not with us.

Yours

J.C. Bose

Transcript of Bose's letter to Josephine MacLeod from
26 October 1911, given above.

93 upper Circular 30th Nov. 11
Road, Calcutta

My heart goes out to you, dear Jaun,
because you knew her as she was,
because you loved her, and she
always rested on your love. Of this she
was absolutely sure. Bless you dear
friend in standing by her being
true to her. Did you ever realise what
privilege it was to know her as a
friend?

Tell me something human. I can
not bear the idea of accepting the loss.
She must be living and with us every
minute! Do you know how these years
one by one everything had given up,
just to carry through a few great
things. Is it possible to work on
under the conditions under which
I was placed, and under such

Bose's letter to Josephine MacLeod dated 30 November 1911, page 1.

isolation? Do you know how it kills one to discover a new thing, and then having no one to tell? *All these* I was reconciled because she was my *pen* and my public. I could dream and work and wait. Now the last *prop* is gone. I could live by work and the *strength & inspiration* from work is crushed.

Such a big world of Science and discovery opened out! Now there are the results coming, and the one who would have welcomed them is away.

But I must not be unmanly. Today is my birthday, this day 17 years ago I resolved to put all my strength for Science. Five years I worked all by

Bose's letter to Josephine MacLeod dated 30 November 1911, page 2.

thoughts. She only instructed
how the women's educational
work is [the] carried out. The
proceeds of her books, the
legacy &c — everything to go for
educational work.

Not one word of impatience
or complaint. Every morning
bright smile and cheerful
words, conscious to the
last minute

"The boat is sinking
but I shall see the
Sun rise"

From the beginning there
was no chance. It was
very little trouble this

Bose's letter to Josephine MacLeod dated 30 November 1911,
page 4. Page 3 is missing.

I enclose some quotations which I found among her papers.

It is a perfect blank now. Only one thing I see clearly: Her school must be maintained, and all her writings must be published.

If I live enough I shall see this done. But I feel so broken down. Write to me often, and tell me how we could best carry out her wishes.

Tell me things she spoke to you. Did she

Bose's letter to Josephine MacLeod dated 30 November 1911, page 6. Page 5 is missing.

really think us as her own?
Did she never feel as if
she was away from home?

God bless you and keep [you]

Yours
J.C. Bose

You may send the letter to
Mr Sharp Lee.

Bose's letter to Josephine MacLeod dated 30 November 1911, page 7.

93 Upper Circular Road
Calcutta

30th Nov., 1911

My heart goes out to you, dear Yam, because you knew her as she was, because you loved her, and she <u>always</u> rested on your love. Of this she was absolutely sure. Bless you dear friend in standing by her and being true to her. Did we ever realise what privilege it was to know her as a friend?

Tell me something human. I can not bear the idea of accepting the loss. She must be living and with us every minute! Do you know how these years one by one everything had (been) given up, just to carry through a few great things. Is it possible to work on under the conditions under which I was placed, and under such isolation? Do you know how it kills one to discover a new thing, and then having no one to tell?? To all these I was reconciled because she was my pen and my public. I could dream and work and wait. Now the last prop is gone. I could live by work and the strength and inspiration from work is crushed.

Such a big world of science and discovery opened out! Now there are the results coming, and the one who would have welcomed them is away.

But I must not be unmanly. Today is my birthday, this day 17 years ago I resolved to put all my strength for science. Five years I worked all by myself, struggling hard. And when my strength was nearly gone, then she came to help me. These 12 years, it has been incessant work, but the hardship was not too much. You know her presence made it so easy to choose all that is great. All small things vanished from life. One can never be contented with smaller things again.

And today I shall try to take up the burden of life in a worthy way.

Transcript of Bose's letter to Josephine MacLeod, dated 30 November 1911, page 1.

She spoke all the time about her woman's work. She deliberately wiped out of her mind all personal thoughts. She only instructed how the woman's educational work is to be carried out. The proceeds of her books, the legacy etc. - everything to go for educational work.

Not one word of impatience or complaint. Every morning a bright smile and cheerful words, conscious to the last minute.

"The boat is sinking but I shall see the sun rise."

From the beginning there was no chance. It was very little trouble this time - hill diarrhœ. Other times we fought successfully, because there was reserve strength behind. This time Dr. Sircar was telegraphed for and was in attendance from the beginning. But since her return from America she had no reserve strength. And it grew daily worse.

Up to her illness you do not know how frequently she used to talk of you. No one could have been nearer. "dear Yam! bless her" Her only anxiety was that you would not survive her. I enclose some quotations which I found among her papers.

It is a perfect blank now. Only one thing I see clearly: Her school must be maintained, and all her writings must be published.

If I (live) long enough I shall see them done. But I feel so broken down. Write to me often, and tell me how we could best carry out her wishes.

Tell me things she spoke to you. Did she really think us as her own? Did she never feel as if she was away from home?

God bless you and keep you.

Yours

J.C. Bose

You may send the cutting to Mr. Thorp to see.

Transcript of Bose's letter to Josephine MacLeod, dated 30 November 1911, page 2.

93, Upper Circular Road
Calcutta.

27. 12. 11

Dear Yam. You do not know how I value your letters at this time. You
will understand how it was a glow of light, a radiance, a living religion
that had been with us. It did not matter in the least whether it was
success or failure. Now that light is gone, the inspiration is gone.
I only wish to carry out things she cared for. I want to bring out her
writings. Then to keep her school. I do not know how all this is to
be done. But what would our friendship be worth if we could not do this
in her memory.

        Mr. Thorp has been wonderfully fine. He knew her.

        She had a small bas-relief made in marble for you. It reached
her the last day. Shall I send it to you and when.

        The other large one is ready. But the cheque came when she
could not sign.

        O dear friend help me to be what she would have wanted us
to be.

                        Yours affly

                                J. C. Bose

        Transcript of Bose's letter to Josephine MacLeod,
        dated 27 December 1911. The original is lost.

IMAGE CREDITS

p. 2   Professor J. C. Bose: Patrick Geddes, *The Life and Work of Sir Jagadis C. Bose*, New York, Bombay, Calcutta, Madras: Longmans Green and Co., 1920.

p. 55   Fig. 3.17(a): Prantosh Bhattacharyya and M. H. Engineer, *Acharya J. C. Bose: A Scientist and A Dreamer*, 1997.

p. 56   Fig. 3.17(b): Ibid.

p. 89   Fig. 4.3: Manoj Roy, G. Bhattacharya, B. Mitra, et al., *Acharya Jagadis Chandra Bose (Basu)*, written in Bengali, Kolkata: Basu Vigyan Mandir, 2008, p. 174.

p. 111   Josephine MacLeod, Sara Bull, Swami Vivekananda, Sister Nivedita: Courtesy of Ramakrishna-Vivekananda Center of New York.

p. 139   Fig. 5.1(c): Geddes, *The Life and Work of Sir Jagadis C. Bose*.

p. 158   Fig. 5.3: Roy, Bhattacharya, Mitra, et al., *Acharya Jagadis Chandra Bose (Basu)*.

p. 160   Fig. 5.4: Ibid.

pp. 161–62   Fig. 5.5 (a), (b), (c): Geddes, *The Life and Work of Sir Jagadis C. Bose*.

p. 199   A photo of the Italian ship, SS *Florida*: Courtesy Rik van Hemmen P. E., owner of the photograph, President, Martin & Ottaway, Inc., 620 Shrewsbury Ave., Tinton Falls, NJ 07701, USA.

p. 200   Guglielmo Marconi: Public domain.

p. 202   Villa Griffone: Wikimedia Commons.

p. 204   Marconi's first transmitter: Appeared in 'Looking back at thirty years of Radio', *Radio Broadcast Magazine*, New York, USA, Vol. 10, No. 1, November 1926. Public domain.

p. 208   Fig 6.2: Courtesy Varun Aggarwal, author of *Leading Science and Technology: IndiaNext?*, Sage Publications.

p. 213   Marconi supervising: Appeared in 'Marconi's achievements', *McClure's Magazine*, New York, USA February 1902. Public domain.

p. 222   Fig 6.4: Courtesy Varun Aggarwal.

p. 253   Mrs Sara Chapman Bull: Public domain.

p. 260   Fig 7.2: Geddes, *The Life and Work of Sir Jagadis C. Bose*.

pp. 269–80   Fig. 7.4, 7.5, 7.11, 7.12, 7.13, 7.14, 7.15: Ibid.

p. 287   Young Sadananda-swami: Public domain.

p. 297   'The Studio House': Courtesy Jeffrey Dodge Rogers.

p. 306   Basiswar Sen: Marine Biological Laboratory Services, 'Basiswar Sen', Embryo Project Encyclopedia (1923), ISSN: 1940-5030, http://embryo.asu.edu/handle/10776/2651.

REFERENCES

1. MAKING OF A NATIONALIST WITH A FLAIR FOR INVENTION

3 'When we get out, we will make the red horse fly.' : Patrick Geddes, *The Life and Work of Sir Jagadis C. Bose*, London: Longmans, Green, and Co., 1920, p. 5.

4 'Father, today I saw a bush on fire.': Ibid.

7 'All this also gave a lower and lower idea of all ordinary worldly success': Ibid.

11 refer to his father as 'a failure that was great': Bose Jagadis Chandra, 'The History of a Failure that was Great', *Modern Review*, Calcutta, February 1917, quoted in Prantosh Bhattacharyya and M. H. Engineer (eds.), *Acharya J. C. Bose: A Scientist and A Dreamer* Vol. 4, Kolkata: Bose Institute, 1997, pp. 227–231.

12 Surprisingly, Bhagaban's refusal as regards that particular career: Geddes, *The Life and Work of Sir Jagadis C. Bose*.

12 '[I]t is impossible for us, with our limited means': T. B. Macaulay, 'Minute on English Education, 2nd February 1835', in H. Sharp (ed.), *Selections from Educational Records Part I, 1781–1839*, Calcutta: Superintendent Government Printing, 1920, pp. 107–117.

14 'My father was one of the earliest to receive': Bose Jagadis Chandra, 'The History of a Failure that was Great'.

19 'My life has been a failure': Geddes, *The Life and Work of Sir Jagadis C. Bose*, p. 32.

20 'I am usually approached from below': Ibid.

2. EDUCATION ABROAD AND STRUGGLE FOR HONOUR AT HOME

24 It is said that Abala used to bring Jagadish: Manoj Roy, G. Bhattacharya, B. Mitra, et al., *Acharya Jagadis Chandra Bose (Basu)*, written in Bengali, Kolkata: Basu Vigyan Mandir, 2008.

3. SUCCESS AGAINST ALL ODDS AND THE EUROPEAN SOJOURN

40 The group had a few British members: Bruce J. Hunt, *The Maxwellians*, Ithaca and London: Cornell University Press, 1991.

42 Unfamiliar with Maxwell's thesis, an Anglo-American: 'David Hughes', Encyclopedia Britannica, 12 May 2021, available at <www.britannica.com/biography/David-Hughes>.

42 In 1879, Helmholtz suggested that Hertz: 'Heinrich Hertz', New World Encyclopedia, 13 Dec 2017, available at <www.newworldencyclopedia.org/p/index.php?title=Heinrich_Hertz&oldid=1008252>.

43 **Hertz succeeded in this endeavour, too:** P. Bhattacharyya and M. H. Engineer (eds.), *J. C. Bose and Microwaves*, Calcutta: Bose Institute, Calcutta, 1995.

44 **Hertz tried to measure the speed of the electric waves:** 'Heinrich Hertz', New World Encyclopedia.

49 **'Hertz failed, however, to conclusively measure':** Ibid.

50 **This notion about the failure of Hertz's speed:** D. J. Cichon and W. Wiesbeck, 'The Heinrich Hertz Wireless Experiments at Karlsruhe in the View of Modern Communication', *100 years of Radio, 5–7 September 1995: Conference Publication*, No. 411, London: IEEE, 1995.

50 **Science historian, John H. Bryant says that Hertz:** John H. Bryant, *Heinrich Hertz, the Beginning of Microwaves: Discovery of Electromagnetic Waves and Opening of the Electromagnetic Spectrum by Heinrich Hertz in the years, 1886-1892*, London: IEEE, 1988.

53 **'Further advance of the determination of':** Geddes, *The Life and Work of Sir Jagadis C. Bose*, p. 56.

54 **An Italian scientist, Augusto Righi, was also:** Augusto Righi, *L'ottica delle oscillazioni elettriche*, Bologna: N. Zanichelli, 1897.

54 **and published a paper on this topic:** Pyotr N. Lebedev, Ueber die Doppelbrechung der Strahlen electrischer Kraft', 'Double refraction of electric waves', *Annalen der Physik*, Vol. 292, No. 9, 1895, pp. 1–17

57 **'The evolution of a suitable generating apparatus':** Geddes, *The Life and Work of Sir Jagadis C. Bose*, p. 63.

57 **According to French physicist M. Poincaré, Bose's receiver was 'exquisite':** Geddes, *The Life and Work of Sir Jagadis C. Bose*, p. 57.

59 **'The object of the present enquiry is to find natural substances':** J. C. Bose, 'On polarization of electric rays by double refracting crystals', *Journal of the Asiatic Society*, Vol. 64, 1895, pp. 291–96.

61 **'The subject dealt with has long been regarded':** Bhattacharyya and Engineer (eds.), *J. C. Bose and Microwaves*, p. 6.

63 **'literally filled with wonder and admiration:** Geddes, *The Life and Work of Sir Jagadis C. Bose*, p. 40.

63 **'For my own part, I hope to take full advantage of the perfection':** Ibid.

64 **'With the ethereal sea in which we are immersed':** Ibid.

65 **In the beginning of 1895, an event was organized:** Roy, Bhattacharya, Mitra, et al., *Acharya Jagadis Chandra Bose (Basu)*.

66 **This experiment might have been performed in late 1894:** Ibid, p. 170.

66 **D. T. Emerson discussed the efforts of Marconi and Popov:** D. T. Emerson, 'The Work of Jagadis Chandra Bose: 100 years of mm-wave research', *IEEE Transactions on Microwave Theory and Technique*, Vol. 45, No. 12, December 1997, pp. 2267–2273.

66 **'J. C. Bose was at least sixty years ahead':** Ibid.

68 **According to the science historian Bruce Hunt, Maxwell's theory:** Bruce J. Hunt, '"Practice vs. Theory": The British Electrical Debate, 1881–1891', *Isis*, Vol. 74, No.

3, 1983, pp. 341–355.

71 'The inventor has transmitted signals to a distance': Bhattacharyya and Engineer (eds.), *J. C. Bose and Microwaves*, p. 48.

71 'Our inventor not only went on signalling through': Geddes, *The Life and Work of Sir Jagadis C. Bose*, p. 62.

72 'The parallel pencil of electric radiation': Ibid., p. 67.

72 his 'coherer' expressing 'surprise that no secret': *The Electric Engineer*, London, 5 Feb 1987, quoted in Bhattacharyya and Engineer (eds.), *Acharya J. C. Bose: A Scientist and a Dreamer*, p. 372.

73 'Through regular publication of the Transactions': Bhattacharyya and Engineer (eds.), *Acharya J. C. Bose: A Scientist and a Dreamer*, pp. 59–71

73 'The originality of the achievement is enhanced by': Geddes, *The Life and Work of Sir Jagadis C. Bose*, p. 67.

73 'The people of the East have just the burning': Bhattacharyya and Engineer (eds.), *J. C. Bose and Microwaves*, p. 48.

4. HELP OUT OF THE BLUE: RABINDRANATH TAGORE, SISTER NIVEDITA, AND THE VEDANTA CIRCLE

75 'It would be conducive to the credit of India': Geddes, *The Life and Work of Sir Jagadis C. Bose*, p. 67.

75 'great importance we attach to the establishment in the Indian Empire': Ibid.

76 'It is worthy of remark that the cog wheels suddenly became mobile': Ibid.

76 'He is now drawing Rs 500 and it is simple nonsense': Author's trans., Dibakar Sen (ed.), *Patraabali*, Kolkata: Basu Bigyan Mandir (Prakaashan Bibhaag), 1994, p. 84.

77 'Mr Bose's distinction is not ordinary distinction': Ibid.

77 'I hear from Lord Rayleigh that he visited the Presidency College': Author's trans., Dibakar Sen, *Bharatiya Bigyan Charchar Janak Jagadis Chandra*, Kolkata: Manisha Granthalaya Pvt. Ltd., 1985, pp. 12–14.

82 'The poet seeing, by the heart, realizes the inexpressible': Bhattacharyya and Engineer (eds.), *Acharya J. C. Bose: A Scientist and a Dreamer*, p. 2.

82 'Years ago, when Jagadish, in his militant exuberance of youthfulness': Author's trans., Sen (ed.), *Patraabali*, p. 202.

83 'He was busy in employing his marvellous inventiveness': Ibid.

85 'We arrived at the denoted hour at the laboratory of the Presidency': Author's trans., Sen (ed.), *Patraabali*.

90 'In a grating we have a structure which is': Bhattacharyya and Engineer (eds.), *J. C. Bose and Microwaves*.

94 'It is perhaps not surprising that crystalline substances should': Thomas Preston, *The Theory of Light*, London: Macmillan and Co., Limited, 1890, quoted in J. C. Bose, 'The rotation of plane of polarization of electric waves by a twisted structure', *Proceedings of the Royal Society*, London, Vol. LXIII, 1898, pp. 146–52.

96   'In order to imitate the rotation produced by liquids like sugar solutions': Ibid.

98   **John F. Ramsay and Ian K. Snook acknowledge Bose in this regard:** John F. Ramsay and S. C. Snook, 'Microwave Model Crystallography', *Electronics and Radio Engineers*, May 1957, pp. 165–69.

98   **He published a paper with his findings:** J. C. Bose, 'On self-recovering coherer and the study of the cohering action of different metals', *Proceedings of the Royal Society*, Vol. LXV, No. 416, April 1899, pp. 166–72.

100 'Very recently I have been able to make a marvellous': Author's trans., Sen (ed.), *Patraabali*.

100 'Bose showed that these short electric waves': Geddes, *The Life and Work of Sir Jagadis C. Bose*, p. 59.

101 'With the rapid progresses in the semiconductor revolution': Probir K. Bandyopadhyay, 'Sir J. C. Bose's Diode Detector Received Marconi's First Transatlantic Wireless Signal of December 1901 (The Italian Navy Coherer Scandal Revisited)', *IEEE Technical Review*, Vol. 15, No. 5, 1998, pp. 377–406.

102 'Detector for Electrical Disturbances' by J. C. Bose: J. C. Bose and Sara Chapman Bull, 'Detector for Electrical Disturbances', 29 March 1904, US Patent No. 755840, available at <en.wikisource.org/wiki/Page:US_Patent_755840_(Bose%27s_Microwave_Apparatus).djvu/2>.

103 'Love India and do for her all you can': Pravrajika Prabuddhaprana, *The Life of Josephine MacLeod, Friend of Swami Vivekananda*, 2nd edn, Kolkata: Sri Sarada Math, 1994.

103 'Mother, I have brought a sky-flower for you': Author's trans., Swami Chetanananda, *Bhagini Nivedita* (Bengali).

104 'When God calls her, let her go.': Ibid.

106 a monk in 'strange orange attire and a yellow turban': Ibid.

106 He had told her that India was the home of the violin: Prabuddhaprana, *The Life of Josephine MacLeod*, p. 166.

107 Her biographer writes, 'Sara's entire life's aim': Pravrajika Prabuddhaprana, *Saint Sara: The Life of Sara Chapman Bull, The American Mother of Swami Vivekananda*, 2nd edn, Kolkata: Sri Sarada Math, 2014, p. 16.

107 When asked for his definition of a saint: Ibid, p. 20.

108 'The fact that metals grow tired and require rest': Ibid, p. 322.

109 He was extremely pleased with her speech: His Eastern and Western Disciples, *The Life of Swami Vivekananda*, 7th edn, Kolkata: Advaita Ashrama (Publications Department), 2001.

109 On 18 March, a lecture by another monk of the order: Ibid.

110 The Swami immediately returned from the mountain resort: Ibid.

110 She wrote about it later to Joe, and drew inspiration: Pravrajika Atmaprana, *Sister Nivedita of Ramakrishna-Vivekananda*, Calcutta: Sister Nivedita Girls' School, Calcutta, 1961.

112 The Swami introduced a new principle to his followers: Ibid.

113 As funding ran out, Nivedita began looking: Reymond, *The Dedicated*.

113 But now, to get rid of the keen suitor, she urged: Swami Chetanananda (ed.), *Swami Akhandananda-ke jerup dekhiyachhi* (As we have seen Swami Akhandananda, Kolkata: Udbodhan Karyalaya, 2011.

114 'I really want to add a new friend to those': Roy, Bhattacharya, Mitra, et al., *Acharya Jagadis Chandra Bose (Basu)*, p. 34.

115 'It was this notion which made me propose that she take charge': Pravrajika Atmaprana, 'Homage to the Founder of the School', *The Divine Legacy*, Pravrajika Jnanadaprana (ed.), Kolkata: Sri Sarada Math, 2017.

116 '...in Bengali, the Swami's various success with the doctrines': Reymond, *The Dedicated*.

117 'She is a jewel of a girl and will do great things': Lizelle Reymond, *The Dedicated: A Biography of Nivedita*, New York: J. Day Company, 1953.

118 the following letter that Josephine wrote to Sara Bull: Prabuddhaprana, *Saint Sara*, pp. 69–70.

121 '"Blessed is the infinite power of human fellowship"': Girish N. Mehra, *Nearer Heaven Than Earth: The Life and Times of Boshi Sen and Gertrude Emerson Sen*, New Delhi: Rupa and Co., 2007, p. 59.

122 'I am informed you had an interview with the': Author's trans., Sen (ed.), *Patraabali*, p. 12.

122 'I know you will suffer much on learning this': Ibid.

122 'Sir, the pose of an alms-seeking mendicant': Ibid.

124 'You ask science for the proof of unity?': Reymond, *The Dedicated*.

124 'I wish you knew how I love the Boses': Prabuddhaprana, *Saint Sara*, p. 454.

124 'You know how to inspire a great man to do great work': Reymond, *The Dedicated*, p. 158.

126 It was Geddes who sent out the invitation to Bose: Prabuddhaprana, *Saint Sara*, p. 454.

127 'I feel sad and low because I shall be away': Author's trans., Sen (ed.), *Patraabali*.

127 'I reached the Congress late': Ibid.

128 'Here in Paris have assembled the great of': Roy, Bhattacharya, Mitra, et al., *Acharya Jagadis Chandra Bose (Basu)*, p. 38.

129 'During the exchange with the ticket vendor': Author's trans., Sen (ed.), *Patraabali*.

129 'Mr Leggett brought about an enormous expense in': Prabuddhaprana, *Saint Sara*, p. 99.

130 'Oh, that's nothing! Bose will make the very pot': Ibid.

130 In Brittany, Sara invited the Swami, Nivedita, and the Boses: Prabuddhaprana, *Saint Sara*.

5. FALL FROM GRACE AND REDEMPTION

131 'Some people in India think that very little': Atmaprana, *Sister Nivedita of Ramakrishna-Vivekananda*.

132 'You must write down all that you are telling me': Reymond, *The Dedicated*.

132 'It is on your heart, I know, as it is on mine': Ibid.

133 'I keep the Maharaja of Tripura well informed': Roy, Bhattacharya, Mitra, et al., *Acharya Jagadis Chandra Bose (Basu)*, p. 39.

133 'The Maharaja of Tripura is now in Calcutta.': Ibid.

134 'There were reasons for apprehension.': Author's trans., Sen (ed.), *Patraabali*.

135 'You must not hesitate even for a moment.': Ibid.

140 'I had planned to do some experiments in the Royal Institution': Ibid.

140 'My paper will probably come next week': Reymond, *The Dedicated*.

141 'Yesterday I heard from Sir William Crookes.': Author's trans., Sen (ed.), *Patraabali*.

142 In July 1901, Sara took Bose to America: Prabuddhaprana, *Saint Sara*, p. 463.

142 On 23 July 1901, Nivedita wrote to Sara, enquiring: Pravrajika Atandraprana, 'Sister Nivedita: Her Contribution to Indian Science', *The Divine Legacy*, Pravrajika Jnanadaprana (ed.), Kolkata: Sri Sarada Math, 2017, p. 82.

142 In *Saint Sara*, Pravrajika Prabuddhaprana has given facsimiles: Prabuddhaprana, *Saint Sara*.

143 Sara stayed with Nivedita in her mother's house: Atandraprana, *Sister Nivedita*, p. 82.

143 Sara sensed that possessed talent and had a noble cause: Prabuddhaprana, *Saint Sara*.

144 'He has devised self-recording and self-stimulating instruments': Ibid, p. 462.

144 'the most wonderful things you ever knew': Ibid, pp. 459–60.

144 'Friend...I know that lady luck is more kind to me': Author's trans., Sen (ed.), *Patraabali*.

147 'Even on the Thursday, the day before the lecture': Ibid.

149 It is believed the man must have been connected to the only rival: Bandyopadhyay, 'Sir J. C. Bose's Diode Detector Received Marconi's First Transatlantic Wireless Signal of December 1901 (The Italian Navy Coherer Scandal Revisited)'.

149 He was tyrannical and when a day of work passed: Reymond, *The Dedicated*, p. 194.

152 'inventions and discoveries belong to the world at large': Joachim Pietzsch, 'Speed read: An illuminating accident', The Nobel Prize, available at <www.nobelprize.org/prizes/physics/1901/speedread>.

154 'The scientists of England are a divided lot': Author's trans., Sen (ed.), *Patraabali*.

155 'While working with the receivers of electric waves': Roy, Bhattacharya, Mitra, et al., *Acharya Jagadis Chandra Bose (Basu)*, p. 173.

155 'I have shown you this evening autographic record': Manoranjan Gupta, *Jagadishchandra Bose: A Biography*, Bombay: Bharatiya Vidya Bhavan, 1964, Appendix III.

156 'Since I received your letter, I am transported': Author's trans., Sen (ed.), *Patraabali*.

159 **These records were presented by Bose in his lecture:** Roy, Bhattacharya, Mitra, et al., *Acharya Jagadis Chandra Bose (Basu)*.

160 **These records were also presented by Bose:** Geddes, *The Life and Work of Sir Jagadis C. Bose*.

164 **'I cannot tell you how busy I truly am!':** Author's trans., Sen (ed.), *Patraabali*.

164 **'It is extraordinary to see Dr Bose':** Reymond, *The Dedicated*.

165 **'"Come now, Bose, what is the novelty"':** Geddes, *The Life and Work of Sir Jagadis C. Bose*, p. 96.

165 **'Well, make us a preliminary communication':** Ibid.

165 **'Friend, I have not had a holiday, even on Sundays':** Ibid.

166 **'I am now a guest of the Maharaja for a few days':** Ibid, p. 86.

167 **'It is a great pity that Professor Bose should leave his own subject':** Ibid., p. 99.

167 **'In reply I said, "scientific terms are not a monopoly of anyone"':** Author's trans., Sen (ed.), *Patraabali*.

168 **'As a consequence, the publication of my paper':** Ibid.

169 **Fn 35: 'I have never seen three sober Englishmen so thrilled':** Geddes, *The Life and Work of Sir Jagadis C. Bose*, p. 103.

170 **'You cannot poach on other people's preserves':** Ibid.

170 **'It seems to me that your experiments':** Ibid.

171 **'I am fully sympathetic and the facts you cite':** Ibid, p. 105.

171 **'I have no patience with you. Eastern courtesy':** Ibid, p. 106.

171 **Before he returned to India at the end of his furlough:** Ibid.

172 **'Dr Bose has had any amount of proof reading':** Prabuddhaprana, Pravrajika, Saint Sara, pp. 489–90.

173 **'Sunshine and the shadow clouds are constantly following':** Author's trans., Sen (ed.), *Patraabali*.

173 **'That I, Sara C. Bull, widow':** Mita Mukherjee, 'Twin Wills that Laid Bose Institute Base', *The Telegraph Online*, 28 October 2016.

174 **Fn 40: A US-based science historian, Probir Bandyopadhyay:** Ibid.

174 **'I have your note of August 9 that the Boses':** Prabuddhaprana, *Saint Sara*.

174 **'Had you seen our condition, you would be in splits':** Author's trans., Sen (ed.), *Patraabali*.

175 **'So far they have been saying that science and India':** Ibid.

176 **'What I have written on plant physiology in my book':** Ibid.

176 **'I was astonished to see a news item in today's paper':** Ibid.

177 **'Previously people thought that only sensitive plants':** Ibid.

178 **'...in the present state of our physiological literature':** Ibid.

178 **'I have been feeling rather low lately.':** Ibid.

179 **'Darling Saint Sara! I suddenly realized':** Prabuddhaprana, *Saint Sara*, pp. 423–25.

181 **'Dr Bose not only demonstrated the existence':** Gupta, *Jagadishchandra Bose: A Biography*.

182 **'Now a few words about you':** Author's trans., Sen (ed.), *Patraabali*.

184 'You will never know what your affectionate': Prabuddhaprana, *Saint Sara*, p. 462.

185 'God impressed a mark of victory on your forehead': Author's trans., Sen (ed.), *Patraabali*.

186 She hopes to make it the ruling impulse: Prabuddhaprana, *Saint Sara*, p. 469.

187 '[Y]ou, Margot, and I are sufficiently one': Ibid, p. 451.

187 One of the leading philosophers of science, Karl Popper: Karl Popper, *The Logic of Scientific Discovery*, London: Hutchinson & Co., 1959.

187 'Many congratulations on your very important': Geddes, *The Life and Work of Sir Jagadis C. Bose*.

188 'I was made familiar from my boyhood': Author's trans., Sen (ed.), *Patraabali*.

190 'I trust, you remember me as a fellow traveller': 'A Meeting On Board The Empress of India', TATA, www.tata.com/newsroom/jamsetji-tata-letter-to-swami-vivekananda.

191 'We are not aware if any project': Ibid.

194 'A Parsi gentleman, Mr Tata, who is anxious': Prabuddhaprana, *Saint Sara*, p. 461.

194 'We have had a Universities Commission lately': Pravrajika Atmaprana, 'Homage to the Founder of the School', p. 14.

195 'The fee for Indian students in the St. Xavier's': Author's trans., Sen (ed.), *Patraabali*.

195 The Swami, however, had sent a request letter: Pravrajika Atmaprana, 'Homage to the Founder of the School', p. 77.

196 Josephine MacLeod wrote to Bose from America: Prabuddhaprana, *Saint Sara*, p. 139.

196 'About Dr Bose's laboratory—one must not talk of it': Ibid.

6. MARCONI AND BOSE: THE PATHS CROSS

198 'When we look deeper...we shall find': Bhattacharyya and Engineer (eds.), *Acharya J. C. Bose: A Scientist and a Dreamer*, p. 227.

200 Marconi never received any formal higher education: Robert McHenry (ed.), Guglielmo Marconi', Encyclopædia Britannica, 1993.

200 'In sketching the history of my association with': Guglielmo Marconi, 'Nobel Lecture: Nobel Prize Outreach AB 2022', NobelPrize.org, available at <www.nobelprize.org/prizes/physics/1909/marconi/lecture>.

201 'Guglielmo lacking regular learning, could not enrol': Degna Marconi, *My Father, Marconi*, New York: McGraw-Hill Book Company Inc., 1962, available at <archive.org/details/myfathermarconi00marc/mode/2up>.

205 Guided by Jameson Davis, on 2 June 1896: Roy, Bhattacharya, Mitra, et al., *Acharya Jagadis Chandra Bose (Basu)*, p. 172.

205 'In 1891, the Navy was seeking some means': 'Obituary Notice', Vol. 124, *Nature*, 1930, p. 59.

207 There was no mention of the reflector now: Roy, Bhattacharya, Mitra, et al.,

Acharya Jagadis Chandra Bose (Basu), p. 172.

207 **It had been demonstrated earlier by Oliver Lodge:** 'Oliver Joseph Lodge', Encyclopedia Britannica, available at <www.britannica.com/biography/Oliver-Joseph-Lodge>.

207 **Fn 50: Bandyopadhyay has credited Marconi with the first use:** Bandyopadhyay, 'Sir J. C. Bose's Diode Detector Received Marconi's First Transatlantic Wireless Signal of December 1901 (The Italian Navy Coherer Scandal Revisited)', pp. 265.

209 **'From the patent which [Marconi] took out':** Silvanus P. Thompson, 'The inventor of wireless telegraphy', *Saturday Review*, Vol. 93, No. 5, April 1902, pp. 424–25.

210 **Marconi hesitated for months, but finally gave in:** Fondazione Guglielmo Marconi, Marconian Digital Archival Biography, available at <www.fgm.it>.

210 **During July and August 1897, Marconi arranged:** Banerjee, Jacquelin, 'Guglielmo Marconi (1874–1937) and the Beginning of Wireless Technology', *The Victorian Web*, 2017, available at <www.victorianweb.org/technology/inventors/marconi/index.html>.

211 **Marconi himself had the fantastic notion that the:** Marconi, 'Nobel Lecture'.

212 **This piece of Marconi's invention and discovery:** Bandyopadhyay, 'Sir J. C. Bose's Diode Detector Received Marconi's First Transatlantic Wireless Signal of December 1901 (The Italian Navy Coherer Scandal Revisited)'.

212 **'[Solari] became Marconi's lieutenant, friend, and confidant':** W. P. Jolly, *Marconi*, London: Constable, 1972, p. 9.

212 **Soon after this visit, on 10 September 1901:** V. J. Phillips, 'The "Italian Navy coherer" affair: a turn-of-the-century scandal', *IEE Proceedings–Science, Measurement and Technology*, Vol. 140, No. 3, 1993, pp. 175–85.

215 **'*Atlantic Wireless Telegraphy*—It is rash to express opinion':** Bandyopadhyay, 'Sir J. C. Bose's Diode Detector Received Marconi's First Transatlantic Wireless Signal of December 1901 (The Italian Navy Coherer Scandal Revisited)'.

215 **'Prof. Oliver Lodge is altogether wrong in':** Ibid.

215 **'I thought that this temporary installation, the first shot':** Ibid.

216 **'At noon on Thursday Marconi sat waiting':** Ibid.

220 **A. Banti, editor of the *L'Elettricista*, claimed:** Phillips, 'The "Italian Navy Coherer" Affair'.

220 **Mr Henniker Heaton, a Conservative Party member of the British parliament:** Ibid.

220 **'The coherer has been with good reason':** Bandyopadhyay, 'Sir J. C. Bose's Diode Detector Received Marconi's First Transatlantic Wireless Signal of December 1901 (The Italian Navy Coherer Scandal Revisited)'.

221 **'Other self-restoring coherers were':** Ibid.

222 **His application for the patent is:** Ibid.

222 **On 10 July 1903, in a letter titled, 'The Real Inventor of the Mercury Coherer':** Ibid.

223 **'Part of my work regarding the utilization':** Marconi, 'Nobel Lecture'.

223 **Braun was recognized by the Nobel committee:** Ibid.

224 **'In view of importance of all that was at stake':** Bandyopadhyay, 'Sir J. C. Bose's Diode Detector Received Marconi's First Transatlantic Wireless Signal of December 1901 (The Italian Navy Coherer Scandal Revisited)'.

224 **'I ran my wire through a window in the barrack':** Orrin E. Dunlap, *Marconi: The Man and His Wireless*, New York: Macmillan Co., 1937, pp. 35–36.

225 **'The kite was rising and falling in the wind throughout':** Bandyopadhyay, 'Sir J. C. Bose's Diode Detector Received Marconi's First Transatlantic Wireless Signal of December 1901 (The Italian Navy Coherer Scandal Revisited)'.

227 **One of the self-recovering coherers described:** J. C. Bose, 'On a self-recovering coherer and the study of the cohering action of different metals', *Proceedings of the Royal Society*, Vol. 65, April 1889, pp. 166–72.

227 **'Another coherer was found apparently irresponsive':** Ibid.

227 **Fn 51: K. L. Groenhaug has rebuilt and tested Bose's mercury coherer:** K. L. Groenhaug, 'Experiments with the replica of the Bose detector', 2015, available at <home.online.no/-kgroenha/Marconi.pdf>.

229 **'A year has elapsed since Röntgen gave us':** H. J. W Dam, 'Telegraphing Without Wires: A Possibility of Electrical Science, (Interview with Marconi)', *McClure's Magazine*, Vol. 8, 1897, pp. 383–92.

236 **'"Marconi's success may be summed up in patience"':** Dunlap, *Marconi*, p. 35.

237 **Bandyopadhyay examined the original *McClure's Magazine*:** Bandyopadhyay, 'Sir J. C. Bose's Diode Detector Received Marconi's First Transatlantic Wireless Signal of December 1901 (The Italian Navy Coherer Scandal Revisited)'.

239 **It cannot be overemphasized that this timeline and all descriptions:** Marconi, 'Nobel Lecture'.

239 **'An invitation letter has arrived from the International Congress':** Author's trans., Sen (ed.), *Patraabali*.

240 **'Sir, I am collecting materials for a book on':** Bhattacharyya and Engineer (eds.), *Acharya J. C. Bose: A Scientist and a Dreamer*, pp. 304–305.

241 **'Your letter dated 11th October has been redirected':** Ibid.

244 **'The practical value of this innovation was':** Ibid.

246 **'I did not consider it advisable for me to say':** Bandyopadhyay, 'Sir J. C. Bose's Diode Detector Received Marconi's First Transatlantic Wireless Signal of December 1901 (The Italian Navy Coherer Scandal Revisited)'.

246 **In this context, the following information is significant:** Fondazione Guglielmo Marconi, Marconian Digital Archival Biography.

247 **'He took the coherer of Branly and Calzecchi':** Ibid.

7. BOSE TURNS TO PLANT PHYSIOLOGY AND TAGORE WINS THE NOBEL

250 **One wintry evening in 1898 or 1899, Abala and Jagadish:** Bhattacharyya and Engineer (eds.), *Acharya J. C. Bose: A Scientist and a Dreamer*, p. 331.

250 **'We have come to you just as we would go to Jesus':** Atmaprana, *Sister Nivedita*

of Ramakrishna-Vivekananda.

251 'Important as well as minor events': Ibid.

252 'She is absolutely staunch. She is gentle and clinging': Ibid.

252 'Christine is, beyond words, soothing, gracious, lovely': Ibid.

252 Unfortunately, Sara had contracted dysentery on board.: Prabuddhaprana, *The Life of Josephine MacLeod*, p. 507.

253 'Margot is here, hard at work upon her book': Ibid, p. 512.

253 'I always enjoy [when] I have had time to see my friends': Ibid.

253 'Christianity is so beautiful that I cannot understand': Atmaprana, *Sister Nivedita of Ramakrishna-Vivekananda.*

254 'Margot's work goes on apace. She is in her': Prabuddhaprana, *The Life of Josephine MacLeod*, p. 513.

254 'The heights have been glorious these two mornings': Ibid.

254 'The past week has given us most lovely days': Ibid, p. 514.

255 'The past week has been devoted to Dr. Bose's work': Ibid.

255 'Dr Bose will have nine glorious papers': Ibid, p. 515.

255 'I shall be your Christmas present!': Ibid, p. 521.

264 'After a while, with a flash, he broke the spell.': Ibid, p. 539.

264 'I have been feeling rather low lately.': Author's trans., Sen (ed.), *Patraabali.*

264 'You will see from the contents, the scope of the book': Prabuddhaprana, *The Life of Josephine MacLeod*, p. 539.

265 'Do you know when I was little': Ibid.

265 'The same jealousy would be found everywhere': Ibid, p. 538.

265 'We are having a lovely birthday': Ibid, p. 539.

266 Now, at the beginning of 1906, Sara offered to meet: Ibid.

266 'To science. The remaining 3000 pounds': Atmaprana, *Sister Nivedita of Ramakrishna-Vivekananda*, p. 236.

266 Stead had some other work on his desk: Prabuddhaprana, *The Life of Josephine MacLeod*, p. 540.

266 'Mother writes to us, full of anxiety.': Ibid, p. 541.

267 'I had a telegram of 15 words from Saint Sara': Ibid.

268 In this respect, our narrative is slightly different from Geddes's: Geddes, *The Life and Work of Sir Jagadis C. Bose.*

274 Modern researchers in the field of plant neurobiology: Prakash Narain Tandon, 'Jagdish Chandra Bose and Plant Neurobiology', *The Indian Journal of Medical Research*, Vol. 149, No. 5, 2019, pp. 593–99.

274 Their work was reviewed by the *New York Times:* Paramahansa Yogananda, *Autobiography of a Yogi*, Kolkata: Yogoda Satsanga Society of India, 2012, p. 71.

280 'It is well that the cook does not know the danger': Geddes, *The Life and Work of Sir Jagadis C. Bose*, p. 133.

282 Just two days hence, on 5 September 1907: Roy, Bhattacharya, Mitra, et al., *Acharya Jagadis Chandra Bose (Basu).*

283 'We had not seen before an embodiment': Atmaprana, *Sister Nivedita of*

Ramakrishna-Vivekananda, p. 239.

284 'No, no,' said the priest: Geddes, *The Life and Work of Sir Jagadis C. Bose*, p. 114.

284 'Hope you remember your promise to make me': Author's trans., Sen (ed.), *Patraabali*, p. 129.

286 She said, 'The selfless man is the thunderbolt': Atmaprana, *Sister Nivedita of Ramakrishna-Vivekananda*.

286 Later, she made a sketch of the thunderbolt: Swami Muktidananda, 'Sister Nivedita: The Western Champion for Indian Culture and Its Revitalization', *The Divine Legacy*, Pravrajika Jnanadaprana (ed.), Kolkata: Sri Sarada Math, 2017, p. 128.

287 His deep voice and Japanese accent: Atmaprana, *Sister Nivedita of Ramakrishna-Vivekananda*.

288 'Sadananda has returned totally exhausted': Author's trans., Sen (ed.), *Patraabali*.

288 'An American has arrived in Mayavati': Ibid.

289 This collection of poems had a dedication: Manju Masi, 'Sister Nivedita, the Poet', *The Divine Legacy*, Pravrajika Jnanadaprana (ed.), Kolkata: Sri Sarada Math, 2017, p. 97.

290 The first poem, 'To be said within the heart': Ibid.

293 It is known that the Boses reached London via Germany: Roy, Bhattacharya, Mitra, et al., *Acharya Jagadis Chandra Bose (Basu)*.

293 'The Government sent Bose in 1907, on his third scientific deputation': Geddes, *The Life and Work of Sir Jagadis C. Bose*, p. 137.

293 'I send you my new book': Author's trans., Sen (ed.), *Patraabali*.

294 'I got into trouble again when I tried to enter': Bhattacharyya and Engineer (eds.), *Acharya J. C. Bose: A Scientist and a Dreamer*, p. 118.

295 'A wonderful year! Began at Dum Dum': Atmaprana, *Sister Nivedita of Ramakrishna-Vivekananda*, p. 209.

296 'How we miss you every day': Prabuddhaprana, *The Life of Josephine MacLeod*, p. 549.

296 'Today everything is snow.... But it is so beautiful!': Ibid.

297 After the lecture, Sara arranged for a tea party: Ibid, p. 551.

298 'You will be happy to know that I was specially': Author's trans., Sen (ed.), *Patraabali*.

298 'The great success of *Comparative Electro-physiology*': Ibid, p. 135.

299 Bhupendranath later wrote in his book: Atmaprana, *Sister Nivedita of Ramakrishna-Vivekananda*, p. 213.

299 'The night you went with me to New York.': Prabuddhaprana, *The Life of Josephine MacLeod*.

299 'We had a pleasant voyage and hope to reach': Ibid, p. 555.

300 'How anxious I am on account of your health': Ibid, p. 557.

301 'I was almost prepared yesterday to send my resignation': Ibid, pp. 463–64.

301 'I have got only one and a half rooms': Ibid, p. 464.

301 Sara disarmed Bose by insisting that it was: Ibid, p. 463.

301 'The work in college is often hampered': Ibid, p. 464.

302 'The real principal of the school was Sister Christine': Ibid.

302 'Literary work absorbed Nivedita too profoundly': Atmaprana, *Sister Nivedita of Ramakrishna-Vivekananda*, pp. 235–36.

302 'Nivedita is well and in Calcutta.': Prabuddhaprana, *The Life of Josephine MacLeod*, p. 565.

303 'I found Nivedita very anxious at Darjeeling': Ibid, p. 537.

303 Learning of this, in June 1910, Sara sent Nivedita: Ibid, pp. 567–68.

304 'You know this school is really yours': Atmaprana, *Sister Nivedita of Ramakrishna-Vivekananda*, p. 236.

304 'Besides writing letters, when we discussed this': Ibid, p. 245.

305 Nivedita went to meet him there on 14 February.: Ibid, pp. 220–21.

305 'I believe that India is one, indissoluble': Ibid, p. 221.

306 Boshi's father Rameshwar Sen, a Kayastha by caste: Mehra, *Nearer Heaven Than Earth*.

308 'Oil in your hair which has dripped on to your coat': Ibid, p. 24.

309 'I became Swamiji's disciple': Ibid.

309 'Blessed are those boys! They are the ones': Arupananda, Swami (1962), Sri Sri Ma-er Katha (in Bengali), Udbodhan Karyalay, p. 197.

310 'Well Boshi. What is the latest in science?': Mehra, *Nearer Heaven Than Earth*.

312 'When you receive this, it will be our beloved': Atmaprana, *Sister Nivedita of Ramakrishna-Vivekananda*, p. 237.

313 'When Olea comes, I don't want': Prabuddhaprana, *Saint Sara*.

313 'We parted last night on a little wave': Prabuddhaprana, *The Life of Josephine MacLeod* p. 584.

315 'Nivedita is in extreme danger': Atmaprana, *Sister Nivedita of Ramakrishna-Vivekananda*.

317 'Dr Bose is much better physically and mentally': Atmaprana, *Sister Nivedita of Ramakrishna-Vivekananda*, p. 237.

317 On 12 October 1912, it was buried, with a Christian ceremony: Reymond, *The Dedicated*, p. 307.

317 'As a woman I knew her in everyday life': Geddes, *The Life and Work of Sir Jagadis C. Bose*, p. 222.

318 'Those to whom she gave the ennobling gift': Ibid.

318 'I owe my science to Sister Nivedita.': Mehra, *Nearer Heaven Than Earth*, p. 55.

320 'These prose translations have stirred my blood': Nilanjan Banerjee, 'Tagore, Gitanjali and the Nobel Prize', *India Perspectives*, Vol. 24, No. 2, 2010.

320 A limited edition of 700 copies was printed: Ibid.

320 Thomas Moore in his individual capacity: Ibid.

321 Initially, the inclusion of Tagore's name was: Ibid.

321 Bose wrote to Tagore in flowery Bengali: Author's trans., Sen (ed.), *Patraabali*,

p. 154.
321 'I can only raise the cup of your honour': Ibid.
322 The story was scandalous and full of ugly innuendos: Ibid, p. 10.
322 Bose has not written anything about this incident: Ibid, p. 154.

8. BOSE INSTITUTE AND SISTER NIVEDITA

325 'I do not think you need be troubled with': Mehra, *Nearer Heaven Than Earth*, p. 67.
325 Boshi has even said that he did certain: Ibid, p. 68.
326 They stayed in the monastery guest house: Ibid.
326 'Boshi, if I transfer all these to your plate': Ibid, p. 27.
327 'His early love for his own village culminated': Ibid, p. 64.
328 Thus was born the oscillating recorder as described: Geddes, *The Life and Work of Sir Jagadis C. Bose*.
328 It seems that the same instrument was also called : Roy, Bhattacharya, Mitra, et al., *Acharya Jagadis Chandra Bose (Basu)*.
330 In 1911, during the coronation of King George V: Ibid.
330 Thus came up Bose's summertime laboratory: Ibid, p. 65.
332 Confirmation came fifteen years later: Karl Umrath, 'Über die Erregungsleitung bei sensitiven Pflanzen, mit Bemerkungen zur Theorie der Erregungsleitung und der elektrischen Erregbarkeit im allgemeinen', *Planta*, Vol. 5, No. 2, 1928, pp. 274–324.
332 'As long as the ship ploughed through Indian ocean': Basishwar Sen, 'Round the World with my Master', *Modern Review*, 1916, p. 84.
334 According to Boshi, this tradition had to be: Mehra, *Nearer Heaven Than Earth*, p. 71.
334 One after another Bose showed how: Ibid.
335 Shaw was known for his quick wit: Ibid.
335 'Do you know whose casting vote prevented': Geddes, *The Life and Work of Sir Jagadis C. Bose*, p. 146.
336 'In a room near Maida Vale there is an unfortunate': Ibid.
336 The *Daily Telegraph* wrote an extensive review: Ibid.
336 The secretary of the Society officially wrote to: Ibid, p. 147.
336 'Ever since I began the study of Botany': Ibid.
336 'Calcutta was far ahead of them in these new lines': Gupta, *Jagadishchandra Bose: A Biography*.
338 On reaching Indian soil, they came to Calcutta: Roy, Bhattacharya, Mitra, et al., *Acharya Jagadis Chandra Bose (Basu)*, p. 690.
339 Geddes mentions that a contribution towards this: Geddes, *The Life and Work of Sir Jagadis C. Bose*.
340 'My wife and I are dedicating all our savings': Roy, Bhattacharya, Mitra, et al., *Acharya Jagadis Chandra Bose (Basu)*, pp. 73–74.
340 'I have recently recovered from an illness': Ibid.

342 'I do not know whether Havell has': Atmaprana, *Sister Nivedita of Ramakrishna-Vivekananda*, p. 269.

342 Soon after the Ajanta visit, Nivedita wrote an article: Pravrajika Bhavaniprana, 'Sister Nivedita: The Writer', in *The Divine Legacy*, Pravrajika Jnanadaprana (ed.), Kolkata: Sri Sarada Math, 2017, p. 92.

342 He started his own school of art, Nihon Bijutsuin: Prabuddhaprana, *The Life of Josephine MacLeod*, p. 120.

343 'Asia is one. The Himalayas divide, only to accentuate': Ibid.

343 The movement went on gathering momentum, and a few years later: Atmaprana, *Sister Nivedita of Ramakrishna-Vivekananda*, p. 271.

344 'The thought of the progress of Indian artists': Pravrajika Asheshaprana, 'Sister Nivedita and the Indian Art Movement', *The Divine Legacy*, Pravrajika Jnanadaprana (ed.), Kolkata: Sri Sarada Math, 2017, p. 160.

344 'Her fervid faith in the long-dreamed-of Research Institute': Geddes, *The Life and Work of Sir Jagadis C. Bose*, p. 222.

344 'Though there are many who are kind to me': Atandraprana, 'Sister Nivedita: Her Contribution to Indian Science', pp. 82–83.

345 He has said that, instructed by Bose, he buried a little box: Mehra, *Nearer Heaven Than Earth*.

345 Fn 79: Reymond has written that, in 1915: Reymond, *The Dedicated*, p. 307.

346 'A small temple in a garden is consecrated': Yogananda, *Autobiography of a Yogi*, p. 66.

349 'O Hermit, call thou in the authentic words': Ibid, pp. 72–73.

349 'I dedicate today this institute': Geddes, *The Life and Work of Sir Jagadis C. Bose*, p. 227.

352 'Far more important for future success': Bhattacharyya and Engineer (eds.), *Acharya J. C. Bose: A Scientist and a Dreamer*, p. 353.

354 He exclaimed, 'I have got it': Mehra, *Nearer Heaven Than Earth*, p. 66.

361 'Surely, the utmost perfection has at last been reached.': Geddes, *The Life and Work of Sir Jagadis C. Bose*, p. 158.

365 'We must ourselves rejuvenate our disease-ridden nation': Roy, Bhattacharya, Mitra, et al., *Acharya Jagadis Chandra Bose (Basu)*, p. 128.

365 'I can clearly see an approaching crisis.': Ibid, p. 82.

367 'I made a portable instrument which I carried myself': Bhattacharyya and Engineer (eds.), *Acharya J. C. Bose: A Scientist and a Dreamer*, p. 118.

368 'We are satisfied that the growth of plant tissues': Ibid.

368 'Criticism which transgresses the limit of fairness': Ibid.

369 'My name was warmly supported by all': Mehra, *Nearer Heaven Than Earth*.

369 'Prof. and Mrs Vines had arrived from Oxford': Roy, Bhattacharya, Mitra, et al., *Acharya Jagadis Chandra Bose (Basu)*, p. 85.

369 'I found Prof. Vines running here and there in frenzy': Ibid.

370 'Just like the telescope and microscope': Geddes, *The Life and Work of Sir Jagadis*

C. Bose.

370 'Monsieur, I see it but my heart still': Roy, Bhattacharya, Mitra, et al., *Acharya Jagadis Chandra Bose (Basu)*.

371 'My stay in Europe was drawing to a close': Bhattacharyya and Engineer (eds.), *Acharya J. C. Bose: A Scientist and a Dreamer*, p. 99.

372 'There have been quite a few remarkable inventions': Roy, Bhattacharya, Mitra, et al., *Acharya Jagadis Chandra Bose (Basu)*, p. 93.

374 Fn 87: We do know that Bose appointed Abani Nath Mitra: Bhattacharyya and Engineer (eds.), *Acharya J. C. Bose: A Scientist and a Dreamer*, p. 391.

375 'that joyous soul Boshi Sen': Mehra, *Nearer Heaven Than Earth*, p. 230.

375 'We want to meet Indians and learn': Ibid.

375 'Couldn't you take two weeks off from Bose': Ibid.

375 'Well, it seems you are losing interest': Ibid.

375 'Sir, I am going to ask for a long leave': Ibid.

376 'This is to introduce Boshi Sen, a live wire': Ibid.

377 'With greatest pain, I find that the only alternative': Ibid, p. 235.

378 'Swamiji Maharaj, I have dared to associate your name': Ibid, p. 236.

379 He was even able to keep an assistant: Ibid.

379 Lytton referred to him as the only Indian: Ibid, p. 238.

9. THE ELDERLY SCIENTIST AND HIS DECLINING YEARS

380 Viceroy Carmichael made a hostile speech: Prabuddhaprana, *The Life of Josephine MacLeod*, p. 151.

381 'Yesterday Mrs Geddes and Tantine [Joe] came to Dr Sircar's': Ibid, p. 155.

381 'Tantine writes that she will be in America soon': Ibid.

382 'a draft of Rupees One thousand from our Tantine': Ibid.

382 'Tantine reached Calcutta last Thursday': Ibid.

386 Constructed by author, from a description of the experiment.: Roy, Bhattacharya, Mitra, et al., *Acharya Jagadis Chandra Bose (Basu)*.

388 The following plant physiologists concurred with Bose: Ibid.

391 'I said to myself that this was the simplicity of the highest genius.': Gupta, *Jagadishchandra Bose: A Biography*.

391 The first imitation was made by his own students: A. Thakurta Guha and B. K. Dutt, 'An Automatic Respirograph', *Transactions of the Bose Research Institute*, Vol. 9 (1933–34), pp. 77–88.

393 He assigned a value of 100 to the rate in red light: Roy, Bhattacharya, Mitra, et al., *Acharya Jagadis Chandra Bose (Basu)*.

396 'I felt great joy when this book arrived': Ibid, p. 96.

396 'Jivaka, who later became the physician': Bhattacharyya and Engineer (eds.), *Acharya J. C. Bose: A Scientist and a Dreamer*, p. 20.

397 'It was a woman in the Vedic times': Ibid.

397 However, there were generous contributions from: Roy, Bhattacharya, Mitra, et

al., *Acharya Jagadis Chandra Bose (Basu)*.

400 The signatories included a large number of eminent scientists: Ibid.

401 Joe proposed that all of them should go: Prabuddhaprana, *The Life of Josephine MacLeod*.

401 '[Bose] took me all about his wonderful laboratory': Mehra, *Nearer Heaven Than Earth*, p. 77.

403 'Boshi Sen! I met Mr Sen in New York': Ibid.

403 'I would be happy to take you and Mr Wedell': Ibid.

403 Even before she could utter a word of apology: Ibid.

404 'She has given her life for India': Ibid.

405 'Why, there is Swamiji!': Ibid.

406 'Hearing about Mr Sen's work from some': Ibid, p. 241.

406 Julian Huxley, E. D. Adrian, and Robert Chambers: Ibid.

407 'Happily, friendly relations were re-established with Bose': Ibid, p. 466.

407 'Having not heard from you for a long time': Ibid.

407 'I dreamt yesterday that Vines had organized': Ibid.

407 'This has been due to the whole-hearted devotion': Ibid.

407 'Great things follow from small beginnings': Ibid.

407 'Is there anything that could give me greater happiness': Ibid.

408 'Beloved Master, my little contribution to physiology': Ibid.

408 'From the least to the greatest living biologist': Roy, Bhattacharya, Mitra, et al., *Acharya Jagadis Chandra Bose (Basu)*.

409 His friend Brojendra Nath Seal, then vice chancellor: Ibid.

409 'Twenty years ago, the scientists of the world': Geddes, *The Life and Work of Sir Jagadis C. Bose*.

410 'The contribution of India in religion, philosophy': Roy, Bhattacharya, Mitra, et al., *Acharya Jagadis Chandra Bose (Basu)*.

410 King Fuad I received the Boses in the Montaza palace: Ibid.

411 'At the time of retirement from the Presidency': Ibid.

411 'I have struggled for the last 40 years': Ibid.

411 At this time, French philosopher Romain Rolland: Ibid.

411 '[Bose] has found that the physiological mechanism': Bhattacharyya and Engineer (eds.), *Acharya J. C. Bose: A Scientist and a Dreamer*, p. 322.

414 He had heard about J. C. Bose and the psychological aspect: Roy, Bhattacharya, Mitra, et al., *Acharya Jagadis Chandra Bose (Basu)*.

415 'How manifold were the blessings she conferred': Atmaprana, *Sister Nivedita of Ramakrishna-Vivekananda*.

415 'Three important style markers—function words': Gaurishankar, Anuradha (1917), Sister Nivedita and her work for the Cause of Indian Science, in *The Divine Legacy*, Edited by Pravrajika Jnanadaprana, Sarada Math, Dakshineswar, Kolkata, p. 265.

416 'In the days of his struggles, Jagadis gained': Atmaprana, *Sister Nivedita of*

Ramakrishna-Vivekananda, p. 238.

418 **The letter to Mrs Wilson was found by more recent researchers:** Atandraprana, 'Sister Nivedita: Her Contribution to Indian Science'.

420 **'Once, when I was trying to engage':** Roy, Bhattacharya, Mitra, et al., *Acharya Jagadis Chandra Bose (Basu)*, p. 118.

421 **'Afterwards he shifted his enquiries from the field':** Author's trans., Sen (ed.), *Patraabali*, p. 202.

422 **'To sum up Bose's contribution to physiology':** Bhattacharyya and Engineer (eds.), *Acharya J. C. Bose: A Scientist and a Dreamer*, p. 401.

423 **Sir Jagadish bequeathed the rest as follows:** Gupta, *Jagadishchandra Bose: A Biography*.

423 **Bose left behind 1 lakh rupees for a memorial:** Atmaprana, *Sister Nivedita of Ramakrishna-Vivekananda*, p. 238.

425 **'Bose made a phenomenal discovery that a unique':** Bhattacharyya and Engineer (eds.), *Acharya J. C. Bose: A Scientist and a Dreamer*.

EPILOGUE

429 **Its core principle was adapted by:** Guha and Dutt, 'An Automatic Respirograph'.

BIBLIOGRAPHY

'Annual Dinner, January 13, 1902', *American Institute of Electrical Engineers*, Vol. XIX, No. 4, April 1902, pp. 481–509.

'Obituary Notice', Vol. 124, *Nature*, 1930.

Aggarwal, Varun, 'Jagadish Chandra Bose: The Real Inventor of Marconi's Wireless Receiver', *ResearchGate*, 31 August 2016.

Arupananda, Swami, *Sri Sri Ma-er Katha*, written in Bengali, Kolkata: Udbodhan Karyalay, 1962.

Asheshaprana, Pravrajika 'Sister Nivedita and the Indian Art Movement', *The Divine Legacy*, Pravrajika Jnanadaprana (ed.), Kolkata: Sri Sarada Math, 2017.

Atandraprana, Pravrajika, 'Sister Nivedita: Her Contribution to Indian Science', *The Divine Legacy*, Pravrajika Jnanadaprana (ed.), Kolkata: Sri Sarada Math, 2017.

Atmaprana, Pravrajika, 'Homage to the Founder of the School', *The Divine Legacy*, Pravrajika Jnanadaprana (ed.), Kolkata: Sri Sarada Math, 2017.

———*Sister Nivedita of Ramakrishna-Vivekananda*, Calcutta: Sister Nivedita Girls' School, Calcutta, 1961.

Baker, Ray Stannard, 'Marconi's achievement', *McClure's Magazine*, Vol. 18, 1902, pp. 4–12.

Bandyopadhyay, Probir K., 'Sir J. C. Bose's Diode Detector Received Marconi's First Transatlantic Wireless Signal of December 1901 (The Italian Navy Coherer Scandal Revisited)', *IEEE Technical Review*, Vol. 15, No. 5, 1998, pp. 377–406.

Banerjee, Jacquelin, 'Guglielmo Marconi (1874–1937) and the Beginning of Wireless Technology', *The Victorian Web*, 2017, available at <www.victorianweb.org/technology/inventors/marconi/index.html>.

Banerjee, Nilanjan, 'Tagore, Gitanjali and the Nobel Prize', *India Perspectives*, Vol. 24, No. 2, 2010.

Bhattacharyya, Prantosh and Engineer, M. H. (eds.), *Acharya J. C. Bose: A Scientist and A Dreamer*, Kolkata: Bose Institute, 1997.

———*J. C. Bose and Microwaves: A Collection*, Kolkata: Bose Institute, 1995.

Bhavaniprana, Pravrajika, 'Sister Nivedita: The Writer', in *The Divine Legacy*, Pravrajika Jnanadaprana (ed.), Kolkata: Sri Sarada Math, 2017.

Blum, Steven, 'Berlin's Einstein of Sex', *Shtetl*, 31 January 2013.

Bose, J. C. and Bull, Sara Chapman, 'Detector for Electrical Disturbances', 29 March 1904, US Patent No. 755840, available at <en.wikisource.org/wiki/Page:US_Patent_755840_(Bose%27s_Microwave_Apparatus).djvu/2>.

Bose, J. C., 'On Self-Recovering Coherer and the Study of the Cohering Action of Different Metals', *Proceedings of the Royal Society of London*, Vol. 65, No. 416, 1899, pp. 166–172.

————'On the Periodicity in the Electric Touch of Chemical Elements. Preliminary Notice', *Proceedings of the Royal Society of London*, Vol. 66, No. 424–433, 1900, pp. 450–51.

————'On the Rotation of Plane of Polarisation of Electric Wave by a Twisted Structure', *Proceedings of the Royal Society of London*, Vol. 63, 1898, pp. 146–152.

————*Abyakta*, written in Bengali, Calcutta: Bose Institute, 1921.

Braun, Ferdinand, 'Nobel Lecture: Nobel Prize Outreach AB 2022', *NobelPrize.org*, available at <www.nobelprize.org/prizes/physics/1909/braun/lecture/>.

Bryant, John H., *Heinrich Hertz, the Beginning of Microwaves: Discovery of Electromagnetic Waves and Opening of the Electromagnetic Spectrum by Heinrich Hertz in the years, 1886-1892*, London: IEEE, 1988.

Cichon, D. J. and Wiesbeck, W., 'The Heinrich Hertz Wireless Experiments at Karlsruhe in the View of Modern Communication', *100 years of Radio, 5–7 September 1995: Conference Publication*, No. 411, London: IEEE, 1995.

Dam, H. J. W, 'Telegraphing Without Wires: A Possibility of Electrical Science, (Interview with Marconi)', *McClure's Magazine*, Vol. 8, 1897, pp. 383–92.

Dunlap, Orrin E., *Marconi: The Man and His Wireless*, New York: Macmillan Co., 1937.

Emerson, D. T., 'The Work of Jagadis Chandra Bose: 100 years of mm-wave research', *IEEE Transactions on Microwave Theory and Technique*, Vol. 45, No. 12, December 1997, pp. 2267–73.

Gaurishankar, Anuradha, 'Sister Nivedita and her work for the Cause of Indian Science', *The Divine Legacy*, Pravrajika Jnanadaprana (ed.), Kolkata: Sri Sarada Math, 2017.

Geddes, Patrick, *The Life and Work of Sir Jagadis C. Bose*, London: Longmans, Green, and Co., 1920.

Groenhaug, Karl-Ludvig, 'Experiments with a Replica of the Bose Detector', 2001, available at <www.kgroenha.net/Marconi.pdf>.

Guha, A. Thakurta and Dutt, B. K., 'An Automatic Respirograph', *Transactions of the Bose Research Institute*, Vol. 9 (1933–34), pp. 77–88.

Gupta, Manoranjan, *Jagadishchandra Bose: A Biography*, Bombay: Bharatiya Vidya Bhavan, 1964.

His Eastern and Western Disciples, *The Life of Swami Vivekananda*, 7th edn, Kolkata: Advaita Ashrama (Publications Department), 2001.

Hunt, Bruce J., '"Practice vs. Theory": The British Electrical Debate, 1881–1891', *Isis*, Vol. 74, No. 3, 1983, pp. 341–55.

————*The Maxwellians*, Ithaca and London: Cornell University Press, 1991.

Jolly, W. P., *Marconi*, London: Constable, 1972.

Lebedev, Pyotr N., 'Untersuchungen über die Druckkräfte des Lichtes', 'An experimental investigation of the pressure of light', *Annalen der Physik*, Vol. 311, No. 11, pp. 433–58.

————'Ueber die Doppelbrechung der Strahlen electrischer Kraft', 'Double refraction of electric waves', *Annalen der Physik*, Vol. 292, No. 9, 1895, pp. 1–17.

Macaulay, T. B. 'Minute on English Education, 2nd February 1835', in H. Sharp (ed.),

Selections from Educational Records Part I, 1781–1839, Calcutta: Superintendent Government Printing, 1920, pp. 107–117.

Marconi, Degna, *My Father, Marconi*, New York: McGraw-Hill Book Company Inc., 1962, available at <archive.org/details/myfathermarconi00marc/mode/2up>.

Masi, Manju, 'Sister Nivedita, the Poet', *The Divine Legacy*, Pravrajika Jnanadaprana (ed.), Kolkata: Sri Sarada Math, 2017.

Mehra, Girish N., *Nearer Heaven Than Earth: The Life and Times of Boshi Sen and Gertrude Emerson Sen*, New Delhi: Rupa and Co., 2007.

Mukherjee, Mita, 'Twin Wills that Laid Bose Institute Base', *The Telegraph Online*, 28 October 2016.

Muktidananda, Swami, 'Sister Nivedita: The Western Champion for Indian Culture and Its Revitalization', *The Divine Legacy*, Pravrajika Jnanadaprana (ed.), Kolkata: Sri Sarada Math, 2017.

Phillips, V. J., 'The "Italian Navy coherer" affair: a turn-of-the-century scandal', *IEE Proceedings–Science, Measurement and Technology*, Vol. 140, No. 3, 1993, pp. 175–85.

Popper, Karl, *The Logic of Scientific Discovery*, London: Hutchinson & Co., 1959.

Prabuddhaprana, Pravrajika, *Saint Sara: The Life of Sara Chapman Bull, The American Mother of Swami Vivekananda*, 2nd edn, Kolkata: Sri Sarada Math, 2014.

———*The Life of Josephine MacLeod, Friend of Swami Vivekananda*, 2nd edn, Kolkata: Sri Sarada Math, 1994.

Preston, Thomas, *The Theory of Light*, London: Macmillan and Co., Limited, 1890.

Rajendra, Seshadri Thiruvenkata, 'Shanti Swarup Bhatnagar, 1894-1955', *Biographical Memoirs of Fellows of the Royal Society*, pp. 81–17, 1962.

Ramsay, John F. and Snook, S. C., 'Microwave Model Crystallography', *Electronics and Radio Engineers*, May 1957, pp. 165–169.

Ramsay, John F., 'Microwave Antenna and Waveguide Techniques Before 1900', *Proceedings of the Institute of Radio Engineers*, Vol. 26, No. 2, February 1958, pp. 405–15.

Reymond, Lizelle, *The Dedicated: A Biography of Nivedita*, New York: J. Day Company, 1953.

Righi, Augusto, *L'ottica delle oscillazioni elettriche*, Bologna: N. Zanichelli, 1897.

Roy, Manoj, Bhattacharya G, Mitra B, et al., *Acharya Jagadis Chandra Bose (Basu)*, written in Bengali, Kolkata: Basu Vigyan Mandir, 2008.

Sen, Basishwar, 'Round the World with my Master', *Modern Review*, 1916.

Sen, Dibakar (ed.), *Patraabali*, written in Bengali, Kolkata: Basu Bigyan Mandir (Prakaashan Bibhaag), 1994.

Sen, Dibakar, *Bharatiya Bigyan Charchar Janak Jagadis Chandra*, written in Bengali, Kolkata: Manisha Granthalaya Pvt. Ltd., 1985.

Tandon, Prakash Narain, 'Jagdish Chandra Bose and Plant Neurobiology', *The Indian Journal of Medical Research*, Vol. 149, No. 5, 2019.

The Editors of Encyclopaedia Britannica, 'Ferdinand Braun', *Encyclopedia Britannica*, 2 June 2021, available at <https://www.britannica.com/biography/Ferdinand-Braun>.

————'Sir Oliver Joseph Lodge', *Encyclopedia Britannica*, 18 Aug 2021, available at <www.britannica.com/biography/Oliver-Joseph-Lodge>.

Thompson, Silvanus P., 'The inventor of wireless telegraphy', *Saturday Review*, Vol. 93, No. 5, 1902, pp. 424–25.

Umrath, Karl, 'Über die Erregungsleitung bei sensitiven Pflanzen, mit Bemerkungen zur Theorie der Erregungsleitung und der elektrischen Erregbarkeit im allgemeinen', *Planta*, Vol. 5, No. 2, 1928, pp. 274–324.

Yogananda, Paramahansa, *Autobiography of a Yogi*, Kolkata: Yogoda Satsanga Society of India, 2012.

INDEX